revision guides

Do**Brilliantly**

GCSE English

Exam practice at its **best**

- **John Reynolds and Andrew Bennett**
- **Series Editor: Jayne de Courcy**

Published by HarperCollins*Publishers* Ltd
77–85 Fulham Palace Road
London W6 8JB

www.**Collins**Education.com
On-line support for schools and colleges

First published 2001
This revised edition published 2004

10 9 8 7 6 5 4 3 2 1

ISBN 0 00 716706 7

British Library Cataloguing in Publication Data
A catalogue record for this book is available from the British Library.

Edited by Jenny Draine
Production by Katie Butler
Original design by Gecko Ltd
This edition designed by Bob Vickers
Cartoons by Dave Mostyn and Sarah Wimperis
Printed and bound by Printing Express, Hong Kong

Acknowledgements
The Author and Publishers are grateful to the following for permission to reproduce copyright material:

Cadogan Holidays The Award Winning Tour Operator (tel. 023 80 828313) for the extract from their Cadogan Holiday Morocco Brochure, October 2002–2003 (p 31); Curtis Brown for the poem 'Island Man' by Grace Nichols (p 39); Heinemann Educational for the poems 'Blessing' by Imitiaz Dharker (p 40), 'The Lake of Innisfree' by William Butler Yeats, with permission of AP Watts Limited (p 44) and 'Vultures' by Chinua Achebe (pp 80–81); Kasbah for the extract from their website **www.kasbah.com** (p 32); MacMillan, London, UK for the extract from *Is that it?* by Bob Geldof (p 9); Oxford University Press India, New Delhi for the poem 'Night of the Scorpion' by Nissim Ezekiel (pp 78–9); © Susan Riley/Mizz/IPC Syndication for the article 'Bouncing back' (pp 24–5); *The Guardian* for John Ezard's account of a tornado (pp 13–14); *The Mail on Sunday* for the articles 'Nightmare of the Grey Goo' by Jonathan Oliver (p 75), 'Tiny robots with massive potential' (p 76) and 'Who will control the nanobots?' by Jonathon Porritt (p 77); *The Times*, London, © NI Syndication, London (20 January 1997) for the article called 'Whose history essay is it anyway?' by Joe Joseph (p 19); Weidenfeld & Nicolson for the extract from *Sahara* by Michael Palin (pp 30–31); also to the following exam board for permission to reproduce GCSE questions: OCR (pp 51 and 85).

Photographs
Andrew Syred/SPL (p 75); Cadogan Holidays The Award Winning Tour Operator (p 31); Eye of Science/SPL (p 77); José Luis Pelaez, Inc./CORBIS (p 19); © Mizz/IPC Syndication (p 24).

Answers to questions taken from past examination papers, and all commentaries, are entirely the responsibility of the author and have neither been provided nor approved by any of the above organisations.

Every effort has been made to contact the holders of copyright material, but if any have been inadvertently overlooked, the Publishers will be pleased to make the necessary arrangements at the first opportunity.

You might also like to visit:
www.**fire**and**water**.com
The book lover's website

Contents

How this book will help you
by John Reynolds

This book takes you through the different kinds of Reading and Writing questions you will come across in your English exam papers. It helps you **identify key words in questions and revise key skills in answering questions**. It makes clear what examiners look for in answers in order to award them high marks.

Reading through this book as part of your revision will **help you with your exam technique and give you the best possible chance of achieving a high grade in your exam.**

The first seven chapters in this book are broken down into five elements aimed at giving you as much guidance as possible:

❶ Typical exam questions

Each chapter contains **two typical exam questions**. For Reading, these are usually part questions, so that they don't take up too much space. For Writing, they are usually complete questions. **I have emphasised and commented on the key words in these questions**. This should help you to understand clearly what is required by the questions which you meet in your exam. So often students lose marks in their exam because they misread or misinterpret the questions.

❷ Extracts from students' answers at Grade C and Grade A

I have included **Grade C** answers to some questions. **I highlight the good points and then show how you could score higher marks.** I have also included **Grade A** answers. Here I **make clear what makes these such good answers so that you can try to demonstrate similar skills in your own exam answers.** In some cases I have used **extracts** rather than complete answers so that you can immediately see the points which are being made and don't have too much to read!

❸ 'Don't forget…' boxes

These boxes highlight **all the really important things you need to remember** when tackling a particular type of Reading or Writing question in your exam. You might like to read these boxes through the night before your exam as a 'quick check' on what to do to score high marks.

❹ Key skill

This section focuses on a **key Reading or Writing skill**. I have written it as **a series of easy-to-remember bullet points** so that you can simply and quickly revise what you have learnt during your English course.

❺ What the examiners are looking for

This page tells you as clearly as possible what an examiner expects from an answer in order to award it a Grade C or a Grade A. **This should help you to demonstrate 'high scoring' skills in your answers to exam questions.**

❻ Practice questions, answers and examiner's comments

Chapters 8 and 9 contain **sample Reading and Writing exam questions**. These questions are for you to try answering once you have read through the earlier chapters.

Hints on exam technique

Before you start

- Although you will have been told what to do by your teacher, read all the instructions on the exam paper carefully. This includes reading those on the front page as well.

- Make sure that you know how many questions you should answer in each section. Check whether there are choices within questions; it's not unknown for candidates to lose concentration and answer more questions than they need to!

- Work out how much time you need to spend on each question. The marks available will be printed after every question; make sure that you use this information to help you divide up your time: you should spend twice as much time on a 20 mark question than you should on one worth only 10 marks, for example.

- Check very carefully which reading passages apply to which questions. Avoid introducing material from the wrong passage as this will be ignored by the examiner as irrelevant.

- Read through and think about all the questions on the paper before you start your first answer. If you know what the questions are about, part of your brain can be thinking about those to come even while you're answering a different one.

- Remember: you do not have to answer the questions in the order in which they are printed on the exam paper. However, you should make it clear to the examiner which question you are answering by writing the number in the margin. This is particularly important when there is a choice of writing tasks on a similar topic.

Hints on exam technique

Questions on non-fiction and media texts

- Make sure that you **read the questions carefully as well as the passages**. Keep the questions firmly in mind as you read the passages and try to identify material which is directly related to answering them.

- Make sure that you **highlight or underline relevant sections** of the reading material.

- **Read actively**; think of the questions your teacher would ask to prompt the right response to comprehension work in lessons and ask yourself (and answer) those questions.

- If the question contains bullet points or mentions specific topics, use these as a backbone for your answer.

- Remember that with reading questions you should spend much of your time doing exactly that. You must understand what you are reading as fully as possible before you start to write.

- Especially with longer tasks, **plan your answer** by making notes from which you can produce a fair version. In particular, decide what your overall approach is going to be and how you are going to conclude your response. Make sure that the points you make illustrate and support this.

- Remember that it is your responsibility to convince the examiner that you have understood what you have read; the best way to do this is to express your answer by **using your own words** and not by just copying words and phrases from the reading material.

- If you use **quotations** to support a comment, make sure that these are the best you can choose for your purpose and remember to explain how they illustrate your point.

- When you are answering questions about the way writers use language, remember that there is no one right answer; think about the writer's choice of vocabulary and the associations of the words used and then explain the effect they have on you.

- When you have finished answering the questions, **check your answers carefully**. In particular, make sure that there is nothing which could mislead or confuse an examiner in your spelling and punctuation.

- Check that you have made clear how your comments relate directly to the question you are answering.

How to avoid common mistakes

- **Spend sufficient time reading the question and the passages**. Too many candidates produce incomplete answers by starting to write before they have a full understanding of what they are reading.

- **Take careful note of the wording of the question.** Distinguish carefully in your answer between questions which contain the word 'what?' and those which contain the word 'how?' The latter will expect you to **analyse and comment**. Make sure you do this in a precise and focused way; vague generalisations will not impress an examiner.

Hints on exam technique

Writing

General points

In any writing that you do under exam conditions, remember the following:

- Spend some time **thinking about and planning what you are going to write**. Don't produce too elaborate a plan, however; a spider diagram or a list of paragraph topic sentences is sufficient as long as you have given thought to how to structure your writing.

- In particular, think carefully about your **opening and closing paragraphs**. Always have a clear idea of how you are going to end your writing; this helps to focus the rest of the plan.

- You only have one chance when writing essays under exam conditions; it is important that you **involve your audience** with your opening paragraph and leave them with a lasting impression through your conclusion.

- Keep thinking about **audience, register and the reader**. The task may give you a specific audience (e.g. your fellow students) and register (e.g. to write the words of a speech). However, your reader is also the examiner. Make sure that your writing can be easily read and that you take care over accuracy. Any slips of expression which prevent the examiner from gaining a clear understanding of what you mean to say are likely to reduce your potential mark.

- Try to write with some **variation of sentence types**; you need to show the examiner that you are able to **control complex structures** and use **interesting vocabulary**. You cannot be rewarded for something you haven't done.

- Remember the basics: the **correct use of full stops, paragraphs and apostrophes** could make the difference between success and failure.

- It is likely that the task will have a suggested word limit; there is no merit in exceeding this. The more you write, the greater the chance of making careless slips of expression.

- Finally, don't forget that this is an examination which tests your skills in reading and writing English; it is not a test of your creative abilities so don't spend too long agonising over how original and imaginative your ideas are. What you write must be **relevant and appropriate**, but usually it is the **quality of your expression** which counts.

Writing tasks to inform, explain, describe

You need to concentrate on:

- **purpose**: what information, explanation or description are you being asked to give and why are you being asked to give it?

- **audience**: for whom is what you are writing intended? Remember to select a register and vocabulary suited to the audience and purpose.

- **focus**: what you write should give clear information or advice. You are being asked to communicate specific details; it is, therefore, a good idea to write in an appropriate tone without too many verbal pyrotechnics.

Hints on exam technique

Writing tasks to argue, persuade, advise

You need to concentrate on:

- the **type of task and the viewpoint**. Are you going to adopt a balanced tone, weighing both sides of an argument or a powerful, rhetorical statement to influence your audience into sharing your opinions?

- the **language** you use. Will you try to convince by using rational, objective vocabulary and controlled sentence structures or will you employ emotive language and forceful rhetorical question? Whatever you decide on, remember – be consistent.

- supporting your argument with **evidence and examples** and ensuring that you make effective use of them.

Writing tasks to analyse, review, comment

You need to concentrate on:

- how best to use any **stimulus material** given on the question paper: will you stay close to it, adapt it for your own purposes or ignore it altogether?

- the **examples and evidence** you are going to use. You must refer to things about which you have sufficient knowledge or experience to make convincingly developed comments.

- the **approach** you are going to take. You should adopt an **objective tone** but it helps to base your comments on an analysis of how you react to your chosen topic.

How to avoid common mistakes

- **Keep focused on the task** and remember the time constraints; don't try to be over-ambitious and try to write too much.

- In general, keep what you write based in your own experience; writing well under exam conditions is difficult enough without the added complications of creating imaginary worlds or situations.

- Remember the **audience and purpose** of your writing and make sure that you use an **appropriate register** for the task.

- Show that you are **in control of the language you use** by using a wide range of vocabulary and grammatical structures. Don't be afraid of using sophisticated vocabulary just because you are uncertain of how to spell some words; you'll still be given credit for knowing them and using them correctly.

Typical exam question

Read carefully Bob Geldof's account of his meeting with Mother Theresa. What do you learn about her appearance and character and how does the writer convey her special qualities?

Refer closely to the content and the language of the passage in your answer. Use your own words as far as possible.

[20 marks]

We were sitting in the departure lounge when Mother Theresa came in with several other nuns all wearing the white habits with blue borders of the Sisters of Charity. She was astonishingly tiny. When I went to greet her I found that I towered more than two feet above her. She was a battered, wizened woman. The thing that struck me most forcibly was her feet. Her habit was clean and well-cared for but her sandals were beaten up pieces of leather from which her feet protruded, gnarled and misshapen as old tree roots.

I bent to kiss her. I do not normally kiss strangers on a first meeting but it seemed like the right thing to do. She bowed her head swiftly so that I was obliged to kiss the top of her wimple. It disturbed me. I found out later she only let lepers kiss her. The photographers crowded round. We sat down. I felt like a clumsy giant next to her. I showed her my shoes which were beginning to fall apart and asked her if she had any spare sandals. She laughed. Actually she cackled out loud. I gave her a copy of the record. I could not think what else to do. I'm sure she got rid of it as soon as she was on the plane for Calcutta. Then she began to tell me about her work in Ethiopia. Her nuns were working in the shanty towns of the capital and they also ran a feeding centre and hospital at Alomata in the famine-stricken province of Wollo where they cared for the old, the blind, the disabled and the incurably ill – the people tragically overlooked by the other agencies who concentrated on trying to save the children, the pregnant and mothers of the very young. It was the same philosophy she adopts in India. I told her that my band had played in India and that, if it seemed a good idea, next time we were there we would do a benefit concert for her mission. She said that she didn't need fund-raising activities – God would provide. She then gave a clear demonstration of the way in which God provided.

While the TV cameras were rolling she turned to Commissioner Dawit Wolde Georgis, the head of the RRC, and said that on the way to the airport she had seen a couple of old palaces which she had been told were empty and she asked him if she could have them as homes for orphans. With the cameras whirring Dawit did a bit of fancy footwork. 'Well, I'm not sure about those particular places. I don't know what they're being used for. But…er…I'm sure we can find you some suitable premises for an orphanage…'

'Two orphanages,' she corrected.

'Two orphanages,' he conceded.

Is That It? by Bob Geldof

What are the key words in this question?

- *Read carefully* This tells you that the examiners will be expecting a response which contains specific **details** taken from the passage. A generalised response will not gain a high grade.

- *What do you learn* This tells you that you must use facts from the passage.

- *Appearance and character* There are **two** points to look for; the first may seem straightforward but it is important not to ignore it.

- *How does the writer convey* You have to write about the way the writer uses language; use quotations from the passage and then explain how they work.

- *Special qualities* There are specific points to look for in terms of what makes Mother Theresa a special person. Remember, some of these are likely to be **implied** rather than openly stated. Answers that search out and explain **inferences** always gain high marks.

- *Use your own words* You need to show the examiner that you have clearly understood the material you have been reading. Using your own words will help to do this.

Penny's Grade C answer

Mother Theresa is a very tiny woman. She has other nuns with her who wear white habits with blue borders. She has gnarled and twisted feet and wears sandals. Although her clothes are clean, the way that her sandals are described suggests that she doesn't worry very much about what she looks like. She is obviously concerned about more important things.

She doesn't like people to kiss her apart from lepers. She seems to be a happy person because she cackles when she laughs. She is obviously a very good person because she works in very poor areas helping the disabled and very ill. She has a very strong belief in God and thinks that he will always help to provide what she wants. She seems to be quite used to appearing on television.

Good points

Penny's response just makes it into Grade C for the following reasons:

CONTENT: There is a sound understanding of the more straightforward points of the passage but they are explained in a rather superficial way.

COMMENT: The comments at the end of the first paragraph show that Penny has some insight into Mother Theresa's character and this is supported by direct reference to the passage.

UNDERSTANDING: The final sentence indicates that Penny has some appreciation of inference (what is not directly stated) but the comment is not developed or explained fully enough.

How to score higher marks

- The answer needs **more detailed explanation**; it contains mainly descriptive statements.
- It would benefit from **greater use of quotations** and some more specific references.
- Penny has **selectively lifted** words and phrases from the original passage. **She needs to use her own words more** to show the examiner that she has genuinely understood the meaning of what she has read.
- **She needs to read beneath the surface of the text** to pull out some of Mother Theresa's special qualities that are implied rather than directly stated.

Mark's Grade A answer

This answer takes account of the points made above.

Mother Theresa is very small – the writer tells us how he "towered more than two feet above her". She is very old and the skin on her face is shrivelled up. She is dressed in a nun's costume which is white with blue borders. The writer was most struck by her feet: she was wearing battered old sandals and her feet were twisted and out of shape. This would suggest that she spends a lot of time walking on them; the description of them as being like "old tree roots" also suggests strength and durability.

Mother Theresa seems to be a woman of very strong principles. Although Bob Geldof is a famous person, she does not allow him to kiss her face as she only allows lepers to kiss her. This shows that she is highly principled and very humble as she doesn't make exceptions or concessions for anybody. She obviously has a sense of humour as she laughs when the writer asks her if she has any spare sandals. Her laugh is, rather surprisingly, described as a "cackle" and this makes her seem more like an ordinary human being and a not entirely respectable one at that. She is obviously very much part of the world about her.

We learn about her charity work, both in Ethiopia and India. The fact that she begins to talk about it almost straightaway shows how important it is to her; she obviously devotes her life to caring for the very sick and needy. Her principles and spirituality are also clear when she mentions that she does not need fund-raising activities, however, as God will provide.

Bob Geldof suggests that Mother Theresa is much more practical than she might appear on the surface and this is what enables her to get what she wants. When she is taking part in a live television discussion with Commissioner Georgis, she very skilfully manipulates the situation to make it very difficult for him to refuse her request for premises for two orphanages. The terse way in which this is described: "'Two orphanages' she corrected. 'Two orphanages,' he conceded," illustrates how effectively she succeeded in getting what she wanted.

What makes this a good answer?

- Mark's answer shows an excellent **overall grasp** both of what the question is asking for and what the passage is about.

- Mark uses his own words to show that he understands what he has read and **the material is well organised into paragraphs**.

- Mark gives many **precise details** about Mother Theresa's appearance. He shows he has a good appreciation of Bob Geldof's opinion of her character and the way in which Geldof uses language to convey this.

- Mark has drawn **several inferences** from the passage about her special qualities. In particular, he expresses clearly the way that the television interview reveals a strongly practical streak beneath her spirituality; and he interprets the reference to her 'cackle' as an indication that there is much about Mother Theresa that is very down-to-earth despite her very spiritual life.

Read carefully John Ezard's account of the effects of a tornado on Oklahoma.

- **What facts have you learnt about the tornado and its effects?**
- **Explain and comment on the writer's thoughts and opinions about what happened.**

[20 marks]

Travel writer John Ezard was in Oklahoma during a tornado. Here is his reaction.

Oklahoma is a highly distinctive American state; and that shows in the reaction of its people to their spasmodic catastrophes. Three years ago when 168 men and women were killed in the state capital's worst single disaster, the bombing of the Alfred Murragh federal headquarters, staff in the city's largest tower block arranged their office lighting so that it projected the sign of the cross. Yesterday morning, as they commuted to work past the confetti-like debris of more than 7,000 homes in the suburbs of Mid West City and Moore City, they did something rare on any freeway and almost unprecedented here. They slowed their cars down to 15 miles per hour.

Mostly it wasn't to gawp because you couldn't see much detail past the police barriers and the tall walls of the highways. It was a mark of respect, almost of reverence, for the ending of 38 lives and, temporarily at least, of the proud, earnest material dreams of thousands more families. The passers by turned their vehicles into an impromptu, collective, funeral cortege. It might so easily have happened to them, the series of vortexes that sucked humans and the fabric or their lives towards the sky and spat them back to earth in these aspiring middle-class satellite townships within a few seconds. At dawn yesterday, which broke with a clear sunny sky after the torrential thunder storms and continuing statewide tornado alerts of Tuesday, you could for the first time realise what had struck these new model Main Streets.

Sound brick houses, built around traditional timber frames, have been at best left looking like shanty town remnants and at worst like Dresden after the fire storm. You can still see what neat places Moore and Mid West used to be. Now they are flimsy death traps which need bulldozing. Yesterday afternoon thousands of survivors were allowed back for a strictly limited two hours to fumble through the ruins of Mid West City and salvage possessions by the car load. They are desperate to retrieve not only their family photos and videos and their children's clothes but their TVs and microwaves. These possessions had to be saved for, or paid off by credit card, and if you can recover them then rebuilding your life is a mite easier. 'First nature shatters my life. Now the government is going to bury my possessions,' said one frantic woman, her face still blood-flecked with cuts from the flying debris.

In time the dead will get their public memorials, like the one which is due to be opened next year to the Murragh bomb victims. Here, the bomb is seen as an incomprehensible atrocity from another planet, an event to be buried deep in memory. But the twisters come every year, their spouts grubbing up and spewing out soil, property and sometimes people, like giant malignant earthworms reaching down from the sky. Moore City had its last tornado as recently as October.

Moving at 35 miles an hour, engorged with sucked-up debris, this evil killer grew to a base more than a quarter of a mile broad which started to twinkle with grey flashes as it brought down power lines. 'My God. This thing is a monster,' said a TV weather man. Then another twister developed nearby and they marched together like twin Hiroshima mushroom clouds. 'God, it just hit. It was so loud, much louder than last time,' Ronna Johnson said. 'Our house was covered with mud. And then I started crying. I said, "This is not right..."'

Within minutes the response was as practised and organised as in a disturbed anthill. Neighbours trained in mouth-to-mouth resuscitation were sought to treat the heart victims that twisters always cause. Six designated emergency hostels were re-opened, and within an hour Wayland Bonds, Moore's schools superintendent, who lost two schools and a technology centre, was planning how to complete the school year without them. Less than two days afterwards, the event is beginning to lose its grip on public interest. Last night, even on local radio bulletins, the topic of tornado damage had dropped to third place. And during the commercial breaks – 'in this difficult time' – the Prudential Insurance Company was urging prudent people to take out policies to protect those material dreams during the next big blow.

What are the key words in this question?

● The first key word here is *what*. The first part of the question asks you to identify information contained in the passage. Notice, however, that you are asked to identify only *facts* related to the tornado and its effects, not **opinions**.

● The second part of the question asks you to *explain and comment on* the writer's *thoughts and opinions*. Here you need to identify the writer's personal response to the tornado, the language he uses to convey this, and the effect he is trying to create on the reader.

The tornadoes struck Mid West City and Moore City in Oklahoma on a Tuesday. Over 7000 homes, mainly in prosperous middle-class areas, were demolished. Many of these were solidly built brick and timber houses and this shows the force of the storm. Even houses that remained standing were covered in mud. In total, 38 people were killed and the lives of the survivors were wrecked as they had lost so much personal property. Power lines, schools and factories were destroyed. Although tornadoes are an annual event in this part of America (and this is shown by the trained and organised response of the people to the disaster, particularly towards helping those suffering from heart problems), this particular one seemed to be exceptional. The base of the tornado was more than a quarter of a mile wide and it was joined by a second tornado; together they produced an extremely loud noise. These are the facts contained in the passage.

In general, the writer's thoughts and opinions about the tornado and its effects concern his sympathy and respect for the people who suffered it and his impression of the tornado itself as a terrifying, unnatural monster.

His respect for the people of Oklahoma is shown by his description of it as a "highly distinctive American state" and his account of the way in which its inhabitants took part in the "rare and unprecedented" gesture of slowing down their cars on the freeway as a mark of respect to the victims.

The language which is used to personify the tornado ("sucked humans and the fabric of their lives towards the sky and spat them back to earth") shows his sympathy for the victims and how he regards the tornado as a heartless monster which feeds off humans and discards them when it has had enough.

The writer seems to be critical of officialdom. He includes a quote from one victim complaining that "the government is going to bury my possessions". This makes the government seem heartless in its rush to clear up the mess before everyone has a chance to salvage what can be recovered.

The writer further represents the twisters as inhuman, terrifying monsters "grubbing up...spewing out...giant malignant earthworms...evil killer". The reference to the mushroom clouds at Hiroshima (where atomic bombs came out of a clear sky and destroyed a city) emphasises the destructiveness of the storm and its unfairness to innocent people.

The concluding paragraph shows that the writer feels the outside world has a very short memory when it comes to other people's problems. He uses irony to highlight the cynicism of the insurance company that wants to cash in "in this difficult time" by "urging prudent people" to protect their "material dreams" against "the next big blow".

What makes this a good answer?

- There is clear evidence that Sophie is **aware of the difference between fact and opinion**. She makes a point of showing this by dealing with the two parts of the question in separate paragraphs.

- The facts relating to the tornado and its effects are **identified and expressed in Sophie's own words**. They are well-organised and do not slavishly follow the order of the original passage. In this way it is clear to the examiner that the candidate has a thorough understanding of the passage.

- When dealing with the writer's opinions and thoughts, Sophie shows she is able to **infer** what the writer thinks and feels from the language that he uses. Not only does Sophie **quote** appropriate examples from the original article, but she also **explains how these selected quotations illustrate the point being made** – so making it easy for the examiner to credit the points made.

You need to make clear to the examiner how well you have understood the question; the examiner cannot award marks for points you haven't made. **Don't assume that some points are so obvious that they are not worth mentioning**; unless you show that you are aware of them, the examiner cannot reward you for knowing them.

It is your responsibility to make your understanding clear. One way of doing this is by **using your own words** whenever possible. (You will not be expected to reword technical vocabulary, however.)

It is the ability to identify and explain points which are **implied** in what you read which allows you to achieve top grades.

Another way of showing your understanding is by **reorganising information** from the original passage to match the requirements of the question.

An understanding of **tone** and **register** and how well they are suited to the chosen **audience** will help in an analysis of the writer's techniques.

Keep focused on the question at all times in your answer. Do not include irrelevant personal opinions or comments.

Key skills

These are the skills which exam questions on non-fiction texts set out to test:

1 **Your ability to distinguish between fact and opinion and to evaluate the ways in which information is presented.**
Remember: a fact is something which can be proved to be true; an opinion is what someone thinks about something but the truth of which cannot be proved. ('Apples grow on trees' is a fact; 'Apples taste disgusting' is an opinion.)

2 **Your ability to follow an argument.**
For example, you may be asked to show that you can do this by expressing something you have read in your own words or by writing an argument against the original to show that you have understood its main points.

3 **The ability to show an understanding of the ways writers use language, structure and presentation to convey their information.**
This involves analysing and explaining **how** these different devices are used, taking examples from the passage you have read and commenting on them in detail.

What the examiners are looking for

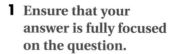
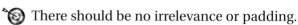

To achieve a Grade C when writing about non-fiction texts you should:

1 Show a sound understanding of what you have read.

🎯 In particular, you should be able to show a good grasp of the straightforward points contained in the original.

2 Select appropriate details from the passage which are relevant to the question.

3 Give evidence that the meaning of the passage has been understood.

🎯 You can show this by making an attempt to use your own words.

4 Select some references and quotations when writing about the writer's techniques and make some attempt to explain *how* they are used.

To achieve a Grade A when writing about non-fiction texts you should:

1 Ensure that your answer is fully focused on the question.

🎯 There should be no irrelevance or padding.

2 Show that you have a complete understanding of the material.

🎯 A consistent use of own words is a good way to give evidence of this and so is rearranging the original material in order to focus directly on the question.

3 Refer to a wide range of appropriate points taken from the original.

4 Give clear evidence that inferences have been clearly understood.

5 Adopt a consistently analytical approach when writing about the writer's techniques.

6 Give detailed references to and relevant quotations from the original to back up original insights and comments that you make.

Typical exam question

Read closely the newspaper article *Whose history essay is it anyway?*

What impression does it give of the way homework is viewed by the writer? In your answer you should comment on:

- **the presentation**   - **the content**   - **the use of language.**

[20 marks]

Whose history essay is it anyway?

DAD'S GOING THROUGH ONE OF HIS REBELLIOUS PHASES WHERE HE JUST CAN'T SEE THE POINT OF DOING MY LATIN HOMEWORK ANY MORE.

The increasing reliance by examiners on coursework (much of it done at home) has only swelled the emotional pressure on parents

THE current generation of homework-doers is fraying from the strain of overwork. Just when they've got home in the evenings and ache to slump in front of *The Simpsons* on TV they have to buckle down to a page of algebra or an essay on Anne Boleyn – although we parents wouldn't mind doing all this extra work if our children showed more gratitude now and then.

Of course, teachers don't actually send home a note saying: 'Dear Parent, draw a cross-section of a leaf cell in your child's biology book.' But sensitive parents feel under great emotional pressure to help out, because they don't want their child to be ridiculed in class the next day by children whose neat leaf-cell diagrams prove that they have made far greater progress in the important educational discipline of blackmailing their parents into doing their homework.

The pressure – if not the responsibility – to make sure that homework gets done falls on parents, which is dispiriting because their heart just isn't in it any longer. If adults once knew why it might have been important to know how to address a table in Latin, then they have certainly forgotten now.

And it's difficult to appear convincing when you tell a seven-year-old that it's crucial to learn the exact length of the Nile, when you know that the exact length of the Nile is a statistic that has proved to be of as much practical value in adult life as knowing which side of the bed the Prime Minister prefers to sleep on. If you ever get around to taking a holiday in Egypt, you can always just look up the figure in a travel guide.

An adult's eyes glaze over at the sight of fractions. Who cares what seven-twelfths divided by two fifths is? Adults know that in the real world there is no such thing as a fraction, at least not for anything an adult might crave: you can't have four fifths of an Aston Martin, or one third of a roulette chip. In the real world knowing fractions is a lot less useful than knowing the name of an accountant who has a spirit of adventure when it comes to tax returns.

There *are* ways of passing the homework buck. One popular option in parts of Hampstead was to hire clever Yugoslav *au pairs* who had fled their homeland and universities when Yugoslavia crumbled: to them, your child's maths homework was a doddle. One downside of peace in the area (Yugoslavia, not Hampstead) is that the supply of these smart *au pairs* has shrivelled.

Another is to slip your children some money and pack them off to an Internet café where they post their A-Level physics homework into cyberspace and wait for show-offs to file back the solutions: an insider advises plumping for German respondents, who are more concise than Americans, which means there is less to download.

The increasing reliance by school examiners on coursework (much of it done at home) for a pupil's end-of-year exam marks has only swelled the emotional pressure on parents. In the old days, if their children failed their exams you could blame *them* – if only they had revised a bit harder!

But now it is the parents who feel guilty. 'Maybe I should have gone to the National Portrait Gallery and bought postcards of Henry VIII's six wives for the history coursework,' they chastise themselves. Not that you can just glue them onto a sheet of A4 any more. Home computers with desktop publishing programs mean that every parent can be enough of a typographer and dust jacket designer to make their children's project really stand out from the rest of the dossiers handed in to the teacher.

Many parents worry that their children might be genetically programmed to find homework irksome, but a visit to a Harley Street specialist will show that there is often a simple treatment for this – known as 'monetary bribes'. Some parents console themselves with the knowledge that Solomon, Chaucer and Shakespeare never did a jot of homework whereas Roy Keane, Kylie Minogue and Gareth Gates did. Discuss.

Other parents like to try out the latest tricks to make homework palatable. A teacher in a Los Angeles school decided to teach maths in an argot more in tune with the rhythms of his pupils' lives and resorted to rap, such as: 'Six times seven is 42, Babe I wanna make love to you.' Try this at home: 'Henry VIII he did not grieve, when he divorced Anne of Cleves.' Still making no progress? What about: 'Write your piece on Paul Revere, or I'll clip you round the ear.'

> 'In the real world there is no such thing as a fraction'

By Joe Joseph for *The Times*, London, 20 January 1997

What are the key words in this question?

● *Read closely* Close reading is a key skill. You should spend at least 10 minutes reading the passage and gaining as full an understanding of it as you can. Keep the question at the front of your mind as you read and ask yourself questions to ensure that you can see how the main issues can be answered.

● *Impression* This means that you should attempt to show an understanding of what you think the writer's purpose is and how effectively it has been passed on to the reader (that is, *you*).

● *Presentation* In general, this refers to the way the writing is presented on the page (the use of columns, photographs, headlines, etc.). However, it also implies that there should be some consideration of the way the writer has presented his argument.

● *Content* This refers to the examples and other points which the writer uses to interest the reader. Does the passage contain facts, opinions or a mixture of both?

● *Use of language* This is an argumentative piece of writing. How does the writer use language to get you to share his point of view? You should consider the **vocabulary** he uses and the **implications** of particular words and phrases. **Identifying and explaining the writer's tone of voice (register)** is also important.

Jason's Grade C answer

The article is set out in columns and is clearly from a newspaper. There is a photograph of a rather bored looking boy trying to do his homework and his thoughts are shown in a bubble. It's quite a large picture and will attract the reader's attention. It might make readers think of their own school days and how they found homework boring too. There's also a quotation in the middle of the page which says "In the real world there's no such thing as a fraction." This also suggests that the writer is not very much in favour of homework.

The writer makes quite a lot of jokes in the article because he talks about parents doing homework for children as if it's something they're expected to do. He says what they really want to do is watch "The Simpsons" instead like a lot of children do. He then goes on to talk about a lot of things which teachers expect you to learn, like the length of the Nile, which are of no use in real life.

Good points

Jason's answer is a sound C Grade for the following reasons:

UNDERSTANDING: There is quite a good understanding of the presentation of the article and some relevant comments which attempt to explain how the presentation conveys the writer's feelings. The final sentence of the first paragraph also indicates a sound understanding of the writer's point of view.

REFERENCES: There are some appropriate references to the content of the article and some relevant details have been identified.

LANGUAGE: Although the comments about the writer's use of language tend to be descriptive, the final point, which shows an understanding of the writer's tone, is sufficient to confirm this as a secure C Grade response.

Then he talks about ways in which parents can get out of doing homework by sending their children off to an internet café so that they can find out the answers and says that old-fashioned famous people like Shakespeare never did homework but modern people like Roy Keane and Kylie Minogue did and that would seem to suggest that homework is a waste of time.

The language the writer uses is usually quite straightforward and easy to understand but he does also use some formal language like "monetary bribes" which suggest that he is writing for a broadsheet newspaper and an educated audience. However, some of his language is quite chatty and he uses slang like "clip you round the ear" which suggests that he's not always being serious.

How to score higher marks

- A better answer would be structured less around description/narrative and would concentrate more on **analysis** and **explanation** of the points made.

- The response should be more **directly focused** on how the writer views homework and how the references used show this.

- There needs to be more detailed explanation about how the examples of content which have been chosen indicate that the writer has some doubts about the value of homework. Remember: you have to convince the examiner that you have understood the question.

- More detailed explanation and **comment about the writer's use of language** would produce a better answer. There should be comment about some of the words the writer uses and why they help to create a particular response from the reader.

- Comments about language should be more **precisely focused on specific examples** rather than generalised assertions.

A better answer

This is a better answer, which includes many of these suggestions:

The writer clearly thinks that doing homework is a waste of time, especially when it seems to be common practice that it's done by parents instead of children. This point is conveyed by the catchy headline "Whose history essay is it anyway?" and the photograph with the article which shows a schoolboy looking fed up because his father is going through "one of his rebellious phases" and can't see the point of doing his Latin homework any more. The joke here is that the language of the boy's thoughts is like that which we usually associate with parents when they complain about their children's attitudes to school work.

In fact, the whole article is written in a rather humorous tone. The writer starts off by reversing the roles of parents and children and makes great use of applying vocabulary usually connected with children to the parents. For example, he talks about parents being "sensitive" and "under great emotional pressure". The whole situation seems to be one in which the children have the upper hand by "blackmailing" their parents into doing homework because they, the parents, don't want their children to be ridiculed in class because their efforts were not good enough.

However, the writer also makes the point that, much as parents want to help their children to do well, they also realise that as you grow older, many of the things which seemed to be so important when you were at school are of no use at all in real life. Studying Latin would seem to have been a particular waste of time if all it can do is enable you to talk to a table and there really is no point in committing factual details like the length of the Nile to memory when they can easily be looked up in a book. He then goes on to suggest ways that parents can avoid the chore of having to do homework, such as by using the internet or hiring intelligent au pairs. These seem to be somewhat extreme methods and the use of hyperbole helps to emphasise how pointless the whole thing is.

The writer does seem to have a more serious point under the generally light-hearted tone, however. He is certainly questioning the relevance of much of what is required to be learnt in schools and he does this by mentioning that great writers and thinkers such as Solomon, Shakespeare and Chaucer never did homework whereas minor modern celebrities did. This suggests that maybe homework is a waste of time, especially as those mentioned as having done it tend to be names of people we may not necessarily take seriously. Towards the end of the article, the writer adopts a more formal tone and makes his point through this mock seriousness. He uses words like "children might be genetically programmed to find homework irksome" and that they should be given the treatment of "monetary bribes". In the context of the article as a whole this overstatement produces an ironic effect. This is further emphasised by the deliberately colloquial closing statement which puts everything back into perspective and makes us realise that one of the main points the writer is making is how easy it is to cheat by getting someone else to do your coursework and homework and if such cheating takes place it really ought to be punished and not accepted as normal practice.

Typical exam question

The article *Bouncing back* gives advice on coping with bullying.

By close reference to the form, layout and language of the article:

1 Explain the audience for whom the article has been written.   [5 marks]
2 Explore how successful you think the writer has been in appealing to that audience.   [15 marks]

Bouncing

BULLYING: Mizz DIAGNOSIS

When you're down, there's only one thing to do: jump right up again...

If anyone's ever told you bullying's just part of growing up, erase that from your memory now. Unlike periods and spots, being picked on isn't something you have to learn to deal with. And it's wrong to think you're weak if you can't cope. It's a major problem that leaves you feeling scared and lonely. In fact, it can totally wreck your confidence.

Some people get so depressed about being bullied that they need counselling. For others, suicide seems to be the only option. Just last September, 12-year-old Emma Morrison from Edinburgh decided to end her own life rather than face her bullies for one more day. It sounds drastic but, sadly, she's not the only one who's felt like there's no way out.

You can get through it, though. If you're being bullied, you have the power to turn the situation around and become a stronger person. Look at Victoria Beckham, Eminem and Gareth Gates. They were all bullied when they were younger, but now they're all mega-strong and an inspiration to loads of people. You can be, too. Just take a seat in our bully clinic and we'll try and patch you up. You'll be on the road to recovery in no time...

back

VE PRESCRIBE: VACCINATION

rotect yourself against the ullying bug…

Whether you've got a problem with a bully or not, you can actively prevent a lly culture from developing by making your hool a "no tolerance" zone. Your school ould have its own anti-bullying policy yway, but you can still help keep the rridors fear-free. Call a meeting with your achers and organise a survey so everyone n have their say. Suggest having an anti-llying week or create an anonymous mments box for people to pop their ncerns into.

Loads of schools have peer-counselling schemes, too, where older pupils talk rough problems with younger students. So art one up. If you raise awareness and get ople talking, a potential bully will think twice out teasing someone.

VE PRESCRIBE: MEDICATION

reat the symptoms of the ullying bug…

First off, don't spend your weekends trying to work out why you're being cked on. It's not your fault. Often, it's just e bullies' way of making themselves feel etter and more secure about their own lives. u'd be doing yourself down if you tried to nange in any way, cos there's nothing wrong ith you. We love you just the way you are.

Tempting as it is to bunk off school so you can avoid being bullied, your place is : your desk. Each time you shout, "Here" hen your teacher takes the morning register, s a triumph over your bullies. That way, u're showing them you've got a right to be ere and they're not gonna win. Besides, you on't want to end up falling behind, do you?

Whenever the bullies are on your back and you're feeling low, remind yourself of everything you've got going for you. C'mon, there's tons! Think of your friends and family that love you, your obsession for Justin T, the hobbies you're fab at. Write down all your talents, and any compliments people pay you. Now feel those positive thoughts flow through you. But if it's still getting you down, give ChildLine a call on 0800-1111 or email Help@bullyingonline.co.uk. There are people out there you can talk to and trust.

Annoyingly, bullies always seem to know exactly how to wind you up. But try not to show 'em that they're affecting you. They're looking for a reaction and will get a kick out of knowing you're upset or angry. No matter what they say to you, stay calm. The next time someone disses you, why not try saying (pleasantly and politely), "You're entitled to your opinion," and leave it at that? Don't get into a slanging match, though – it might escalate into something worse. Probably the best thing to do is ignore them. It's tough but they'll get bored eventually, honest!

When you're out and about, remember to stand tall. If you shuffle along with your head down, hoping not to get noticed, a bully might think you're an easy target. The more invisible you try to be, the more you tend to stick out. Instead, you wanna be striding when you walk, with your head held high. Practise it now in your mirror. Next time you go through the school gates, you'll send out the message that you're strong, confident and won't tolerate bullying. It works – even if you're shaking inside.

It's really helpful to learn some avoidance tactics. If you get bullied in the playground at lunchtimes, go and sit somewhere else. If it means hanging out in the canteen with loads of staff, then so be it. Yeah, it's unfair that you have to stay indoors, but while it's getting resolved, it'll help. Similarly, try to go to the loo in a group, and sit near the driver on the school bus. If you walk home, change your route whenever you can, so there's no chance the bully could be waiting for you somewhere.

In sticky situations, like if a gang confronts you, stay calm. Look 'em in the eye and ask them firmly to stop. Don't fight back. It solves nothing and might make things worse. If they're demanding cash, hand it over. Remember, you're more valuable than a pile of pennies. Then leave as soon as you can, and go spill to the nearest adult.

Bullying's a massive blow to your confidence. So how 'bout taking up self-defence, judo or karate? Not so you can bash 'em though. It'll help rebuild your courage cos you'll know you can defend yourself if you ever need to. Even if that's not your thing, you should still start a new hobby or join a youth club. You'll meet new friends and your self-esteem will soar.

WE PRESCRIBE: A CURE

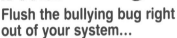

Flush the bullying bug right out of your system…

The only way you're gonna rid yourself of the bullying bug is to tell someone what's going on. It can be any adult you trust – your ma, gran, dad, sis, anyone. If you need support, take a friend with you. If talking about it is too tough, write it down in a letter. Lots of people find it helps to keep a diary about what's been happening…

Alternatively, you can talk to a teacher. Your school has an obligation to protect you from bullies. But they need to know about it first. If you're not sure how to bring it up, pretend you need some homework help and stay behind after class so you can have a quiet word with your teacher. Or get your folks to go and see the Head. Don't worry, they won't tell everyone about it in assembly the next morning. If the bullying doesn't stop and you feel your school's not doing enough, your folks can make a formal complaint to the Local Education Authority. But if you're still not happy, you could always discuss moving schools. It might seem a bit extreme, but you don't have to stay put and suffer.

You're not being a grass when you tell an adult about a bully. You're just fighting for the right to live your life how you want. Feeling better yet?

AFTER-CARE

Oh, just one more thing. Even after the bullying stops, it'll still take you time to get over what's happened. So don't give yourself a hard time. You'll need time to recover.

What are the key words in this question?

- *Form* This refers to the type of article which it is; for example, is it a narrative story, a newspaper or magazine article, an interview, etc.?

- *Layout* This refers to the ways in which print, headlines, photographs, illustrations, etc. are included in the article.

- *Explain* State your understanding based on what you have interpreted from the **analysis** of layout, content and language.

- *Audience* This refers to the particular group of people for whom the article is intended to appeal.

- *Explore* Write at some length about the different ways in which the writer sets out to interest his or her chosen audience.

Lyndsay's Grade A answer

1. This article would seem to have been written for a teenage magazine. Its headline is colourful and informal in appearance and it uses different colours of print throughout the article. The article is broken up by sub-headings and at the end a final point is emphasised by being placed within a circle which makes it stand out from the rest of the article. The overall appearance of the page is friendly and informal and this would be likely to appeal to a teenage audience as they wouldn't feel threatened by something which looks too much like a text book. There is a photograph of people's faces and all of them are smiling; this would help to reassure readers who might be worried about being bullied themselves. All the faces in the photograph are of girls which would seem to suggest that this is a magazine aimed mainly at girls.

2. The article is also laid out to look like it's giving advice for dealing with an illness or medical problem as each section begins with the words "We prescribe" and contains illustrations of medicine being poured into a spoon. As well as this, each paragraph has a cross at the start. The cross is associated with first aid and this clever piece of layout also succeeds in making the readers realise that the issue they are dealing with is a serious one but one which can be cured.

The comparison with a medical article runs all the way through the article. The words "vaccination", "medication" and "a cure" are all highlighted in bold black type and they're all presented as part of the process of dealing with the bullying bug. A bug is usually thought of as something which is irritating and inconvenient but not particularly serious and so this again suggests that although bullying may be annoying, it can be cured if you follow the right procedure. The language used throughout the article is colloquial and friendly in tone, for example, it uses abbreviations like "cos". The writer also uses the second person pronoun "you" so the reader feels that she is being spoken to personally and is therefore more likely to take note of much of the good advice that it contains. The tone of the article seems to hit exactly the right note; the content indicates that the writer has a very thorough knowledge of the many different issues concerned with bullying, but does not present them in a dull or boring way and also does not talk down to the readers. It's friendly and comforting and shows concern and understanding – the closing question "Feeling better yet?" is very effective and overall the article is very successful in achieving its purpose.

What makes this a good answer?

- Lyndsay's comments are **clearly focused on the question**. The first sentence states who the audience for the article is and this is followed by explanations which are fully illustrated by **quotations and references**.

- The answer is a very full one; Lyndsay not only appreciates that this is a magazine article aimed at teenage girls but **explains her reasons** for concluding this.

- All the elements of the question are fully covered in both parts of the answer in such a way that a **full overall understanding** is revealed. A less good answer would simply make the points as a list without connecting them together.

- Lyndsay is not afraid to look for and explain some **more inferential details**, e.g. by linking the red crosses to the idea of first aid and healing.

- There is a **clearly stated conclusion** in which Lyndsay sums up the points made and brings her answer back to the question being answered.

Don't forget ...

When writing about media texts you must show that you understand the writer's **purpose and attitude** and how these are communicated to the reader.

You must express yourself precisely and **your arguments should be clearly structured**; the easier you make it for the examiner to follow what you are saying, the better the mark you are likely to gain.

You will be expected to explain how print and image are used as well as language and how they have an effect on the reader.

You should show awareness of **the writer's use of fact and opinion**. Media texts are often intended to **persuade** you to agree with a point of view and you should comment on how the writer sets out to achieve this. You should consider the effects achieved by the use of **emotive language** (words and phrases that appeal to the emotions rather than the head).

You should be prepared to **give your own personal response** and explain how the article affects you and why it does so.

At all times you should **justify any comment** you make by using evidence – references to or quotations from the text.

Key skill: analysing the use of print and image

- If a question asks you to write about the use of **print and image** (this may also be referred to as layout or presentation) you should think about:
  - how the words look on the page (the font style and size; use of bold, italic or underlining and colour, shading, etc.);
  - the use of headlines, captions, subheadings, bullet points;
  - the use of illustrations, photographs, graphs, statistical tables, etc.;
  - the way the material is presented on the page. For example, the relationship between text and image (are illustrations integral to the written text or are they placed apart from it? Is the page set out as landscape or portrait? Are borders or other design features used?

- To gain a Grade C and above, it is important that you explain how these various features are used to create a particular effect. Simply describing them is unlikely to give evidence that you have understood how they have been used.

- A good answer will make good use of **appropriate terminology** such as that used in the bullet points above. You should become familiar with these terms but keep in mind that this is an English exam and not a Media Studies one. You will not be required to use the specialist jargon you may have learnt when studying that subject!

What the examiners are looking for

To achieve a Grade C when writing about media texts you should:

1 Make a clear, competent attempt to engage with media concepts.

- This means that you should give a clear indication that you understand the purpose for which the text was produced.

2 Write a structured response which selects and comments on different aspects of the text.

- As always, you should keep a clear focus on the question; you may have to write about different media features (layout, the use of images, etc.) so you should make sure that you quote or refer to appropriate examples.

3 Make competent use of some appropriate technical terminology.

- You should be able to use correctly terms such as *headline, caption,* etc.

4 Show a clear appreciation of the links between image and text and give a clear explanation of how layout and presentation contribute to the writer's effects.

- You should be able to make relevant comments about how photographs, illustrations and other such devices are used to influence the audience.

To achieve a Grade A when writing about media texts you should:

1 Show a clear and detailed understanding and explanation of how form, layout and presentation are used.

- You should show a complete understanding of how the different media features used in the text combine to create the intended effect on the target audience.

2 Construct careful and logically structured arguments and explanations.

- Your answer should deal fully with all aspects of the task and develop logically towards a conclusion which provides an answer to the question and shows that you have a complete understanding of what is required by it.

3 Make sure that references to and quotations/examples from the text are fully absorbed into the answer and shaped for purpose.

- The comments you make should be explained in detail and supported by appropriate quotations and references which are fully focused on the question.

4 Show a sophisticated and convincing use of technical terminology to describe media features.

- You should be confident in your use of media terminology in support of your comments. This means that you should use it naturally as and when appropriate but not just to show off that you know the terms!

Typical exam question

Compare Passage 1, a non-fiction text, with the two media texts, Passages 2a and 2b.

Compare:
- **the form, layout and presentation of the articles**
- **what they have to say**
- **the language used to say it.**

[20 marks]

Passage 1

The walls of Marrakesh reflect this red land with a beguiling rosy glow which deepens as the afternoon light fades. Running unbroken for over 6 miles, their towers and battlements throw a spectacular cloak around the city. But if Fez was enclosed, almost hidden away behind its walls, Marrakesh is bursting out of them. The new town pushes right up close. It's colourful and expansive with broad avenues and a Las Vegas-like dazzle and swagger. Slab-like resort hotels with names like Sahara Inn jostle alongside a brand new opera house. This is an old city desperate to accommodate the modern world.

I'm disappointed. I'd expected something exotic and unpredictable. After all, Marrakesh has the most romantic connotations of any city in this romantic country. Perhaps it's because the snow-capped range of mountains that frames the city in every tourist brochure is virtually invisible in the haze. Perhaps it's because almost everyone I've seen so far is white and European like me, or perhaps it's because I feel, on these tidy tree-lined streets that I could be anywhere.

Then someone suggests the Djemaa el-Fna.

To get to it I have to leave the wide streets and bland resort hotels of the New Town and pass inside the peach-red city walls through the twin arched gates of Bab er Rob and Bab Agnaou.

Once inside the gates the atmosphere is transformed. Tourist buses prowl, but they have to move at the pace of a largely African throng. The tallest building is not an international hotel but the elegant and decorative minaret of the Koutoubia mosque, rising to a majestic height of 230 feet, from which it has witnessed goings-on in the Djemaa el-Fna for over 800 years. There is an entirely unsubstantiated story that because the minaret directly overlooked a harem, only blind muezzins were allowed up it.

The Djemaa el-Fna is not a beautiful space. It's a distended rectangle, surrounded by an undistinguished clutter of buildings and lines of parked taxis. Its name translates as 'Assembly of the Dead', which is believed to refer to the practice of executing criminals here.

It's bewildering. There's so much noise that they could still be executing criminals, for all I know. There seems no focal point to the commotion – no psychic centre. At one end, where gates lead into the souk, tourists take tea on the café balconies and overlook the action from a safe distance. The locals favour the food stalls, which are drawn up in a circle at the centre of the Djemaa, like Western wagons waiting for an Indian attack. They are well-lit and the people serving the food have clean white coats and matching hats. This concession to First-World hygiene is deceptive. The rest of the Djemaa el-Fna is a realm way beyond protective clothing.

Sahara by Michael Palin

Passage 2a

Marrakech

Against the back-drop of the snow-capped peaks of the High Atlas and set in a 1000 year-old palm grove lies the Imperial City of Marrakech. Every morning as the sun rises over the ramparts, the population awakens to the call of the muezzin from the towering Koutoubia Mosque, and a multicoloured crowd flows into the medina. Another day has begun. Plunge yourself into the souk's fascinating maze of stalls and discover carpets in colourful designs, fine jewellery, hand-made pottery and numerous items crafted from wood, leather and wrought iron, as well as sweet or pungent-smelling spices, oils and herbs. The focal point of Marrakech is the great

Djemaa el-Fna square. Providing an ever-changing source of entertainment, it undergoes an astonishing and magical transformation at dusk. Tourists and locals wander amongst the singers and dancers, snake charmers and story tellers. There are acrobats, tumblers and preachers, jugglers, magicians and rows of stalls selling a variety of mouth-watering foods including fresh citrus fruit. At one end you can take time to sit on a balcony and watch the whole spectacle as you sip a glass of mint tea. It is often called 'the greatest free show on earth' – though you are expected to pay for taking pictures or filming. Marrakech is rich in restaurants serving delicious local cuisine in atmospheric settings but even more exotic is a visit to a Fantasia – a lavish Berber dinner where, after a wholesome feast, the amazing cabaret is performed in a great open arena.

Cadogan Holiday Morocco Brochure, October 2002–2003

Passage 2b

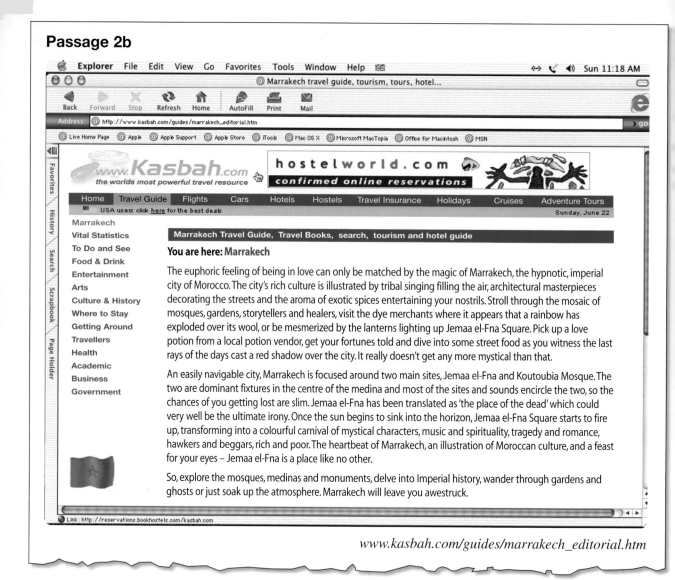

www.kasbah.com/guides/marrakech_editorial.htm

What are the key words in this question?

- *Compare* This means that you should write in some detail about not just the similarities in the passages, but also the **differences**.

- *Non-fiction text* This is a piece of writing whose main purpose is to **provide information in a factual way**.

- *Media text* This is a piece of writing whose main purpose is to **persuade or influence** the reader into sharing the writer's point of view. It is likely to use pictures, illustrations and other presentational devices as well as print.

- *Form* The form of an article could be that of a newspaper article, an advertisement, a website, an extract from an autobiography, etc.

- *Layout and presentation* These words refer to the ways the material is set out on the page and its overall appearance; they are very important issues to consider when analysing the effect of a media text.

- *What they have to say* This means you should write about the content of the articles.

- *Language* This refers to the words used by the writers, the **tone of voice** they use, the range and **variety of sentence structures**, and the effects they achieve through the use of similes, metaphors and other **figures of speech**.

Michael Palin's description of Marrakesh is set out in paragraphs and looks as if it has been taken from a book. The second passage is from a holiday brochure and contains some photographs of the country. These make this passage seem more eye-catching. The third passage is from a website.

All three passages are about Marrakesh in Morocco. At first, Michael Palin isn't very impressed; he thinks the place is colourful but he's disappointed because it isn't very romantic and that it's just like anywhere else. He uses words like "slab-like" and "bland" to describe the hotels. However, when he visits the Djemaa el-Fna he finds somewhere which is different; it's not a beautiful space but it's full of local people (the rest of the town seemed to be full of white European tourists) and is much more bewildering because of the noise. His attitude towards it seems to be a little uncertain; he says it's "undistinguished" and it sounds as if criminals are being executed there. His last sentence suggests that it's also not very hygienic.

The writer in Passage 1 is describing somewhere that he's visited and is trying to help the readers understand what he thinks about the place. The writers of the other two passages are trying to persuade their readers to come and visit Marrakesh and so they write about the town in a much more attractive way. Both of them talk about how attractive the sunset is there and use words like "magic", "hypnotic" and "mesmerised" to suggest that it's very exotic. The writers of these passages also talk directly to the reader, e.g. "Plunge yourself", whereas Michael Palin just describes things from his point of view.

Good points

This is a potentially good answer but doesn't make the most of the points it mentions.

CONSISTENTLY COMPARATIVE APPROACH: Sarah makes a good attempt throughout her answer to compare the different passages and shows that she has a good understanding of the differences in their content.

USE OF QUOTATIONS: Sarah's answer also shows a good understanding of the difference in the tone and purpose of the passages and uses relevant quotations to support this. She also makes some attempt to explain how these quotations help to convey the writers' points of view.

FOCUS ON TASK: Sarah keeps the requirements of the task clearly in mind; her introductory paragraph states her intention clearly and her conclusion returns to the main point of the task.

What would make a better answer

- Sarah needs to adopt a more **consistently analytical approach**. Remember that in this type of question, the examiner wants you to show *how* a writer achieves a particular effect. Sarah tends to describe the similarities and differences between the passages without making any detailed comments on them. This is particularly the case with the comments on the layout and presentation of the passages where the only comment is that the use of pictures makes the brochure more 'eye-catching'. A better answer would have developed this comment.

- More detailed references would lead to evidence of clearer understanding.

- Greater **depth and detail** in the comments would show a more thorough understanding of what the writers are trying to do. For example, Sarah's comments on Michael Palin's attitudes are insufficiently developed to show whether or not she has understood them fully.

- It's a good approach to think to yourself 'Why?' after every statement you make and then answer that question in the next sentence you write.

Niral's Grade A answer

An answer which followed this advice would read something like this:

All three passages write about the Moroccan city of Marrakesh. Passage 1, by Michael Palin, is an extract from a piece of travel writing, and records the writer's impressions of the city; his concern is to record these honestly and to give a clear account to the reader of what the town seemed like to him. The other two passages are written with a different purpose as they are from a travel brochure and a website, both of which are trying to attract their readers to visit the city. Consequently, the language they use is more emotive and they also make use of photographs which illustrate the exotic beauty and appeal of the town and which are intended to attract and interest the reader. The extract from the holiday brochure also uses different colours of print which makes it look far more interesting than the formal layout of Palin's travel book.

Michael Palin begins by describing the new town of Marrakesh; he finds it rather disappointing as it appears to have deliberately set out to lose its traditional qualities and attract tourists by building hotel blocks which are exactly the same as those to be found anywhere else in the world. He describes them as "bland" and "slab-like" with a "Las Vegas-like dazzle and swagger" which suggests that he considers them to be rather garish and unattractive. Marrakesh is "an old city desperate to accommodate the modern world". The word "desperate" shows that he thinks that Marrakesh is not being particularly successful.

However, when he visits the Djemaa el-Fna, he finds it much more interesting. The single sentence paragraph "Then someone suggests the Djemaa el-Fna" is a very effective way of emphasising the importance of this visit. It is when he starts to describe this place that the most direct comparisons can be made with the other articles. They both emphasise that this is the part of Marrakesh which tourists are likely to find most attractive. They do this by using language which emphasises it as being a place which is beyond the everyday experience of most people by using vocabulary which presents us with positive images of the place. We are told about the exciting entertainment to be found there consisting of, for example, acrobats and magicians; the food on sale is "mouth-watering" and "delicious"; "the magic of Marrakesh" is compared to "the euphoric feeling of being in love". Wherever you go you are surrounded by "the aroma of exotic spices"; you can "pick up a love potion from a local potion vendor" and watch the "mystical beauty" of the sunset. The square is a "carnival of mystical characters" and is full of life – a far cry from its name which means "the place of the dead".

All of these descriptions and activities are intended to attract the readers to visit a place which is presented to them as exotic and mystical; the writers of the passages are concerned with this alone. Michael Palin mentions many of the same things; for example, he mentions the square's name as meaning the place of the dead, but gives it a more sinister interpretation by saying that the name derives from the practice of executing criminals there; he then suggests that these executions might still be going on with the amount of noise which can be heard. Because he is not trying to encourage people to visit, his impressions are quite honest. He finds the atmosphere "bewildering" with "no focal point" and "no psychic centre". He is more cautious when writing about the food; although he mentions the appearance of hygiene, his final paragraph is more critical and this reflects the tone of his whole description. The other passages conclude with more positive statements referring to "amazing cabarets" and Marrakesh leaving you awestruck which reflects the different purpose of their writers.

What makes this a good answer?

- Niral has shown a **good overall understanding** of all three passages.
- He has made a consistent attempt to compare the passages following the guidance of the question.
- This overall understanding is reinforced by Niral's references to **specific details**.
- The response covers all elements of the question but in particular, Niral shows a good appreciation of the writers' use of language and how it is tailored to a specific audience and for different purposes.
- His comments are backed up by **quotations and references** and, in turn, these are explained to the reader.
- Niral's concluding sentence **focuses directly on the question** and provides a direct answer to it.

Don't forget ...

Writing a comparison means that you should show an understanding of what the passages have in common and also the differences between them.

When you are comparing a non-fiction text with a media text you should show an awareness of the **different purposes and audiences** for which they were written and how they set out to appeal to them.

You should always back up your comments with **quotations** from the passages or **references** to particular details of the content or of the layout/presentation.

You do not have to say which of the passages you prefer unless the question particularly asks you to do so.

It is not enough just to state differences and similarities; you must **explain** the effects the writers are trying to achieve by **commenting on the techniques** they use.

It is the ability to respond perceptively to the ways the writers use language which is likely to identify the best answers. In particular, consider the devices such as humour, emotive language, etc. which are used by the writers, and how effective their use is.

Don't be afraid to refer to your own **personal response** to the passages; if they have a particular effect on you (for example, if you feel that you have been persuaded to share the writer's point of view), explain what has done this – what works with you is likely to work with other readers.

Look closely at the ways the writers use **fact and opinion** and, particularly with the media texts, whether opinions have been presented as if they are facts (a fact is something which can be proved by external evidence; an opinion is simply what the writer thinks is so).

Key skill: making cross-references

- Show a clear awareness of the **purpose and audience** of each text. This will give you and the examiner a clear point of reference for the comments you are going to make.

- It is best to start from an **overall standpoint**. For example, you could talk about the use of photographs and illustrations and then compare how the different texts make use of them.

- Try to adopt a **consistently analytical approach**. Don't write about each text independently and then try to make points of comparison in a concluding paragraph.

- You may find that it helps you to make a comparison by thinking which text you personally prefer and why, but you should try to relate this to how successful each has been in carrying out its specific purpose.

What the examiners are looking for

To achieve a Grade C when comparing non-fiction and media texts you must:

1 Write a structured and full response.

🎯 You must organise your answer so that the line of your argument is clear and covers all aspects of the task.

2 Show a clear attempt to engage with media concepts.

🎯 You should make it clear that you have a sound understanding of the purpose of a media text and what distinguishes it from other types of writing. To do this you should show that you are familiar with appropriate terminology.

3 Explain clearly how form, layout, presentation and content contribute to the effect of the text.

🎯 The important point here is that you make a consistent attempt to explain how these features contribute to the overall effect of the text.

4 Show some appreciation of the way the writers use language.

🎯 Explain how the writer's choice of words helps you to understand meanings and inferences.

Support this understanding with appropriate quotation and reference.

To achieve a Grade A when comparing non-fiction and media texts you must:

1 Write a complete answer, covering all elements of the question and adopting a consistently comparative approach.

🎯 You must show an appreciation of the whole task and compare the texts by relating specific details to an overview, explaining and justifying your points and references.

2 Show a full understanding of what the task requires.

🎯 You should structure your answer so that it is fully focused on the question and include clear reasons for and evaluations of your comments.

3 Show a clear and detailed understanding of how form, content, layout, presentation and language contribute to the effect of a text.

🎯 You must refer to all the elements of the question and show a consistently analytical approach to explaining how the writers make use of them. Don't be afraid to include your personal responses as long as you can justify them by reference to the texts. At this level, well-developed and fully justified explanations of the writers' use of language to achieve their purpose are particularly important.

4 Show careful and logical organisation.

🎯 Material should be fully absorbed and shaped for the purpose with a consistently comparative approach and a conclusion which clearly attempts to answer the question.

5 Show a sophisticated and convincing use of critical terminology to describe media concepts.

🎯 You should be fully confident in your use of technical terms as part of your overall response; A Grade responses are distinguished by the fact that these terms are absorbed into the answer and indicate that the writer is thoroughly familiar with them without feeling the need to explain them every time they are used.

I   POETRY FROM DIFFERENT CULTURES

Typical exam question

Compare *Island Man* with *Blessing* showing how poets convey their feelings about the particular cultures they are writing about.

[20 marks]

Island Man

(For a Caribbean island man in London who still wakes up to the sound of the sea.)

Morning
and island man wakes up
to the sound of blue surf
in his head
the steady breaking and wombing

wild seabirds
and fishermen pushing out to sea
the sun surfacing defiantly
from the east
of his small emerald island
he always comes back   groggily groggily

Comes back to sands
of a grey metallic soar   to surge of wheels
to dull North Circular roar

muffling muffling
his crumpled pillow waves
island man heaves himself

Another London day

                                        Grace Nichols

Blessing

The skin cracks like a pod.
There never is enough water.

Imagine the drip of it,
the small splash, echo
in a tin mug,
the voice of a kindly god.
Sometimes, the sudden rush
of fortune. The municipal pipe bursts,
silver crashes to the ground
and the flow has found
a roar of tongues. From the huts,
a congregation: every man woman
child for streets around
butts in, with pots,
brass, copper, aluminium,
plastic buckets,
frantic hands,

and naked children
screaming in the liquid sun,
their highlights polished to perfection,
flashing light,
as the blessing sings
over their small bones.

Imtiaz Dharker

What are the key words in this question?

- *Compare* This means you should write about both **similarities and differences** between the poems. You can compare them in different ways such as content, style and language, etc.

- *Convey* This means that you have to show an understanding of the ways in which the poets communicate their **thoughts and feelings** to the reader. You must show that you understand what the poems are saying and how the way in which they're written relates to this. You should write about the **structure and form** of the poems and, in particular, about the poets' **use of language** (imagery, metaphors, similes, choice of vocabulary, etc.). Remember that **explaining** *how* these devices help your understanding is a key skill.

- *Cultures* It is expected that your writing about poems will be informed by an appreciation of the **social, cultural and historical background** in which they were written. However, don't forget that this is an English and not a Sociology, Geography or History exam. Sometimes – especially when you're in an exam – it's very easy to fall back on repeating notes you may have made about the poets' backgrounds and lose sight of the fact that you should be writing about the poems themselves!

Both of these poems are from different cultures. Grace Nichols is a Caribbean poet who lives in England and Imtiaz Dharker lives in India. They are both women. "Island Man" is set in England and describes how a Caribbean immigrant to this country still misses his homeland, especially the sea. In London, instead of waking up to the sound of the waves, all he can hear is the constant traffic on the North Circular Road near his house. The sounds of the sea and the sea birds are always in his head and even the "muffling" pillow on which he has been sleeping appears to have wave patterns. The last line of the poem "Another London day" is set out as a line on its own and seems to suggest how boring and uninteresting his life is now compared to what it was like in the Caribbean.

Grace Nichols is sympathetic to the feelings of the man she's describing as he's living in a foreign land but can't escape from the memories of the country where he was born where the weather was much warmer and the life was more relaxed. In the Caribbean there is sun and "blue surf" but London is "dull" and "grey".

In "Blessing" Imtiaz Dharker writes about how important water is to some people in different parts of the world especially in somewhere like India. "There never is enough water" she says. She asks you to imagine the sound as it drips into a tin mug and says that it is like the voice of a kindly god. Sometimes the town water pipe bursts and the people are able to have a bonus supply of water so they rush out to collect as much as they can in all sorts of containers from brass pots to plastic buckets. The young children of the town dance naked in the water which the poet describes as a blessing.

Imtiaz Dharker tells us how much water is depended on by people of different cultures. It is seen as

Good points

UNDERSTANDING OF THE TEXT: Neil has shown a clear understanding of what both poems are about and paraphrased their ideas quite thoroughly. He has included some quotations, especially from *Island Man* and has made an attempt to explain how they help to convey the poet's thoughts.

FOCUS ON THE QUESTION: The opening paragraph indicates that there is a clear awareness of the need to compare the two poems and makes a sound attempt to do this. Neil's comments on both poems also indicate that he understands the need to explain the ways the poets write about their cultures.

something holy and precious as it is described as a being like a god and a blessing. The poem makes us realise that something we may take for granted is really very important to people's lives.

How to score higher marks

SUMMARY OR ANALYSIS? Although Neil's answer indicates that he has a good understanding of the poems, this is mainly through explaining what they are about in his own words. In fact, the comments on *Blessing* read very much as if they are remembered class notes and would benefit from being more **closely rooted in the text**.

REFERENCE TO THE TEXT: Neil's textual references are somewhat superficial and could be improved by more detailed comment; what effect do the poets achieve by their choice of vocabulary, the use of repetition, etc.?

FOCUS ON THE QUESTION: Neil's answer could also be improved by making more consistent and specific comparisons between the poems.

A better answer

This is a better answer and includes many of these suggestions:

Both "Island Man" and "Blessing" begin by referring to water. In "Island Man" it is the sound of the "blue surf" with its "steady breaking and wombing" which is in the head of the Caribbean man waking up in the midst of London's "dull North Circular roar". The poet, Grace Nichols, presents us with the experience of this man living in a culture different from that of where he was born. There, the morning suggests life and vitality; the sun surfaces "defiantly" and the fisherman are "pushing out to sea" to the sound of the "wild seabirds" from his "small emerald island". Words such as "defiantly" and "steady" suggest strength and purpose and the reference to "emerald" gives the impression that there is a precious permanence about his island home. The "wild seabirds" give us the idea of freedom and the difficult word "wombing" describing the sea suggests that the sea, such an important feature of the man's life, is responsible for giving birth to all life on earth.

Ironically, "Island Man" has left his Caribbean home to live in a much larger island where he is not in close proximity to the freedom and life of the sea which is so much part of the culture in which he was born. He wakes up slowly and with difficulty; this is emphasised by the repetition of "groggily groggily" as the sounds of his dream blend into the sound of the traffic outside his room. The poet cleverly transposes vocabulary here, as "soar" and "surge" are words more commonly associated with the sea. Finally he wakes, leaving his dreams on his pillow, to the monotony of "Another London day". Grace Nichols has effectively conveyed to the reader how powerfully someone's background influences their life and no matter where they are, how difficult it is to escape from the culture you were born into.

To Imtiaz Dharker, water is seen as something which is essential to life and how, in her culture, it is a precious blessing. The parched land "cracks like a pod" as water is scarce. Simply to imagine the sound of it — the poet refers to a "drip" which to us would seem a very insignificant amount — is like hearing "the voice of a kindly god". This makes us understand how much water is seen as a blessing. The rest of the poem describes a particular incident when the municipal water pipe burst. This occurrence is seen as something of a mixed blessing. The people of the town rush out to collect water as the drip has now turned into "a roar of tongues" calling them. They use whatever containers they can find to preserve this blessed substance collecting it with "frantic hands". Presumably, the townspeople are aware that the burst pipe could mean problems with the water supply in the coming days. The innocent, naked children, however, look upon the gushing water as a "liquid sun" and perform a dance of joy as it "sings over their small bones". The last line reminds us of the joy and comfort which water brings but also of its importance in ensuring that "small bones" are able to grow and develop. By presenting us with a vivid snapshot of this incident, the poet conveys how essential water is to her culture and how precious such a blessing is.

Typical exam question

Compare *The Lake Isle of Innisfree* **with** *Upon Westminster Bridge* **and show how the poets have used language and imagery to convey a sense of peace and tranquillity.**

[20 marks]

The Lake Isle of Innisfree

I will arise and go now, and go to Innisfree,
And a small cabin build there, of clay and wattles made:
Nine bean-rows will I have there, a hive for the honey-bee,
And live alone in the bee-loud glade.

And I shall have some peace there, for peace comes dropping slow,
Dropping from the veils of the morning to where the cricket sings;
There midnight's all a glimmer, and noon a purple glow,
And evening full of the linnet's wings.

I will arise and go now, for always night and day
I hear lake water lapping with low sounds by the shore;
While I stand on the roadway, or on the pavements grey,
I hear it in the deep heart's core.

William Butler Yeats (1865–1939)

Upon Westminster Bridge

Earth has not anything to show more fair:
Dull would he be of soul who could pass by
A sight so touching in its majesty:
This city now doth, like a garment, wear
The beauty of the morning; silent, bare,
Ships, towers, domes, theatres and temples lie
Open unto the fields, and to the sky;
All bright and glittering in the smokeless air.
Never did sun more beautifully steep
In his first splendour, valley, rock, or hill;
Ne'er saw I, never felt, a calm so deep!
The river glideth at his own sweet will:
Dear God! the very houses seem asleep;
And all that mighty heart is lying still!

William Wordsworth (1770–1850)
(Composed upon Westminster Bridge, 3rd September 1802)

What are the key words in this question?

- *Language and imagery* These words are telling you that your response should include an understanding of the effects achieved by the words the poets use. Imagery refers particularly to the **similes and metaphors** contained in the poems; language covers such things as the use of rhyme, rhythm and other poetic devices as well as the poet's choice of vocabulary. Remember that simply identifying poetic devices is not enough: you must explain their effect.

- *Peace and tranquillity* Again, these are words which should help you to **focus your response**; they tell you that the poems are intended to create such feelings and you should use this knowledge to structure your answer.

Lorna's Grade A answer

Both Yeats and Wordsworth write about peace and tranquillity. Yeats is in the middle of a city, surrounded by "pavements grey" (the unusual word order places particular emphasis on the dull colour) and is dreaming of escaping to a secluded island which he knows in the middle of a lake in the Irish countryside. Wordsworth, writing at the time of the Industrial Revolution, is in the middle of London early in the morning and is surprised by the peace, quiet and beauty of the scene before him.

Yeats' poem begins with a statement implying decisive action: "I will arise and go now". He intends to leave his present surroundings and escape to the isle of Innisfree – no doubt the word's second syllable "free" reinforces its attraction. Once there, he wishes to live a simple, self-sufficient life; he'll build a simple cabin (nothing as grand as a house) made of natural materials ("clay and wattles"). He intends to plant "nine bean rows" and have a "hive for the honey bee". The precise number "nine" suggests the modesty of his ambition, but there may also be a suggestion that it possesses some mystical power as nine is a potent magic number and Yeats' poetry contains many references to Irish myths and legends. The next line also makes his intentions clear: he wishes to "live alone in the bee-loud glade" and the peaceful sounds are echoed in the onomatopoeia of the open vowel sounds in this line.

Life on the lake island will provide the poet with the peace that he wants. Indeed, peace seems to fill the whole surroundings as it comes "dropping slow" throughout the day. The repetition of the participle "dropping" effectively slows up the line to emphasise the peace he feels and which lasts all day "from the veils of the morning to where the cricket sings".

The final stanza of the poem takes us back to where it begins; the tranquillity of the lake island is at present only in the poet's imagination.

Although in his mind he always hears the lake waters lapping, he is still standing in the roadways among the pavements grey (the harshness of the surroundings is emphasised by the harsher rhythm) and the poet realises his need to return to the place which is firmly fixed in his "deep heart's core".

The situation is somewhat reversed in the sonnet "Upon Westminster Bridge". Wordsworth is a poet usually associated with writing about the beauties of the countryside but in this poem he expresses pleasurable surprise at the beauty which can be found in a large city. London at this time in the morning is a sight "touching in its majesty". He has caught the city before it is awake and he is aware of the beauty of the buildings rather than the noise and bustle which is usually associated with them. Everything is "bright and glittering in the smokeless air". To the poet, this scene is more beautiful than anything he has ever witnessed in the countryside and he has never felt "a calm so deep". It is as if he has caught the city unawares and has been made aware of a glory within it as it sleeps with its mighty heart lying still. The final line of the poem reminds us of the tremendous power and strength in the industrial and commercial qualities of the city which are the attributes people usually associate with it.

In conclusion, both poets describe scenes of tranquillity, although Wordsworth is physically present in his whereas Yeats views his scene only in his mind. The language of both poems emphasises the beauties and special qualities of the places and both poets write in a measured, gentle rhythm which supports the scenes they are describing.

Why this scores high marks

COMPARISON: Lorna has shown a good understanding of the way the poets treat the same topic and has referred to this consistently throughout her answer. She has also clearly identified the **differences** in their situations and the way they have treated the subject.

ANALYTICAL APPROACH: Particularly in her comments on *The Lake Isle of Innisfree*, Lorna has shown that she is aware of the complexities of the poet's thoughts and of the **meanings below the surface of the poem**.

LANGUAGE: Lorna has shown a perceptive appreciation of the poets' **linguistic techniques** and has not only quoted relevantly in support of her comments, but has also explained how these quotations illustrate the point she is making.

TECHNICAL VOCABULARY: Technical terms like *onomatopoeia* have been used correctly and with confidence but not self-consciously.

Don't forget ...

Writing about poetry requires you to look closely at the poet's **use of language** and, in particular, to be aware of the **associations** of the words used. There are no right or wrong interpretations of a poem and it is your job to identify the **different layers of meaning** which may be suggested by the poet's choice of words.

When writing about poetry, you will need to refer to some **technical details** such as the poet's use of rhyme and rhythm and the regularity (or otherwise) of the poem's stanza pattern. Remember it is not enough simply to identify a rhyme scheme (abba abba, etc.); what matters is that you can **comment on the effects** the poet achieves by it.

Precise and relevant quotation from the poems is necessary to make your arguments convincing. However, you must make sure that you **justify** your reason for choosing a particular quotation and explain how it **illustrates the point** you are making.

You will also be expected to have some knowledge of **technical vocabulary** (such as metaphor, alliteration, etc.). However, writing about poetry involves more than the ability to spot such literary devices ('There is some alliteration in this line…'); you must comment on **the effect achieved** (e.g. 'The use of alliteration effectively slows down the line…').

It is more effective to work short quotations from the poems into the fabric of your essay rather than quoting at length; remember to indicate quotations by placing them within inverted commas.

You must express yourself clearly and coherently; think about what you are going to say before you start to write. **Focus your comments** clearly on the question and make sure that you conclude with a definite statement which refers back to it.

Key skill: comparison

- All GCSE poetry tasks are likely to require you to compare at least two poems.

- Remember that comparison means writing about **similarities** *and* **differences**.

- **Don't over-complicate your response.** It is almost certain that the poems you are set to write about will be on a similar theme or topic which will provide you with an overall area for comparison. Once you have identified this then you should consider the different ways in which the different poems treat this topic. You can do this either by writing about the poems in turn and drawing points together in your conclusion, or by writing about them both together.

- There are more things to compare than just topics and subject matter, for example, the form of the poems, the use of rhyme and rhythm, etc.

- When you are revising and preparing for the exam it's a good idea to try to find how many different ways you can group poems together as well as by subject matter, e.g. by form (sonnets, odes, etc.); by date of composition; by background culture; poems written by women poets; poems which rhyme and poems which don't and so on. How many other ways can you think of?

What the examiners are looking for

To achieve a Grade C your response to reading poetry must:

1 Show an effective use of quotation and reference to support your comments.

You must use quotations to show your understanding of what the poet is saying but you should also be able to explain how the quotations illustrate this.

2 Make some cross-references between different poems.

You should be able to write sensibly about the way different poets treat the same topics.

3 Show an awareness of the poet's techniques and purpose.

You should be able to indicate that you have some understanding of the ways in which the poets achieve their effects through their use of poetic devices.

4 Show an understanding of the poets' feelings, attitudes and ideas.

You must not only explain the surface meaning of the poems but show some awareness of the meaning beyond the literal.

To achieve a Grade A your response to reading poetry must:

1 Contain well-selected quotations and references closely integrated into your argument.

Your response must be tightly structured and the quotations you use should clearly and seamlessly be linked into your explanation of how the poets achieve their intentions.

2 Show close and detailed analysis of the poets' techniques.

You must be able to show a sensitive and consistently detailed appreciation of the poet's language, form and structure.

3 Show a sustained exploration of and sympathetic understanding of the poet's ideas and attitudes.

You must show a developed understanding both of the main points of the poem and also consistent and imaginative insight into the underlying issues and themes which the poet is expressing implicitly through the associations of language, imagery, etc.

4 Show a consistent and detailed appreciation of the relationships between two or more poems.

Your answer must show a consistently comparative approach; this does not mean that you have to write about both poems at the same time, but you must show a developed awareness of the different ways in which poets treat similar issues and themes.

Typical exam question

Write a letter to a cousin who is just about to start Year 7 at your school.

Describe some of the problems which might arise in the first week and explain how best to deal with them. Your letter should be lively and interesting and written from the point of view of someone who knows the ropes!

You do not need to include your address or the date. Begin your letter 'Dear…'

[20 marks]

What are the key words in this question?

- *Describe* and *explain*   These instructions remind you that the purpose of this piece of writing is to give information to somebody and to provide some practical suggestions of how to deal with difficulties.

- You have been given clear instructions as to the **form** of the task and the **audience** that you are addressing. The **tone** of your letter should be informal and appropriate to a younger relative. You should ensure that you conclude with a suitable valediction.

- You have been told to make your letter *lively* and *interesting* and have also been given the angle (that of someone who knows the ropes) from which to write it. You should, therefore, include not just **facts** but also some personal **comments** and **opinions** which convey 'insider' knowledge.

Extracts from Alice's Grade C answer

The beginning

Dear Natalie,

   How are you and the rest of the family? Mum tells me that your mum says your a bit worried about starting at the new school so as I've had several years of experience of the place, I thought I'd give you some advise about how to survive here. It's really not too bad and don't forget you'll always have me to look after you.

Good points

TONE AND FOCUS: Natalie has shown a good grasp of the appropriate tone to use and has made a direct attempt to answer the question.

AWARENESS OF THE NEEDS OF THE READER: She has gone straight to the point so her reader is immediately involved in what she has to say.

TECHNICAL ACCURACY: Overall, her spelling and punctuation are quite secure, but she's made a couple of slips. Can you spot where they are?

- As an opening paragraph, this has a **suitable tone and register**, however, Alice could have given a little more thought to its **structure**. The final sentence contains two ideas which might have been better treated separately and she may have given herself a problem in making it link smoothly with what is to follow on.

- The spelling and punctuation slips are really due to carelessness; a higher grade piece of writing would avoid such errors although it might make others as a result of using more ambitious vocabulary, sentence structures, etc.

The middle

Alice's letter goes on to tell Natalie about the school and of what she will be expected to do on the first day there. It contains quite a lot of useful information and gives a clear indication that she is writing from her expert knowledge of the school. This information is presented almost as a list, but in places it becomes a little muddled as the points aren't always carefully structured. Here is an extract:

> The school is very big and you'll most probably get lost quite a lot. The science rooms are altogether at one end of the building and some of the science teachers can get really angry if you're not on time for their lessons. The gym is at the opposite end of the school and if you have science after PE it can take you a long time to get changed and then you'll be late and be given a detention if you're not carefull.

Good points

USE OF RELEVANT EXAMPLES: Alice is continuing to write in an appropriately informal tone and has clearly identified a particular problem which her cousin might meet. Her inside knowledge of the science teachers is a helpful piece of information.

How to score higher marks

CONTENT: Although the information that Alice gives is helpful, it's a little disjointed and there's no clear focus on the requirement to explain how to deal with the problem.

STYLE: The sentence structures are accurate but rather repetitive. Alice should try varying the openings of the sentences instead of beginning each one in the same way. For example, she could start the last sentence like this: 'This can lead to a really big problem if you have Science straight after PE because…' in order to give some variety.

STRUCTURE: The structure is rather loose. Alice has a tendency to put down ideas as they come into her head without selecting them or thinking about how best to order them. She could profitably spend some time planning ideas carefully before starting to write.

The ending

Well, I hope what I've written here will have given you some idea of what to watch out for and how to deal with problems when you come across them. In particular, remember what I've said about teachers. Most of them aren't that bad really and there human enough to understand if you've got problems. The important thing is not to be afraid to ask them and, remember, you've always got me to sort them out if things don't work out for you. I'll see you in September.

Good points

LINKS: Alice has made a positive attempt to round off the letter with a conclusion which refers to and sums up the ideas which she's mentioned earlier.

TONE: Alice has maintained a consistently informal and friendly tone throughout the letter. Her sentence structures are more varied in the conclusion as well.

How to score higher marks

STRUCTURE: There are several positive qualities in Alice's conclusion but there's a tendency to cram ideas together without developing them quite as fully as she could do. For example, her final point about her being there to sort things out isn't clear. Does she mean that she will sort out problems or teachers?

STYLE: Those irritating spelling slips are still occurring and the letter would have been improved by including a correct valediction such as 'With love and best wishes' followed by Alice's name.

Typical exam question

Describe a dangerous place which is known to you and explain what makes it dangerous.

[20 marks]

What are the key words in this question?

- *Describe* This tells you what the specific purpose of your writing is; you need to give **precise details** about the place: where and what it is; what it looks like, etc.

- *Explain* You should give reasons based on your description as to why the place is dangerous.

- **You are not given a precise audience for your writing;** you should, therefore, assume that the audience is someone who does not know the place and requires particular details of it.

Extracts from Dan's Grade A answer

The beginning

I live near the seaside. Close by to me there is a famous beauty spot which is a high cliff jutting out into the sea. It is about 75 metres high and there is a precipitous drop on to the sharp rocks at its base; the sea boils and seethes around these rocks continuously and if anyone were to fall over the edge they would be caught up in the fierce maelstrom of eddying water and swiftly drowned – that is, if they survived the fall in the first place!

Why this scores high marks

- There is a **direct opening** which gives a **clear focus** to the writing. Dan then goes on to elaborate on the opening statement by giving **precise details** and then a clear reason as to why the place is dangerous. By using the first person pronoun, 'I', Dan also makes it clear to the reader that the place is known to him.

- **LANGUAGE:** Dan has used precise and **original vocabulary** which is sophisticated in places. (Words such as 'seethes', 'fierce maelstrom of eddying water' are evidence that Dan has thought carefully about choosing **interesting descriptive words** to give a clear picture of what he is describing.)

- **STYLE:** Dan has varied his sentence structures effectively to make his writing interesting. He starts with a short, direct opening sentence which immediately involves the reader and then ends the paragraph with an involved complex sentence which describes the dangers and, incidentally, shows that he can use **sophisticated punctuation devices** such as the semi-colon and dash.

The middle – an outline plan

This type of writing needs to be carefully structured and organised. Dan has described the place as dangerous and now needs to go on and identify specific reasons as to what makes it particularly dangerous.

For example, he could describe what precautions are taken (if any) to prevent people falling over the edge. He needs to include a description of what the top of the cliff is like and the dangers it presents to different types of people (children, sightseers, etc.).

The end

So, this place is dangerous for several reasons: it is an easily accessible beauty spot which is visited throughout the year by people of all ages from all walks of life. The safety precautions (a not particularly suitable wooden fence and some faded warning notices) are inadequate preventative measures either to restrain exuberant young children or to deter foolhardy adventurous types who want to go too close to the edge. Every year several people accidentally lose their lives here; there is clearly a need for the local authority to provide more effective safety measures, but perhaps they fear that if the element of danger is taken away its popularity may disappear. I know I would prefer to be able to visit and enjoy the beauty of the scenery without feeling my life was at risk and so would all my friends.

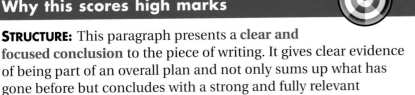

Why this scores high marks

STRUCTURE: This paragraph presents a **clear and focused conclusion** to the piece of writing. It gives clear evidence of being part of an overall plan and not only sums up what has gone before but concludes with a strong and fully relevant personal statement giving Dan's own point of view which clearly addresses his audience.

LINKS: Dan begins with a connective, 'so', which relates directly back to his preceding paragraph and clearly introduces the summative points which will follow.

LANGUAGE: Dan's continued to use **precise, appropriate and sophisticated vocabulary** ('inadequate preventative measures', 'restrain exuberant young children') and has shown that he can spell some potentially problematic words correctly.

STYLE: Dan has continued to use some **complex sentence structures** and written consistently in a register which is both personal and informative, which is what this task requires.

Don't forget ...

The **purpose** of this type of writing is to convey information; you must avoid the temptation to write a narrative.

The reader will require **precise facts and details** to understand fully what you are describing or explaining.

Planning and structuring your work is important; your paragraphs should be logically sequenced and organised and you should keep the requirements of your reader in your mind at all times.

Although you should use language appropriate to the task and remember that your main purpose is to provide information, you can still include some personal touches and opinions as long as they are suited to the task.

The triplet 'inform, explain and describe' allows for a wide range of tasks to be set; some may be more factual than others. Make sure that you adapt the tone of voice you use in your writing to match the exact type of task you are answering.

Key skill: structuring your work

- Organising your writing into carefully **linked and logically connected paragraphs** is an essential skill to use in this type of writing.

- A carefully focused **introductory statement** is necessary to convey the main purpose of what you have to say to your reader.

- Each paragraph you write should contain a **topic sentence** which encapsulates the main point which you are describing or explaining.

- Your paragraphs should develop logically from each other; remember to use **linking devices** which indicate how they are connected.

- There should be a **clear sense of development** of ideas throughout the piece of writing which culminates logically and inevitably in a concluding statement. An essay with a **positive conclusion** is a more impressive piece of writing than one which simply stops.

- Even when working under time restrictions, it is a good idea to make **a plan** of your writing. This should not be too detailed, but writing out your topic sentences is a good approach; there is then something for the examiner to refer back to if, by any chance, you fail to finish in the time available.

- As with all writing tasks it is important to show that you can **vary your sentence structures** to interest and involve the reader. The ability to use complex sentences with confidence is a clear indication of a writer who has a sophisticated control of English. There are three types of sentences; good writing uses a mixture of all three as appropriate:
  - **Simple sentences**: I know a dangerous place. It is a very steep cliff. It is near where I live.
  - **Compound sentences** (these are simple sentences made into one by the use of connectives): I know a dangerous place and it is near where I live as it is a very steep cliff.
  - **Complex sentences** (these are more grammatically sophisticated sentences which combine the simple sentences in a much tighter and more focused way): I know a dangerous place which is a very steep cliff, situated near to where I live.

What the examiners are looking for

To achieve a Grade C, your writing which aims to inform, explain or describe must:

1 Show you have a clear understanding of what you are writing about and the audience for whom you are writing.

🎯 You must show that you are clear as to the purpose of your writing and you must give evidence that you understand why your reader requires the information. It is a good idea, whenever possible, to base your information on your own knowledge and experience.

2 Be structured and clearly focused.

🎯 Your paragraphs should be linked both by content and through language (e.g. the use of connectives).

3 Interest and involve your reader.

🎯 You could do this by referring directly to your personal experiences and/or by addressing the reader directly to provide him or her with relevant information.

4 Be generally secure in spelling and punctuation.

🎯 This means that your spelling of straightforward vocabulary should be consistently accurate and that of more complex and ambitious words should be generally secure. To achieve a Grade C in a writing task, you should be confident in your use of full stops to separate sentences.

5 Show some variety of sentence structures and types.

🎯 There should be evidence that you can control some compound and complex sentences and that by doing so you can provide order and clarity in the information, explanations and descriptions that you give.

To achieve a Grade A, your writing which aims to inform, explain or describe must:

1 Use form, content and style which are consistently matched to audience and purpose.

🎯 Your writing should be clearly focused on the subject and contain a wide range of relevant and interesting details. You should show a clear understanding of the reader's specific requirements and subtlety in the way you present the material to meet these.

2 Show clear evidence of confident and sophisticated control of your material through structure and crafting.

🎯 Your writing should consistently show coherent and fluently linked sentence structures and paragraphs. You should show a varied range of ways of demonstrating information about the subject appropriate to your audience.

3 Show an extensive and original vocabulary range.

🎯 Your choice of words should be precise, appropriate to the task and interesting. At this level it is important that you show that you are in control of the words that you use and aren't just choosing the first ones to come into your head.

4 Use a wide range of punctuation with precision, contain correct spelling across a wide range of vocabulary and use a wide range and variety of sentence structures with purpose and precision.

🎯 Remember, that it is your responsibility as a writer to show the examiner that you are in control of the structures and technicalities of writing English and that you are choosing those which are most suited to your purpose. An examiner can only reward what he or she can see!

Typical exam question

Write the words of a speech to be given to your year group at school in which you try to persuade them that to travel is better than to arrive.

[20 marks]

What are the key words in this question?

- *Write the words of a speech* You are being given the format of the task; you are therefore expected to show an awareness of this and make some attempt to use an **oral register** (but don't forget that you will be assessed on your writing skills).

- *Your year group* You have also been given the **audience** for your speech; you should show an awareness of this in the content of your argument.

- *Persuade* What you write must be convincing and you should show that you can use language and content in such a way that it will influence your audience into accepting your point of view.

Extracts from Chris's Grade C answer

The beginning

I think that there's a lot to be said for travelling and I'm sure that you'll agree with me. Last year I went with my family on holiday to the USA. Dad gave us the choice between staying in a fairly lively hotel in Florida or hiring a car and visiting different parts of the country. At first I wanted to stay in Florida as I thought that there would be loads of activities to do but everyone else wanted to hire the car and now that we've done it I'm very glad that we did.

Good points

OPENING: Chris has written a direct, clearly focused opening which relates directly to the question and is likely to attract and hold the attention of the reader.

IDEAS AND STRUCTURE: There is a clear indication of the direction which the essay is going to take (although it may become unnecessarily anecdotal).

EXPRESSION AND ACCURACY: What Chris has written is a direct treatment of the question, written in an accurate if unambitious way. Although the sentence structures are somewhat limited, they are accurately expressed with no immediately apparent errors.

How to score higher marks

EXPRESSION: Although the opening has some good colloquial vocabulary, it lacks the overall **register of a formal speech**.

STRUCTURE AND FOCUS: There's a suspicion that the essay could go off at a tangent; Chris has introduced his family holiday but there's no indication that the essay will continue to focus clearly on the benefits of travelling; there's a possibility that it might turn into another of those 'What I did on my summer holidays' pieces of writing. To avoid this Chris should:
- decide on how he intends to conclude the essay
- keep his conclusion in mind to ensure staying on task
- make a plan of the main points he will make in order to reach that conclusion
- remember that each of these points should be developed on in order to produce a **fully coherent and convincing argument**.

The middle

It was in the middle of the second week that I realised why I enjoyed travelling. We had visited several exciting places such as the Grand Canyon. We had also been to a couple of big and exciting towns. We had seen a lot of different scenery. I realised that I wouldn't have seen as much if we had stayed in one place.

Good points

RELEVANCE: This paragraph is clearly linked to the topic and is well placed to explain Chris's response to the task.

How to score higher marks

REGISTER: Although the content is relevant to the task, Chris is writing in a narrative register. It would help to adopt a more **consistently oral tone**.

STRUCTURE: The explanation of why he enjoys travelling is clearly conveyed but it reads a little like a conclusion. Chris may find it difficult to develop the argument from this point without repeating himself.

SENTENCE STRUCTURE: The sentences are accurately expressed and correctly punctuated. However, there is a lack of variation in their openings; more variety would improve the grade.

The ending

So, by the end of the holiday I'd seen more than I'd ever dreamed of. I have a lot of interesting memories and they mean a lot to me. I told my Dad that I was glad that he suggested the idea. When you travel from place to place you have a great sense of freedom and you don't have to do what other people want. I got a lot of enjoyment from wondering what the places would be like which we drove to and I can definitely say that I enjoyed going to them as much or more than arriving.

Good points

CONTENT: Chris has kept focused on his argument and gives good reasons for holding his opinion.

CONCLUSION: Chris has made a positive attempt to refer to the topic in his concluding paragraph and has summed up his argument quite effectively.

ACCURACY: Chris's expression is accurate and his tone has been consistent throughout the essay.

How to score higher marks

FOCUS ON TASK: Although Chris has produced a consistently developed argument, he has not paid much attention to the need to persuade which is one of the key requirements of the question. He has relied on his argument convincing people rather than using any specific **persuasive linguistic devices**.

EXPRESSION AND TONE: Chris's tone is rather passive and descriptive; he has been asked to write the words of a speech and a greater indication that he is aware of ways of communicating dramatically and effectively with his target audience would be to his advantage.

Typical exam question

'The younger generation see reading as a thing of the past; we should close down libraries and turn them into internet centres.'

Argue your point of view about this statement.

[20 marks]

What are the key words in this question?

● *Argue your point of view* You have not been given a specific audience for this task so you should address your ideas to the examiner who is the reader. *Argue* suggests that you should construct a logical (and persuasive) piece of writing. *Your point of view* means that you can take either aspect of the statement to write about and that your argument need not be balanced. A good response is likely to show an appreciation of the points of view of both sides, however.

Extracts from Mary's Grade A answer

The beginning

And why shouldn't we do so? Is there really any point in maintaining these draughty, unwelcoming places with their dull rows of shelves all creaking under the weight of dry and crumbling volumes which give off clouds of dust and pollute the atmosphere? Far better, I suggest, to throw their musty contents on to the rubbish heap and refurbish their newly naked insides with bank upon bank of glittering screens passively awaiting the influx of eager technokids bursting with excitement to acquire the latest crumbs of knowledge which the world wide web can offer or to pass their valuable free time in downloading and playing the latest version of *Rampant Racing Road Rage Turtles!*

Why this scores high marks

READER INVOLVEMENT: Mary **begins with questions**. The first is short and sharp; the second longer and more complex. The reader is immediately involved by this confident opening.

VOCABULARY AND SENTENCE STRUCTURES: Mary's **vocabulary is wide and original** and clearly suggests an enjoyment in writing. **There is a good and varied range of sentence structures and types** which keeps the reader interested.

TONE AND PURPOSE: Apparently the content of this opening paragraph suggests that Mary is adopting a **deliberately challenging and controversial approach** to the topic which is likely to provoke a response from the reader; however, there are sufficient hints in her choice of vocabulary and in the rather overstated way in which some of the comments are expressed to suggest to the reader that perhaps she may be about to present a more conventional viewpoint in an original way.

Extract from the middle

In the white heat of our technologically-challenged world, the younger generation have no need or time to engage in the quiet and reflective pleasures to be gained by sitting in a comfortable armchair and allowing themselves to be transported into the world of the imagination created for them by writers such as Dickens and Jane Austen. No, it is far better for them to watch scenes of excitement and violence played out before their eyes as they are involved in the latest adventures presented to them by the great range of reality TV shows available for their consumption; the effort involved in using their imagination and engaging in the demanding and tiring task of thinking, is immediately removed.

Why this scores high marks

DEVELOPMENT: This shows a consistent development in tone and attitude from the opening. Mary's **ironic approach** to her topic is becoming clearly and effectively apparent.

CONTROL: The writer is clearly **in control** both of her argument and in the way she is **manipulating her reader** into sharing her point of view.

LANGUAGE: The language used is fully appropriate to the content; the **use of the semi-colon to balance the final sentence** and to throw emphasis on the latter part of it is particularly effective.

The end

So, in conclusion, what, may I ask, are the important values which should be instilled into us, the younger generation? Should we be passively fed with pre-digested entertainment and information which we can obtain at the push of a button or the click of a mouse or should we be encouraged or even forced into making the effort to research and evaluate information for ourselves, even if it means exercising our minds in order to do so? Do we really want our brains to become stagnant? A world run by machines may offer comfort and ease but what would our future be if the machines ever break down and no-one knows how or where to find the information to repair them? Libraries, and the books they contain, must be preserved.

Why this scores high marks

STRUCTURE: Mary has **sustained her approach and tone** throughout the essay but has acknowledged her conclusion by emphasising strongly what her real opinion is and leaving the reader with a forceful statement of it.

PERSUASIVE LANGUAGE: The response shows a very clear awareness of the need to argue and persuade and the **series of rhetorical questions** with which this conclusion begins is a very effective way of influencing the reader into sharing the writer's point of view.

RHETORIC: What makes Mary's conclusion particularly powerful is the **control she shows over the rhythms of her sentences** which involve and convince the reader of the truth of their argument.

Don't forget ...

The purpose of your writing is to argue, persuade or advise. This means that you must try to **convince an audience** to believe or do something.

You will need to show that you have a **confident grasp of your subject** so you should **support your argument with facts and evidence**.

The **structure** of your writing is particularly important; **plan and organise** your ideas thoughtfully and make sure that you have a **striking opening and convincing conclusion**.

Make sure that your tone and register match the demands of the task: *advise* means that your writing should be convincingly supported by facts; *argue* requires you to **present considered opinions**.

The purpose of your writing is to convince your audience of something; in order to do so, your **language must be precise** and you should show a clear awareness of how to use the **power of words** to influence the emotions of your readers by using humour or anger, for example.

Always **keep the audience of your writing clearly in mind**; you can argue much more effectively if you do this.

Key skill: structuring your argument

- With anything you write, your **thoughts must be effectively connected** to help your readers follow your ideas and understand exactly what you are thinking.

- **Your vocabulary needs to be precise** and carefully chosen; try to ensure that you can choose the right word to produce exactly the response you want from your readers.

- **Your sentences should be clear and complete units of sense and be logically linked to each other** through the use of appropriate conjunctions such as therefore, however, nevertheless, etc.

- In particular, you should pay careful attention to your paragraphing. Each paragraph should focus on a particular idea, be structured around a topic sentence and be linked to the paragraphs which precede and follow it. When you are planning your writing it's a good idea to **use topic sentences to provide the skeleton of your ideas**.

- In all your writing, but particularly that to argue, persuade or advise, **opening and concluding paragraphs are especially important**. Your opening paragraph should involve your reader and give a clear indication of the direction your writing is taking; your conclusion should sum up all that has been said and refer back to the main point of your introduction. Remember, there's a great difference between a piece of writing which concludes with a well-planned and focused ending and a piece which just finishes because the writer has no more to say.

What the examiners are looking for

To achieve a Grade C, your writing which aims to argue, persuade or advise must:

1 Clearly present the writer's point of view.

🎯 Show a **clear understanding of the purpose of your writing** and be consistent in the way you construct and present your ideas.

2 Keep closely to the format required by the task.

🎯 Pay particular attention to what the task tells you about **the audience and format of your writing**; if you are required to write the words of the speech, you should show the examiner that you have an awareness of the need to use an oral register. Beginning your writing with a statement such as 'Fellow students…' is a simple but effective way to do this.

3 Show an ordered and logical development of ideas.

🎯 Your writing should be **paragraphed** and show **evidence of planning and structure**. There should be a clear indication that your **paragraphs are linked** and that you have given some thought to how your points follow on one from another.

4 Show some variety of sentence structures and vocabulary.

🎯 You should show that you have an appreciation of how **varying your sentence structures and vocabulary** can be used to influence your readers to gain the effects you want. For example, short sentences can be used to emphasise a point and thinking carefully about your choice of words is an extremely important way to create a response in your reader.

5 Be secure in punctuation and spelling.

🎯 You should show that you are capable of being able to **use punctuation devices effectively to help shape your meaning**; in particular, you should be confident in using full stops to separate sentences. In order to produce the required response from your readers you cannot afford any possibility that they may lose track of what you are saying through failure to punctuate or spell correctly.

To achieve a Grade A, your writing which aims to argue, persuade or advise must:

1 Contain confidently and convincingly presented views.

🎯 You should show that you are **fully in control of your arguments** and that what you write is knowledgeable, informed and clearly aware of the need to persuade or convince an audience. Your writing should be **clearly focused on the question** and the content should be varied, interesting and relevant.

2 Closely observe the required format.

🎯 Read the question carefully and ensure that your writing consistently follows the format of the task in register and tone.

3 Be effectively and logically structured.

🎯 Show that you have clearly thought through and planned your writing. **Paragraphs should be logically structured** and expressed cogently and coherently.

4 Show a varied and controlled range of sentence structures and vocabulary.

🎯 Show that you have both the vocabulary to communicate the range and complexity of your thoughts and the ability to convey them convincingly **through complex sentence structures which will engage and control the reader's response to what you have written**.

5 Show controlled and accurate spelling and punctuation.

🎯 You must show that you are in **complete control of punctuation and the spelling of the words** you use. Writing which deserves a Grade A mark should use a varied and sophisticated vocabulary and the spelling of this should be accurate. (Examiners will allow a few slips, however!)
Punctuation should be fully secure and used positively to produce the required responses from your reader. In particular, you should show that you are **confident in using the more sophisticated punctuation devices such as the semi-colon**.

'Nearly all popular TV programmes are mindless entertainment; they are no more than moving wallpaper.'

'Popular TV programmes reflect real life and help the viewers to understand the world of which they are part.'

Analyse one of the statements above and, by referring to one or two TV programmes, comment on how far you think it can be justified.

[20 marks]

What are the key words in this question?

- *Analyse* *Analyse* **means to break something down into its component parts.** You should, therefore, indicate that you have a good understanding of all the implications of the statement about which you are writing.

- *Referring to one or two TV programmes* You need to write in detail about **actual examples to support your analysis**; make sure that you choose programmes about which you have sufficient knowledge to write convincingly.

- *Comment* This means that after you've considered your chosen programme(s), you should state how they help you to **justify the point** you are making.

Extracts from Jayne's Grade C answer

The beginning

I think television programmes tell us alot about real life, my family watch programmes like Casualty and The Bill and we all agree that their full of people you can believe in who do real things.

Take Casualty for example. You can learn a lot about what happens in hospital emergancy departments and realise that the doctors and nurses are just the same as ordinary people with their own

Good points

FOCUS ON TASK: Jayne has shown a good understanding of what the task requires and has made her position clear in her opening paragraph.

ARGUMENTS: Jayne's second paragraph, in particular, shows that she has some relevant ideas and points to make about this topic.

personal problems and worries. You also learn quite alot about operations and different illnesses and some of the things they show might help if you ever needed to give first aid to someone who was in trouble. It also helps you to understand the problems hospitals have with finding enough money to keep them going.

How to score higher marks

STRUCTURE: Although what Jayne has written shows that she has some good ideas about the topic and has chosen some relevant examples, they could be **more carefully structured**. The ideas appear to be written down just as she thinks of them rather than being logically ordered. A better response would treat the different ideas in her second paragraph separately and develop each of them into a paragraph of its own.

AWARENESS OF GENRE: Although Jayne is writing about specific programmes as requested, there could definitely be a more **analytical approach** in the way she treats them.

EXPRESSION: There are some **spelling mistakes of basic vocabulary** and on one occasion **a comma has been used to separate sentences rather than a full stop**. Jayne has also forgotten to place the names of the television programmes within inverted commas. Overall, her vocabulary and sentence structures are quite sound but unexciting and too many slips like those mentioned could easily reduce her grade.

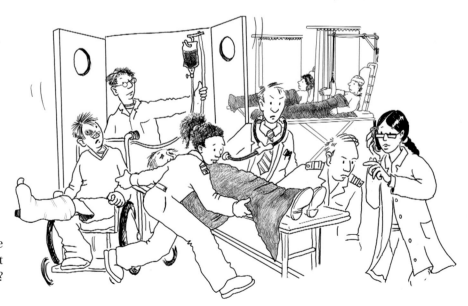

TV programmes like *Casualty:* realistic or just entertainment?

So as I've said, Casualty helps us to understand what goes on in hospitals today. Sometimes you might think that to much happens at once in the same episode. For example, there is nearly always someone who has a rare disease which is only cured at the end of the programme and there is always a surprising number of road accidents and other such matters. Usualy, in the final episode of a series something spectatular happens such as the hospital is attacked by suicide bombers or one of the main characters is killed off or accused of doing something wrong. This is a bit far-fetched and not always like real life but it does show you how people cope in an emergency and also reminds you that nobody is perfect or lives forever.

Good points

RELEVANCE: Jayne has continued to keep closely focused on the task. She is making some relevant comments and criticisms about the television programme and is also giving some reasons to support these comments.

STRUCTURE: This paragraph sums up the first section of Jayne's essay and relates it back to the topic. She is now in a position to move on to comment on another television series and has left herself several options by which she can link into her next paragraph.

EXPRESSION: Overall, Jayne's sentences show some variation of length and she has not repeated the sentence separation error which occurred in her opening paragraph. The ability to use full stops consistently correctly is one of the main features which distinguishes Grade C from Grade D writing.

How to score higher marks

DEVELOPMENT OF IDEAS: Jayne is clearly an intelligent candidate who makes some perceptive comments about the television series. However, she has a tendency to state a criticism and then move on to another. It would help to improve her grade if she were to devote some more time to **developing and explaining the points she makes in greater detail**.

MATCHING STYLE TO CONTENT: Jayne writes fluently and apart from the occasional slip in spelling and punctuation, her work is accurate. However, the register she uses is somewhat colloquial and as a result comes over as quite limited. A more sophisticated use of language and a **slightly more objective tone** would improve the impression she gives.

The conclusion

So, after considering two popular TV series, we can agree that popular television programmes do reflect real life. Both series contain characters who are convincing and could easily be members of your family or your next door neighbours. This makes you realise that people like doctors, nurses and policemen are real people with ordinary worries and problems. The reason we think this is because the acting in the programmes is good and because the storeys are well written. Both series show us life as it really is, they dont set out to make things more attractive than they really are and so we can believe in what they show and imagine how we would behave in the same situation. Their not like some films, such as Spiderman which has got nothing to do with real life at all.

How to score higher marks

FOCUS AND STRUCTURE: As already mentioned, this is a good concluding paragraph but it could still be tidied up and **focused more tightly**. The final sentence is not necessary and gives the impression of being an afterthought. Jayne should either have developed it into a separate paragraph or omitted it altogether. **The final sentence is always important as it leaves a lasting impression in the examiner's mind.**

EXPRESSION: Jayne's written expression is of a consistent standard. As already mentioned, a little more variety and sophistication would help. As a general rule, Grade C writing is accurate but lacking in range and variety. **Once examiners become aware of more variety in sentence structure and vocabulary, then they start to think of the highest grades.**

Extracts from Leroy's Grade A answer

The beginning

British-made television soap operas certainly set out to reflect the lives of real people and to deal with issues which are of concern to their viewers. However, it should be remembered that they are produced not with a sociological purpose, but with the intention of attracting and entertaining more viewers than those of similar programmes on rival channels. So, although the first half of the statement can be quite easily proved to be true, the second part, as to how far these programmes help viewers to understand their own lives, needs greater consideration. Although the success of soaps depends on presenting characters living recognisably ordinary lives, it does not necessarily mean that viewers identify and empathise with them on more than a superficial level. In order to consider this point further it is necessary to look closely at some specific examples.

Why this scores high marks

EXPLANATION: Leroy has made a **strong opening statement** in which he indicates a mature understanding of the implications of the statement about which he is writing and clearly **indicates the direction** his comments will take.

STRUCTURE: Leroy has decided to focus his response on TV soaps; this means that he has avoided the temptation to make too many unsupported generalised comments and has **developed his argument** in such a way that he can move smoothly on to **considering specific examples** in the following paragraphs.

REGISTER: As this is a topic which requires an objective approach, Leroy has appropriately decided to write in **an impersonal register** (e.g. 'it does not mean') which gives a more convincing effect than using the personal pronoun, 'I'.

LANGUAGE: Leroy has used a **mature and sophisticated vocabulary** which is appropriate to the task (e.g. 'empathise'; 'superficial'). His spelling of potentially problematic words (e.g. 'recognisably') is accurate and he is confidently **using complex sentence structures to convey the complex ideas** which he is expressing.

Most British-made soaps present recognisable characters living in a convincing background and this is enough to allow their audiences to identify with the characters' attitude and concerns. It should not be necessary to live in the north-west of England or to have been born within the sound of Bow bells to share the worlds of "Coronation Street" and "Eastenders" respectively. What is important is that the fictional characters who inhabit these worlds experience the same emotions and problems as those of viewers of the same age group and gender. This sense of identification is important in other ways too as it is an important means whereby families are drawn together and encouraged to share their problems. Soaps provide genuine family viewing as they are watched by different generations of the family together. I always watch soaps with my parents and sister, and even my grandparents if they are visiting.

Why this scores high marks

TOPIC SENTENCE: Leroy's opening sentence clearly **signals the main point of the paragraph** and provides plenty of opportunity for development and explanation of this point.

ANALYTICAL TONE: Leroy is continuing to write in an objective, impersonal tone to create a **scientific, analytical register** which helps to make his comments sound convincing.

DEVELOPMENT: Towards the end of the paragraph, Leroy introduces a **refinement of his topic sentence point** (the reference to soaps as family viewing) **which will enable him to develop this idea further** in the next paragraph.

The conclusion

In conclusion, it can be said that soaps are a valuable means of helping people come to terms with their own experiences and those of their family members. This is largely due to the skills with which the programmes are researched, scripted and acted. The audiences believe in the characters in the programmes as they can recognise them as being just like themselves, suffering from similar trivial but personally important problems. In my opinion, it is only when the plot lines become over-sensational (for example, when a character turns out to be a serial killer) or over-didactic (such as when a public moral issue such as abortion is dealt with in a somewhat self-conscious way) that the programmes lose their basis in real life and become no more than mere entertainment; in general, however, this seldom happens and a large number of viewers from all walks of life benefit from what they can offer.

Why this scores high marks

ANALYTICAL APPROACH: Leroy has considered the various implications of the topic and weighed them up through looking at specific examples, but, at the same time, has indicated that there are not necessarily any right or wrong conclusions to be drawn. All he has done is to **show a keen awareness of the possible interpretations**.

DRAWING POINTS TOGETHER: There is a positive sense of conclusion in Leroy's final paragraph. He is showing that this is a point at which he definitely plans to finish his essay and has **drawn together the main points** he has made earlier.

STRUCTURE: Leroy's conclusion shows an awareness of two very important techniques: he has brought up reference to the opening of his essay to show a completeness to his thinking but has also introduced a new idea which, although complete in itself, nevertheless leaves the way open for further consideration and indicates his **understanding of the analytical processes**.

Writing to analyse, review or comment means that you should show an **awareness of the different ways a topic can be considered**; it is important that you indicate to the examiner your appreciation of the importance of this.

You should try to show that you have some **knowledge of the topic about which you are writing** by using examples and evidence to support the abstract points that you are making.

Once you have considered different interpretations of a topic, you should weigh up the validity of each one; your language should reflect this (e.g. 'on the other hand'; 'however, it can be argued...', etc.).

You should not just review and consider different ideas but also follow them through to consider **how effectively they support your overall judgements** about your chosen topic.

In particular, try to show that you can **make connections between the different points of view** and examples which you have considered; this is a way of showing how perceptive your thinking is; if you can follow through connections in the implications of different ideas, you are doing this at quite a high level and will be rewarded for original thinking.

Key skill: writing for different purposes and audiences

- First of all, consider the key words in a writing task, for example, *analyse*, *inform* or *persuade*. These words are central to telling what the purpose of your writing is to be and you should think about the **appropriate language to use to create the required effect on your reader**. For example, you will use a different type of language depending upon your purpose:
  - *analyse* means that you are likely to use a rather **objective tone** as analysis is a scientific process and your writing should convey a balanced and thoughtful approach; you may use abstract terms and a speculative approach which could be reflected in **complex sentence structures and the use of questions**;
  - *inform* means that your writing should be less complex; your concern is to convey some information as clearly as possible and you should use **simple, clear vocabulary and sentence structures** so that the reader can concentrate on what is being said rather than how you are saying it;
  - *persuade* suggests that you wish to make your readers share your viewpoint even though initially they may not want to; you are likely to use **rhetorical devices** in your writing such as many questions which lead the reader to only one possible answer (that is, the one you want) and **emotive language** which will help to influence the reader's emotional response.

- At all times you must **keep your audience in mind** and think about what they are already likely to know and how to choose the appropriate vocabulary and tone of voice to involve them in what you are writing; you would need to adopt a different approach if you were giving information to your headteacher from what you would use if talking to a friend.

Key skill: presenting an overview

- You should attempt to **show an overall understanding** of the main implications of the issues about which you are writing.

- This type of writing involves showing an awareness of the possible different interpretations and judgements that can be made about your chosen topic.

- Follow through your different ideas and try to balance them together; it is likely that your conclusion will draw from them rather than finishing with simply accepting one to the exclusion of all others.

- In order to show your overall understanding you need to try to **make connections and relationships between apparently different ideas**.

- Remember that you need to **give examples and provide evidence** to support your comments. It is a good idea to keep to examples which are within your own experience.

What the examiners are looking for

To achieve a Grade C, your writing which aims to analyse, review or comment must:

1 Be supported by appropriate and relevant examples.

🎯 These can be used to illustrate your analytical comments.

2 Present a clear overview of the task.

🎯 You should relate this to the reader through a **consistent tone and appropriate vocabulary**.

3 Give a clear indication of your intended approach in the opening.

🎯 This should then develop in some detail to a **sensible and focused conclusion**.

4 Be organised into paragraphs of varying length which help to shape and convey meaning to the reader.

🎯 These paragraphs should be **linked by straightforward connectives**. The spelling of commonly used vocabulary should be secure and punctuation will be used generally to clarify meaning.

To achieve a Grade A, your writing which aims to analyse, review or comment must:

1 Show a sharply focused perceptive insight into the topic.

🎯 This can be achieved by **detailed analysis of specific examples** supported by **relevant and appropriate personal comment**.

2 Show a complete grasp of the topic.

🎯 Explore it thoroughly revealing a **varied tone and fully appropriate and sophisticated technical vocabulary**.

3 Show a very effective opening which engages directly with the topic.

🎯 This should develop into a fully coherent and sustained development and lead to a **convincing and balanced conclusion**. Paragraphs should show skilful construction and be purposefully varied in length, and linked through a range of connectives and connective devices which reinforce **a sense of cohesion in your argument**.

4 Be expressed through varied and elaborated sentence structures.

🎯 Spelling of a wide range of vocabulary should be fully correct (although a few slips are acceptable). There should be a good range of punctuation correctly and positively used to create specific effects.

NON-FICTION TEXTS

This is not intended to be a complete paper. What follows are three articles which are representative of the sort of articles you will meet in your exam and a range of questions on them. If you try answering all the questions, you will be practising all the skills and techniques you will need (whichever specification you are following).

Question 1

1   **Read Item 1, *Nightmare of the Grey Goo*. You are being asked to distinguish between fact and opinion.**

   Choose 3 opinions. Write each down and explain how you know each is an opinion and not a fact. [6 marks]

2   **Read Item 2, *Tiny robots with massive potential*. You are being asked to select material appropriate to purpose.**

   Explain, using your own words, what the article tells you about nanotechnology and advantages and problems which could arise from it. [10 marks]

3   **Compare Item 1 with Item 2 and identify similarities and differences.**

   Compare:
   ●   what they have to say
   ●   the language used to say it. [10 marks]

4   **Read Item 1, *Nightmare of the Grey Goo* and Item 3, *Who will control the nanobots?* Compare how the writers of both articles express their concerns over nanotechnology.**

   In your answer you should look closely at how the articles use presentation, content and language. [20 marks]

Item 1

Nightmare of the Grey Goo

PRINCE CHARLES has warned that life on Earth could be wiped out by scientists 'playing God' with potentially lethal new technologies.

The Mail on Sunday has learned that the Prince has summoned experts to a crisis summit over fears that the planet could be engulfed in a so-called 'grey goo catastrophe' caused by experiments going wrong.

The campaign reflects his continuing concern over environmental issues following his successful crusade in highlighting the dangers of genetically modified food, and centres on nano-technology, the cutting-edge new science that involves meddling with molecules and atoms that make up the universe.

His intervention last night set him on a collision course with the Government, which has given its full support to scientists involved in this controversial research, claiming it could be worth a fortune for British industry.

Tony Blair himself has described nanoscience as 'startling in its potential'.

But Charles won powerful support from Britain's best-known Green campaigner, Jonathon Porritt, who said: 'This research has radical consequences and we need to be much more alert about its implications.'

The row follows claims by some experts that nanotechnology could spark a freak accident – the so-called 'grey goo' nightmare – where tiny nanobots could gobble up the Earth.

Environmentalists deny it is science fiction fantasy and say it could happen if governments fail to impose strict controls on maverick scientists.

Enthusiasts say nanotechnology could create new miracle light-weight materials, cures for deadly diseases and super-fast microchips. Research is already taking place at some of Britain's most prestigious universities including Oxford and Cambridge.

The Americans see the potential of the technology for new defence equipment – including body-armour and light-weight fighting vehicles.

If the Prince continues to oppose Government policy, he risks a constitutional crisis. While he is free to vent his views on 'non-political' issues, such as modern architecture, as a member of the Royal Family he is forbidden from going head-to-head with the Government on matters of public policy.

Charles's worries were triggered by old-Etonian environmental campaigner Zac Goldsmith, who is emerging as one of the Prince's most important advisers.

Mr Goldsmith, editor of *The Ecologist* magazine, defended the Prince's decision to get involved in the row.

'He can play an enormously important role in leading the debate,' he said. 'The potential is there for the grey goo effect. It is a Pandora's box.

'With nanotechnology there is massive room for disaster. It is quite terrifying that there has been no debate on this issue. Some people may say the genie is out of the bottle already.

'But in fact it will only be pushed out of the bottle with billions of pounds of research money. There is still time to ask if we are wise enough as a species to handle this new technology.'

The Big Down report, published earlier this year by the Canadian-based ECT Group, is seen by ecologists as the definitive work on nanotechnology.

The survey recommends an international agreement restricting nanotech research. It also warns that even if the grey goo nightmare proves to be unfounded, nanotech poses other threats to the planet.

For example, it argues, some of the new miracle materials could have unforeseen side-effects – rather like asbestos, once hailed as a wonder-substance, which was later revealed to pose deadly risks.

Ottilia Saxl, chief executive of the Stirling-based Institute of Nano-technology said the new technology would bring huge benefits.

'There are great prospects, particularly in medical research. This is not about unlocking a Pandora's box. The idea of self-replicating nanorobots is pure science fiction,' she said. 'You cannot regulate every aspect of nanotechnology. We need to have a commonsense approach.'

Tiny robots with massive potential

Mail on Sunday Reporter

THE concept of nano-technology was first suggested by legendary US physicist Richard Feynman more than 40 years ago when he predicted the future thrust of technology would not be to build large machines, but incredibly small ones.

However, it was not until 1990 that the new science had a real breakthrough. A team of IBM researchers managed to manipulate 35 individual atoms so that they spelled out 'IBM'.

At its simplest, nano-technology is technology on the scale of a billionth of a metre or about 100,00th of the width of the human hair. It is science on the level of individual atoms and molecules – and it is only recently that microscopes powerful enough to study these basic materials of matter have been developed.

This new technology allows scientists for the first time to move around and, crucially, alter the individual building blocks that make up the universe.

Already experts have produced a powerful microchip just one millimetre across – so small it can be held in the mandible of an ant. Another breakthrough has been a tiny pill-sized submarine with a camera that, when swallowed, can spot internal bleeding or tumours.

However, most of the potential benefits – and risks – lie in the future. Experts say it will enable the development of artificial substances which could lead to ultra-lightweight aircraft or 'smart' bandages for faster healing. And according to nanotech's enthusiasts, even this is just the beginning. The next step would be to create 'universal assemblers': tiny robots or 'nanobots' that can be programmed to build just about anything, atom by atom, from the raw materials. In theory this would allow the manufacture of aircraft or cars that are 100 per cent perfect. Experts believe the first prototype nanobots could be developed by 2010.

There is another step envisaged by the nanotech scientists. They want to build more efficient nanobots that could make copies of themselves – to reproduce like bacteria. This is, in essence, what life does. A tree sucks air and water out of its environment and uses the power of sunlight to turn them into wood.

Scientists claim a self-replicating nanobot could 'feed' in a bucket of iron, sand or wood and in an hour it might make a trillion copies of itself.

But what if a nanobot fails to stop replicating itself? Doom-mongers warn that a mutant strain of these tiny robots could escape to a laboratory and begin 'feeding' on the matter around them. This is where the 'grey goo' theory comes in.

There are fears that these technologies could run wildly out of control. In the worst case scenario, the entire planet could be engulfed, the nanobots leaving behind nothing but a formless 'grey goo'.

Scientists disagree about whether we will ever be able to develop these self-replicating robots, although some believe the concept will be a reality in just ten or 20 years.

Item 3

Who will control the nanobots?

MY SUMMER holiday reading last year included Michael Crichton's book, *Prey*.

It's an entertaining bit of nonsense about a group of ruthless scientists working on a high-tech military contract who accidentally end up releasing a swarm of self-replicating, man-eating 'nanoparticles' into the Nevada desert.

The hero scientist just manages to save us all from global catastrophe. So prepare to be sort-of scared when the film comes out later this year.

To get your head round all this nano stuff, you have to think very small indeed. Imagine a length of cloth one metre long, and then slice it up into a billion fragments. Each of those would be one nanometre wide. A human hair is about 100,000 nanometres wide.

So how can anyone be talking about technologies operating at such an impossibly small scale? Astonishingly powerful microscopes now allow scientists to manipulate materials at the atomic level, atom by atom. And they're well on the way to building tiny robots (nanobots!) to carry out assembly work following sophisticated computer programmes.

That means there's already a lot of money going into nanotechnology – from governments (there's nearly £2 billion of global government expenditure per annum) and big business.

Britain has a reasonably good record in nanoscience, and the DTI has committed around £50 million to support a new UK strategy for Nanotechnology.

Some people see it as the most important breakthrough since the wheel; others believe it threatens the end of life as we know it.

Here's a classic bit of nano-hype from Mark Modzelewski, director of the Nanobusiness Alliance: 'The importance of nanotechnology to the future of mankind cannot be overstated. Nanotech's promise is clean industries, cures for disease, nearly unlimited energy supplies and perhaps the end of hunger.'

Erich Drexler, the 'father' of nanotechnology, enthuses about the potential for nanobots to whiz around cleaning up pollution we cause, or to 'cohabit' inside our bodies, eliminating cancers or prolonging life indefinitely.

On the other side of the divide are the prophets of doom. Bill Joy, of Sun Microsystems, conjures up a world in which nanobots get out of control, breaking everything down into a 'grey goo' in an uninhabitable wasteland.

And what if these technologies fell into the wrong hands, with weapons of mass destruction being superseded by weapons of nano-destruction?

Current reality is more prosaic than these scenarios. Some sun-screens now use nano-sized zinc oxide particles, and cosmetics company L'Oréal markets anti-ageing 'nanocreams' that it claims work by getting deep down into the skin. And a vast number of new developments are in the pipeline. The number of new patents (civil and military) rises steeply every year.

So should we celebrate the genius of our scientists – or gear up for public protests to stop the nano-juggernaut in its tracks?

I haven't a clue. As an environmentalist, I find the potential for reducing pollution and increasing the efficiency with which we use natural resources exciting.

If it is possible to revolutionise solar cell technology or grow products atom by atom, clean up our contaminated land or nuclear waste, then I'd have to be a curmudgeon to look this gift horse in the mouth. All I do know right now is that we have to engineer a far more engaged public debate about such world-shaking technologies. And we would surely be well advised to proceed with a great deal more caution and forethought than is currently the case.

By Jonathon Porritt

Question 2

Compare the ways in which the poets of *Night of the scorpion* and *Vultures* use living creatures in their poems.

[20 marks]

Night of the scorpion

I remember the night my mother
was stung by a scorpion. Ten hours
of steady rain had driven him
to crawl beneath a sack of rice
Parting with his poison – flash
of diabolic tail in the dark room –
he risked the rain again.
The peasants came like swarms of flies
and buzzed the name of God a hundred times
to paralyse the Evil One.
With candles and with lanterns
throwing giant scorpion shadows
on the mud-baked walls
They searched for him: he was not found.
They clicked their tongues.
With every movement that the scorpion made
His poison moved in mother's blood, they said.
May he sit still, they said.
May the sins of your previous birth
be burned away tonight, they said.

May your suffering decrease

The misfortunes of your next birth, they said.

May the sum of evil

balanced in this unreal world

against the sum of good

become diminished by your pain.

May the poison purify your flesh

of desire, and your spirit of ambition,

they said, and they sat around

on the floor with my mother in the centre,

the peace of understanding on each face.

More candles, more lanterns, more neighbours,

more insects, and the endless rain.

My mother twisted through and through,

groaning on a mat.

My father, sceptic, rationalist,

trying every curse and blessing,

powder, mixture, herb and hybrid.

He even poured a little paraffin

Upon the bitten toe and put a match to it.

I watched the flame feeding on my mother.

I watched the holy man perform his rites

to tame the poison with an incantation.

After twenty hours

it lost its sting.

My mother only said

Thank God the scorpion picked on me

and spared my children.

Nissim Ezekiel

Reproduced by permission of
Oxford University Press India, New Delhi

Vultures

In the greyness
and drizzle of one despondent
dawn unstirred by harbingers
of sunbreak a vulture
perching high on broken
bone of a dead tree
nestled close to his
mate his smooth
bashed-in head, a pebble
on a stem rooted in
a dump of gross
feathers, inclined affectionately
to hers. Yesterday they picked
the eyes of a swollen
corpse in a water-logged
trench and ate the
things in its bowel. Full
gorged they chose their roost
keeping the hollowed remnant
in easy range of cold
telescopic eyes…
Strange
indeed how love in other
ways so particular
will pick a corner
in that charnel-house
tidy it and coil up there, perhaps
even fall asleep – her face
turned to the wall!

…Thus the Commandant at Belsen
Camp going home for
the day with fumes of

human roast clinging
rebelliously to his hairy
nostrils will stop
at the way-side sweet shop
and pick up a chocolate
for his tender offspring
waiting at home for Daddy's
return…

Praise bounteous
providence if you will
that grants even an ogre
a tiny glow-worm
tenderness encapsulated
in icy caverns of a cruel
heart or else despair
for in the very germ
of that kindred love is
lodged the perpetuity
of evil.

Chinua Achebe

Examiner's hints
You will have studied both of these poems in advance of the exam and so you should have gained a good understanding of what they are about and the techniques their writers use. However, you won't know exactly what the question on the poetry anthology will be until you see the exam paper. It is, therefore, important that you read it carefully and decide exactly what it requires. Be careful to answer the question which is printed on the paper and not the one you hoped was printed there!

Question 3

Compare the ways the poets of *The send-off* and *The hero* write about soldiers involved in war.

[20 marks]

The send-off

Down the close darkening lanes they sang their way
To the siding-shed,
And lined the train with faces grimly gay.

Their breasts were stuck all white with wreath and spray
As men's are, dead.

Dull porters watched them and a casual tramp
Stood staring hard,
Sorry to miss them from the upland camp.

Then, unmoved, signals nodded, and a lamp
Winked to the guard.

So secretly, like wrongs hushed-up, they went.
They were not ours:
We never heard to which front these were sent;

Nor there if they yet mock what women meant
Who gave them flowers.

Shall they return to beating of great bells
In wild train loads?
A few, a few, too few for drums and yells,

May creep back, silent to village wells,
Up half-known roads.

Wilfred Owen

The hero

'Jack fell as he'd have wished,' the Mother said,
And folded up the letter that she'd read.
'The Colonel writes so nicely.' Something broke
In the tired voice that quavered to a choke.
She half looked up. 'We mothers are so proud
Of our dead soldiers.' Then her face was bowed.

Quietly the Brother Officer went out.
He'd told the poor old dear some gallant lies
That she would cherish all her days, no doubt.
For while he coughed and mumbled, her weak eyes
Had shone with gentle triumph, brimmed with joy,
Because he'd been so brave, her glorious boy.

He thought how 'Jack', cold-footed, useless swine,
Had panicked down the trench that night the mine
Went up at Wicked Corner; how he'd tried
To get sent home, and how, at last, he died,
Blown to small bits. And no one seemed to care
Except that lonely woman with white hair.

                                        Siegfried Sassoon

Examiner's hints
You will have studied these poems in preparation for your exam. You are being
asked to write a comparison of the way different poets treat the same subject. You
will gain high marks by showing a good understanding of the poets' feelings
towards their subjects and of the way they use linguistic devices to convey them.

WRITING TO ANALYSE, REVIEW, COMMENT

Question 1

'This year it is nanotechnology; forty years ago it was nuclear power; no doubt some early man had doubts about the wheel.'

There are always concerns about any new advances in science and technology. Analyse and comment on some examples of such inventions and the concerns associated with them.

[20 marks]

Examiner's hints

This task asks you to analyse information and to comment on it. Quite possibly, the exam paper will contain some stimulus material to help you to organise your ideas. I have given a suggested plan below for approaching this topic which can act as stimulus material. Examiners will be looking for a logically structured piece of writing which uses an objective tone to make judgements about the particular topics to which you refer.

SCIENCE AND TECHNOLOGY
Key discoveries

Electricity
- Natural resource
- What it's done to improve human living conditions
- It's allowed people to control their lives and not be subject to daylight, etc.
- Any real problems?

Computer technology
- Transformed our lives in less than 50 years
- List and comment on advantages
- What were the main fears?
- Is there a danger of computers taking over?

Internal combustion engine and flight
- Opened up travel opportunities
- Linked different parts of the world
- Dangers to life
- Pollution of environment

Nanotechnology
- Good example of the unknown
- Potential benefits
- Unforeseen dangers

Conclusion
- All discoveries have potentially dangerous side effects
- However, we tend to accept them and focus on benefits
- Once the knowledge is there it cannot be removed

WRITING TO INFORM, EXPLAIN, DESCRIBE

Question 2

Explain what you have learnt about yourself and others through playing games.

[20 marks]

Examiner's hints

This is a writing task which requires you to inform and explain. It is important that you follow the instruction and write about yourself and your own experiences. You have a free choice as to how exactly you define the words 'playing games' but remember that the task requires you to explain what you have learnt about yourself and not to describe the games you enjoy playing.

WRITING TO ARGUE, PERSUADE, ADVISE

Question 3

'We all need some excitement and risk in our lives.'

Write the words of a speech in which you try to persuade members of your year group to agree with this point of view.

[20 marks]

Examiner's hints

This task requires you to write to persuade and you should, therefore, choose your vocabulary carefully to make the most of emotive language. You should also think about using examples and references to support and reinforce your argument. Finally, note that you are being asked to write the words of a speech; it is important that you make some attempt to adopt an oral register and include some rhetorical devices in your answer. However, you should also try to avoid writing an over-colloquial response; this is, after all, a test of writing!

NON-FICTION TEXTS

Question 1

All the answers in this section are A/A* grade answers. The examiner's comments explain why they are very good answers. Compare your own answers with them and decide whether your answers contain all the features that are needed in order to achieve the top grade.

The three opinions in the article which I have chosen to write about are as follows:

"Prince Charles has warned that life on Earth could be wiped out by scientists 'playing God' with potentially lethal new technologies."

The first half of this statement is almost certainly a fact as it would be possible to check with newspaper reports, etc. whether Prince Charles did actually make this statement. However, what he is claimed to have said is certainly an opinion. This is indicated primarily by the vocabulary, as the article uses the conditional tense "could" which implies that what was said is speculation. The word "potentially" is also used and this too suggests that there is only a possibility that the Prince's fears may come true. Finally, there's the obvious point that as the technologies described have not yet been fully developed, no-one can know for sure whether these dangers will happen or not.

"The row follows claims by some experts that nanotechnology could spark a freak accident – the so-called 'grey goo' nightmare – where tiny robots could gobble up the earth."

Again, this statement uses the word "could" twice and this implies that there is no absolute guarantee that such an outcome would occur. It is also stated that these are "claims" made by "some experts". "Claims" means that these ideas are unsupported speculations and not provable facts and the fact that only some experts think this could happen (and these experts aren't named) is an indication that not all experts agree which they would do if the comment could be proved as true.

"The idea of self-replicating nanobots is pure science fiction."

This statement would seem to suggest that such a situation could never happen. Although there is no proof that it could, equally there is no absolute proof that it couldn't and so it must be an opinion rather than a fact. It is also worth noting that it was made by the Chief Executive of the Institute of Nanotechnology who would be likely to want to present a positive view of nanotechnology and she also goes on to say that "you cannot regulate every aspect of nanotechnology" which would seem to contradict her earlier statement.

Examiner's comments

There are six marks available for this question which means that a maximum of two will be given for each example chosen. This answer **identifies three opinions** taken from the passage and **focuses clearly and economically on explaining** why they are so. The answer deals with both the **language** used (remember that a skilful writer can make opinions appear to be facts through choice of vocabulary) and with the **content** of the passage. It also shows an awareness of some of the **limitations of the writer's argument**. There is **precise and appropriate use of quotation and reference** and the points made in this way are thoroughly **explained and directly related to the task**.

Nanotechnology is a scientific process which is based on the use of incredibly small parts of matter – individual atoms and molecules – in order to make a wide range of materials. It was first thought of about 40 years ago when some scientists realised that the future was in the use of very small, rather than increasingly larger machines. It only really became a feasible option in 1990 by which time microscopes which were sufficiently powerful to study these miniscule forms had been produced. The process of nanotechnology allows scientists to manipulate (and alter) the fundamental basis of all living matter and already they have succeeded in producing extremely small microchips.

There are many potential advantages that can be gained from this process, particularly in medicine. For example, it is possible to produce tiny machines which can study the development of tumours from within and nanotechnology techniques can also be used to speed up the healing processes. It is also thought that it will be possible to make extremely light materials to be used in the manufacture of aircraft.

The most far-reaching claim for nanotechnology is that, within the next ten years, scientists will produce miniscule robots which will be able to assemble anything, atom by atom, to produce a perfect object. It is also thought that it will be possible to programme these "nanobots" to replicate themselves.

It is this point that gives the greatest cause for concern as some people fear that, if things go wrong, this replication could go on without stopping and that a mutant strain of billions of these robots could escape from the laboratory and, by feeding on whatever matter they find around them, consume the entire planet.

Examiner's comments

This response shows a very thorough **overall understanding** of the material. It selects many **details** from the passage, all of which are **specifically related to the question**. The student demonstrates her understanding by **re-ordering and synthesising points** – this shows that connections between different ideas have been fully taken on board. There is also good use of the student's **own words** and an attempt to expand on some points in order to make their **implications** clear. Finally, the student has **kept all strands of the question in focus** throughout which helps to bind the answer together.

Both articles are about nanotechnology and both make the point that it is something which could have potential dangers, in particular the "grey goo" effect. The first article adopts a more sensational approach as is suggested by the language of its headline, "Nightmare of the Grey Goo" and this is continued by its opening which refers to Prince Charles's concerns that that scientists may be "playing God" with "potentially lethal new technologies". By using such an important public figure as the heir to the throne, the writer of the article encourages his readers to question the wisdom of these scientists.

Throughout this article, the writer is adopting a negative approach to the subject of nanotechnology and most of the sources he refers to such as Jonathon Porritt and Zac Goldsmith are environmentalists who, not surprisingly, express their concerns about what might happen. Although the article makes some references to the possible beneficial effects of this technology, they are hidden away in the middle and described in language such as "miracle lightweight materials" which suggest that perhaps they are not to be taken too seriously. It should also be noted that those in favour of nanotechnology are described as "enthusiasts" which implies that they may have more enthusiasm than common sense and that one of the people who is quoted as being in favour of nanotechnology is none other than the Prime Minister himself. The implication here is that, if the Prime Minister is in favour then perhaps we shouldn't really trust him which is an attitude usually conveyed by the Mail on Sunday in which this article was printed.

The second article uses much less sensational language; rather than having science fiction suggestions in its headline it takes a much more balanced approach: "Tiny robots with massive potential". It is interesting to note that this is written by "A Mail on Sunday Reporter" rather than by a named writer. This article uses much more formal language and adopts a more informative approach. It explains the development of nanotechnology and supports this with facts and figures ("the concept will be a reality in just ten or 20 years"). These facts and the writer's generally balanced tone allow the readers to weigh up the points made in the article and to feel that they are being given reliable and correct information. Therefore, when the writer mentions what could be a serious danger resulting from nanotech experiments, the readers are prepared to take it seriously rather than to dismiss it as a piece of over-excitable journalism.

Examiner's comments

There are 10 marks available for this question and so there is no need to write at extreme length. However, it is important that you show a good grasp of the main similarities and differences between the two passages and can illustrate and explain these clearly.

This response shows a **sound overall understanding of the different ways the two articles deal with material on the same topic** and scores its marks in particular by the ways in which it comments on the way the first article uses references to individual figures to comment on and support its ideas. It also shows a good understanding of how the article is **aimed at a particular group of readers** with particular attitudes and there is good analysis of the writer's use of sensationalist language.

The contrast between the different approaches of the two articles is clearly shown by the way in which the student writes about the two headlines and the **references to the writer's tone** in the second article is a perfectly valid response to the use of language.

Both articles are intended to make the readers question the values of nanotechnology and both use headlines which focus attention on the potential dangers which may arise from such research. In fact, both headlines sound as if they could be the titles of science fiction films although "Nightmare of the Grey Goo" suggests something more frightening and unknown than "Who will control the nanobots?" This science fiction nightmare approach is also conveyed by the photographs which accompany each article. The picture of the magnified ant which is at the head of the Grey Goo article is particularly scary and the

ant appears as if it's some monster from outer space. The writer's clear intention here is to provoke a scared response in his readers with visions of giant ants taking over the world. This is a very effective way of influencing the readers' response to the article especially as nowhere does it make any reference to this in its content! Jonathon Porritt's article also has a photograph which looks like a spacecraft about to land but is, in fact, an artist's impression of a tiny robot inside a human artery being used in medical research.

The writers of the articles express their concerns over nanotechnology in slightly different ways. The author of the Grey Goo passage is clearly setting out to make his readers take a negative approach to the research he describes. He quotes from people concerned with the environment (including Prince Charles), all of whom express serious concerns about what may happen. The implication here is that all of these experts know more about the dangers of what may happen than do the politicians and enthusiasts who are in favour of the research. The writer quite cleverly builds up the suggestion that there is a conspiracy on behalf of governments and institutes of nanotechnology to keep the potential dangers a secret. Another way he does this is by stating that the Americans are likely to use the technology to develop weapons for defence purposes.

The language used in the Grey Goo article is deliberately chosen to provoke an emotional response from its readers with words and phrases such as "wiped out", "grey goo catastrophe", "meddling with molecules" (the use of alliteration here helps to emphasise the point), "freak accident", "nightmare" and "gobble up the Earth". The effect of this vocabulary is to create a tone of fear and threat and it results in the readers questioning the motives of those who engage in research into nanotechnology and prejudices them against such research.

Jonathon Porritt, who is quoted in the Grey Goo article, nevertheless adopts a more reasoned and balanced approach in his own article. He begins by bringing in his personal response; he tries to explain what nanotechnology involves and emphasises that, as yet, we don't know its full potential: "Some people see it as the most important breakthrough since the wheel; others believe it threatens the end of life as we know it." He appears to be rather sceptical of the claims made about nanotechnology as he talks about "a classic bit of nanohype" and he refers to nanobots whizzing around cleaning up pollution as if they're some kind of child's toy, but, on the other hand, he also refers to those who question nanotech's potential as "prophets of doom" which suggests he is not fully in support of their attitude either.

Porritt, in general, appears to be presenting an honest evaluation of his own feelings and this is very effectively conveyed in his short, sharp statement which follows quite a long sentence questioning whether we should support or oppose nanotech scientists, "I haven't a clue." This is a very effective use of a colloquial statement and encourages the reader to share the writer's concerns but in the same balanced way that Porritt has expressed them. It would be a shame to lose the possible benefits of nanotechnology, he says, although we must be aware of its potential dangers. The writer's suggestion that we should "proceed with a great deal more caution and forethought than is currently the case" is a logical conclusion expressed in a balanced and reasonable tone and successfully encourages the readers to share his point of view without scaring them into it with tales of global disaster.

Examiner's comments

This is a **thorough and detailed response** which shows a clear awareness of the differences between the two passages. It also explains the methods used by both writers to persuade us to share their viewpoint and **concludes with a judgement** on which has been more successful.

The answer shows a good understanding of the ways in which the photographs are used to enhance the content of the articles and also explains this clearly; it is important to remember that with this type of question, explaining **how and why** writers achieve particular results is central to scoring high marks. The answer **focuses on relevant details** of the writers' arguments, **paraphrases them to show understanding** and also shows a **perceptive appreciation of the vocabulary and register** used in the articles and how this is part of the writers' method of persuading their readers to share their points of view.

POEMS FROM DIFFERENT CULTURES

Question 2

Both poems are about living creatures and both are about living creatures which are generally considered to be unattractive, unpleasant and dangerous. Nissim Ezekiel's poem is about a scorpion and recalls an incident in his childhood when his mother was stung by one. Chinua Achebe writes about vultures which are also unpleasant carrion creatures.

Both poets begin by describing the weather which provides a background to the events. In Ezekiel's poem, the scorpion had been driven to seek shelter in their house as a result of the heavy rain; the setting for Achebe's poem is the "greyness and drizzle" of "one despondent dawn". The ways in which the poets treat the setting is indicative of their differing treatment of their subject matter. Ezekiel deals with a domestic incident; his mother is stung by accident and the poet uses this incident and its aftermath to illustrate the responses such an incident provokes from a range of people. Achebe is concerned with making a wider point about the nature of evil and its existence in the world. In his poem, the vultures are seen as part of the generally threatening nature of the universe; Ezekiel focuses on the general limitations of human behaviour.

Ezekiel describes the scorpion as "the evil one" which has come into the poet's home; the idea of it being like the devil is reinforced by the description of its tail as "diabolic". This tail flashes in the dark room and stings the poet's mother; the peasants of the village come in buzzing like a swarm of flies (the simile suggests that perhaps to the poet's family they are an unwanted irritation) and pray to God to paralyse the evil one. The poem then continues to present a vividly dramatic picture of the scene in the hut. Now that the scorpion has done its deed, it is no longer a central figure in the drama.

In contrast to the frantic human activity being described in Ezekiel's poem, Achebe focuses in an almost objective way on the activity of the vultures. They are sitting on a "dead tree"; the male vulture's head is described as "bashed-in" and like a pebble. The birds' eating habits are described in bald detail, "picked the eyes of a swollen corpse…ate the things in its bowel" after which they are "gorged". There is nothing poetic or attractive about these creatures and yet the male is described as inclining "affectionately" towards his mate and the poet comments how strange it is for love to "pick a corner in that charnel-house".

This observation is extended to a comment on human nature. Even the Commandant at Belsen, says Achebe, must have had some human feelings for his own family: after a day burning the flesh of his victims (the impersonal cruelty of the vultures is used to emphasise the inhuman attitude of the Nazis) he would stop to buy chocolate for his children on his way home. Achebe admits that he is unsure what this reflection means; does the affection of the vultures and the parental love of the Commandant indicate that love can be found even in the midst of evil or does it simply suggest that love and evil are inseparable and that the latter grows within love? This comment and the tone of the poem as a whole leaves the reader questioning whether there is any divine influence on our lives at all or whether the universe is simply indifferent towards us.

In its own way, Ezekiel's poem raises similar considerations. The evil scorpion has done its deed and the eager villagers are each suggesting their own remedy to deal with it. They appear to be relishing the excitement of the incident and pass on much of their local wisdom to the mother, for example, "may the poison purify your flesh of desire, and your spirit of ambition, they said". The poet repeats the phrase "they said" in order to emphasise the ritualistic way in which the peasants are speaking. Although the poet's mother is in the centre of all this attention, there is

very little mention of her in this part of the poem. All the attention is on the villagers going about their ritual and the implication is that they are more concerned with the opportunity the situation gives them for moralising than for the victim herself.

In fact, we are given the impression that the mother's suffering provides the villagers with an opportunity to escape from their mundane lives. More candles, neighbours and insects arrive as the mother twists in agony "groaning on a mat". Her husband, despite his scepticism about superstition, tries every curse and remedy he can think of. Finally, he tries to purify the poison by pouring paraffin on the mother's toe and lighting it. Only at the end of the poem does attention turn to the mother herself whose main concern is for others: "Thank God the scorpion picked on me and spared my children" – her quiet love for her family contrasts with the bustle and activity of the main part of the poem.

Both poems reflect the different cultures of their authors in their setting and background. Neither poem uses rhyme and both are written in a form of free verse which allows a clear and precise picture of the different episodes to be built up in the readers' minds. Achebe's poem, in particular, conveys the harsh indifference of the vultures and what they represent through his choice of words such as "broken bone of a dead tree", "bashed-in head" and "icy caverns of a cruel heart". Ezekiel uses repetition effectively to get across the urgency in the room as the mother twists and groans in pain.

Both poems, while on the surface dealing with living creatures, also address themes and issues which are universal. Achebe writes about the way in which positive human emotions (family love) can still be present even among those responsible for the most appalling acts of human cruelty; the vultures are ugly, unattractive creatures who with no compunction feed off the corpse they have found in a ditch, but nevertheless show what appears to be affection for each other. The poet uses them to represent symbolically the actions of human beings who practise genocide – something just as relevant to Achebe's Africa as it was to Second World War Europe. The objective tone of his poem allows the readers to draw their own moral from the episode and his closing lines emphasise the ambivalence of his feelings:

"Praise bounteous
providence if you will
that grants even an ogre
a tiny glow-worm
tenderness encapsulated
in icy caverns of a cruel
heart or else despair
for in the very germ
of that kindred love is
lodged the perpetuity
of evil."

We are left wondering whether love can redeem evil or whether the "perpetuity of evil" in some way derives from love; the tone of the poem would perhaps suggest that the latter view is more probable.

On the other hand, Ezekiel uses the scorpion to represent the unpredictable presence of evil in the world and the reactions of the villagers and the poet's father reveal how limited our knowledge is in dealing with it. The conclusion of his poem, however, which focuses on the natural love and concern of a mother for her children, suggests a more positive feeling about human nature than the rather bleak attitude suggested by Achebe:

"My mother only said
Thank God the scorpion picked on me
and spared my children."

Both poets, therefore, through dealing with incidents specific to their own cultures use living creatures to make us reflect on the more universal issues of human nature and the relationship between love and evil in our lives.

Examiner's comments

This is a **full and detailed** answer which deals thoughtfully with the texts **selecting and highlighting key points** on which to comment. It shows **good appreciation of the writer's attitudes and ideas and quotes appropriately** to support its arguments. There is also a **very clear awareness of the wider issues** which both poems deal with and there is a **clear awareness of the need to make consistent comparisons and contrasts** between the two poems. There is also a good understanding of the ways in which the poets have used **language** to create their effects.

POETRY POST 1914

Question 3

Although both poems are concerned with soldiers fighting in the First World War, the poets approach their subject in different ways. Wilfred Owen describes a group of soldiers as they are about to leave their camp in England for the trenches. Sassoon's poem describes the scene when a mother is informed that her son has been killed in battle. What links the two poems is the writers' attitude towards war; both are angry about the unnecessary waste of young lives and also about the hypocritical attitude which those in important positions adopt towards those they send to their deaths. Both poets show pity for the young soldiers and succeed in conveying this very forcefully to their readers.

Owen's poem is set at night; the recruits sing their way through "close darkening lanes" as they make their way to the "siding-shed". The alliteration of the letter "s" makes it sound as if someone is whispering and that the whole episode is some kind of conspiracy. The soldiers wait to board the train with "faces grimly gay" and the oxymoron in the last two words again hints at something unnatural taking place. The soldiers have been decorated with flowers but the poet compares them to the wreaths placed on dead bodies and again alerts the reader to the likely fate of these men. Owen continues to create the impression that there is something secret and shameful about the way these men are being packed off to war. The only person likely to miss them is a tramp and the only other people present are the "dull porters" who watch them – almost with the suggestion that they are there to prevent them from escaping. The sense of conspiracy is increased when Owen personifies the signals nodding and the lamps winking; both of these objects seem to know more about the soldiers' fate than they do themselves.

There is a phrase in the fifth stanza which perfectly sums up the attitude of the authorities towards these men; they leave secretly, "like wrongs hushed-up". This is followed by the blunt statement, emphasised by being a single, short line, "They were not ours". Nobody, it seems, wants to take responsibility for these men or for what may happen to them. Up to this point the poet's attitude has not been fully clear. Has he been writing as a detached observer or as one who feels pity for the soldiers? In the final stanzas his sense of pity is clearly conveyed. It is clear to him that these recruits are being sent to their deaths and it is too much to hope that they will return "to beating of great bells". Only a very few are likely to survive the war and those who do will "creep" back (the air of secrecy is being sustained) and they will have been so changed by their experience that they will only half know where they are going.

Owen famously said that his subject was war and the pity of war, "the poetry is in the pity". In this poem in a quiet, ironic and understated way he conveys this sense of pity very powerfully.

Sassoon also uses irony in his poem but in a much more savage way than Owen. The title of the poem is itself ironic as we learn that Jack, in fact, did not die a hero's death and that the officers had very little respect for him. The poem is written in three six line stanzas which rhyme aa bb cc, etc. This plain and simple format is very effective as it suggests both the naivety of the mother and the cynical attitude of the officer who brings her the news of her son's death.

The poet very skilfully controls the reader's responses. At the beginning of the poem the mother receives the news of her son's death in a letter so nicely written by the Colonel. "Jack fell as he'd have wished". The mother's comment about being "so proud of our dead soldiers" indicates that she has been convinced by the propaganda put out by those who control the war and does not know anything about the true conditions in the trenches.

In the second stanza, however, we are allowed an insight into the mind of the Brother Officer who appears to embody the attitude of those nameless and faceless characters responsible for sending Owen's soldiers off to war. He is scornful towards the mother "the poor old dear" to whom he'd told the lies she wished to hear about the death of her

"glorious boy". Far from being a hero, Jack had proved to be a "cold-footed, useless swine" who panicked and was unheroically "blown to small bits". Not one of his colleagues seemed to care and the only person to grieve would be "that lonely woman with white hair". This line reminds us that the son's death has left his mother alone in her old age. By the end of the poem, Sassoon's anger has become clearly established. The reader does not care that the son has died unheroically but rather is bitter at the hypocrisy of the officers and of the whole system which is ashamed to admit to the lies it tells the population about the glories of the war to which it is sending them to be slaughtered.

Together, these two poems present a powerful criticism of the system which allows such things to happen and between them deal with the complete cycle of the fate of many young men involved in the First World War. Owen's poem describes the recruits leaving for the front; Sassoon's presents the all too familiar scene of a mother being informed of the death of her soldier son. What links the two poems in their treatment of war is the poets' anger and bitterness at the hypocrisy of those responsible for sending so many men to their deaths by making them believe that war is something heroic and glorious. Both Owen and Sassoon were directly involved in the fighting in the trenches and they were committed to describing the war as it really was rather than to going along with the official propaganda; their attitude did much to influence the attitudes of later generations.

Examiner's comments

This is a very **detailed response** which shows a perceptive appreciation of the poets' techniques and which makes **consistently relevant and thoughtful comparisons** between the poems. There is a **close textual analysis**, particularly of the Owen poem, and the student shows a good appreciation of the way the poets use words to influence the reader's response. The student also shows a **good knowledge of figures of speech** such as alliteration and oxymoron but, more importantly, is able to **explain how they are used to create a particular effect**. The student has clearly responded strongly to the poems and this answer shows evidence of a **convincing and sincere personal response**.

WRITING TO ANALYSE, REVIEW, COMMENT

Question 1

It is human nature to be curious and to want to know how things work. Throughout history this has led to mankind inventing and discovering many things which, in the long run, have proved beneficial to our lives. Nearly all of these discoveries have the potential to be used for good or ill. In this essay I shall consider a few of them and assess their value to our lives.

First of all, let us consider electricity. This is something which we take for granted. When we watch television, use the computer or take a shower we don't really think about what gives these things the power to work. It's electricity, it's there and we use it. However, it's only during the last 200 or so years that mankind has had this privilege. Before the discovery that the power of electricity (which is a natural force) could be controlled, people's lives were much different. Without artificial light the working day was controlled by the hours of daylight; people went to bed and got up as the sun set and rose. Without the understanding of electricity, even highly civilised people like the ancient Romans could not make the most of their knowledge.

Of course, not all uses of electricity are good; timers used to detonate bombs and other devices also rely on it but very few people now would want electricity banned as its good points far outweigh the bad.

The same could be said for the invention of computers. Within half a century our lives have been totally transformed by these machines and it is not necessary to repeat all the advantages they offer. However, when they were first being developed many people expressed fears about them. They felt that they would make us too dependent on them, that we would become lazy and that computers would take over the world. That hasn't happened. Computers are widely used

and are essential to the smooth running of businesses, transport systems and to education. The internet has opened up a wealth of information which is readily accessible and e-mail has revolutionised communications. Admittedly, there are websites which contain obscene and violent material and it can be argued that some people, especially teenage boys, waste much of their time playing computer games but, overall, these are minor limitations and very few people would deny the importance of computers to our lives.

Transport and travel have been considerably improved by the invention of the internal combustion engine which led to the invention of the car and the aeroplane. Although these machines have some problems connected to them such as the risks attached to human life in using them and the fact that the fumes and noise they produce are adding to the pollution of the environment, nevertheless, they are an integral part of our lives and we would find it very difficult to live without them.

And now, some scientists are expressing concerns about the developments of nanotechnology. These concerns are, no doubt, very similar to those expressed when computers, electricity and cars were first being developed. It is right that these worries should be made public so that they can be looked into. However, it also appears that nanotechnology offers some potentially very exciting opportunities and it is almost certain that scientists will work on developing those and let the more dangerous side effects take care of themselves. Our experience over the centuries has shown that it is human nature to investigate and discover new things; once a piece of knowledge is in the human mind it cannot be removed and no-one would want to stand in the way of progress.

Examiner's comments

This is a **well-constructed and clearly expressed** piece of writing. It successfully analyses some examples of technological developments and makes some excellent comments about them. It **begins with a direct statement** which immediately engages the reader. There is a **logical development through well-linked paragraphs** and the essay concludes by reinforcing the statement with which it opens. The student's vocabulary is well-chosen and well-suited to the purpose and there is a skilfully controlled **range of sentence structures and types**. The conclusion is a little hurried as time was obviously getting tight. However, overall this is a **maturely argued, detailed piece of writing** and deserves a top grade mark.

WRITING TO INFORM, EXPLAIN, DESCRIBE

Question 2

As a child I was lucky to have a vivid imagination. As my much older siblings had left home I was mostly left to my own devices (aided by a treasure trove of wonderful toys) to amuse myself, and enjoyed being alone. With the introduction of a play-group into my day, I was forced to interact with other children – a pastime I came to thoroughly enjoy, and something I often blame for my desire to constantly socialise instead of study...

I am a strong believer that the environment one is brought up in, and how one is introduced to pleasure and pain (and subsequently ways of dealing with both) is crucial to emotional evolution. For example, if a child is kept in isolation, he or she will be unable to interact naturally with peers, and quite possibly develop social problems later in life. Basic lessons like personal space and sharing are taught very early on in one's life, and are vital skills for the rest of one's existence.

As a result of my upbringing, I have evolved into someone who loves to be surrounded by people, a good communicator, but someone who highly values solitude. I get crowded very easily, and sometimes need to be able to disappear. I have learnt this over time, mostly through playing and interacting with other children.

"Play time", I find, always brings out people's true characters. Whether seven or seventeen, certain traits are always exposed when the need for team-work arises. For example, not everyone's a team-player, and the person with a hidden agenda stands out a mile when unity is needed. Programmes like "Big Brother" are interesting on this subject, as the contestants are needed to play as a team half of the time, and as driven individuals for the rest of it. It erases most of the scope for falsities, and encourages raw character analysis.

I remember a very old friend of mine once had an Easter egg hunt in her garden. It was boys against girls, and the person with the most eggs overall would also get a special prize. It was interesting to observe the ways in which the different sexes dealt with the task. The girls decided to all get as many as they could individually, and then choose someone to "win" and each give them half their eggs. The victor would in return share their prize amongst the team. The boys, however, started tearing around, each man for himself, shoving and pushing – competing right from the word "go". I can't remember who won, but it really showed up the differences between boys and girls.

I always think games, in whichever guise they appear, should remain a vital part of one's life. Role-playing and team efforts help us to understand ourselves and each other, and provide a little light relief from playschool, GCSEs, University or a job. Don't tell anyone, but I still pretend to be different people all the time. Sometimes I'm Ella, an art student from Sydney who collects curtains; sometimes I'm Ruby from New York who's 19 and is married to a fifty year old sugar daddy; or Esperanza, a

Spanish gymnast who is running away from her ex-boyfriend who's just got out of prison. Don't laugh at me! These weird and wonderful characters let me totally step back from myself, and unravel my psyche from the complications of being almost sixteen. I also love the different reactions I get from people when I tell them my story, and the greatest challenge of all is trying to get them to believe some of my wilder concoctions.

You may now think I am a mentally unbalanced danger to the community, or simply a teenager who still enjoys being seven, and doesn't want to let go of her childhood. I'll leave it up to you to decide which is closer to the truth.

Examiner's comments

This is a **detailed, original and fully appropriate response** to the task. There is a **clear attempt to answer the question** and the student has selected episodes from her own experience on which to base her explanation of how playing games has taught her to understand herself. She makes this interesting by showing a **continued awareness of the reader** and, at times, addressing the reader directly. This is particularly well done in the concluding passage as the writer is clearly aware of **the importance of leaving a strong final impression in the reader's mind**. The writer has a wide vocabulary and is especially strong at using abstract terms which are important to this type of topic. However, these are balanced by **a quiet but effective tone** which adds to the appeal of the writing.

WRITING TO ARGUE, PERSUADE, ADVISE

Question 3

In ancient times, when man was at his "manliest"(!), we did not believe in such nonsensical things as laws and rules! Our raw, natural impulses had freedom of speech. This basic, "primal" instinct remains within us, even today, albeit suppressed by the restrictions of society: the instinct to seek danger – to take risks. By taking risks, we experience excitement, and by overcoming them, we feel satisfaction! It is by introducing risk, and creating a challenge, that we are truly satisfied. As J F Kennedy once said – "We choose to go to the moon – not because it is easy, but because it is hard." What is life without that underlying element of risk? Why is it that such pursuits as drinking, smoking and taking drugs are so much more exciting when they are illegal? It is due to the "buzz" and exhilaration of defying rules, taking chances and going against the grain. Another famous quote reminds us to "never forget that only dead fish swim with the stream".

Therefore, I believe that we do all need excitement and risk in our lives. The dawn of this new "cyber-era" has modernised life to such an extent that our lives have become too restrained, too predictable. However, our ancient instinct for danger remains intact. We have started to find ways of venting our desires through "extreme sports" – what is the appeal of bungee-jumping and kayaking? It is the thrill of confronting danger and overcoming it. Similarly, what is the fun in a rollercoaster which turns you upside down? Or a 50 foot waterslide? Once again, it is the simulation of danger. We have managed to elude society's restricting grasp. However, our forefathers would laugh at the complexity of the methods we have employed to recreate emotions which they could experience so easily.

Another form of escape has recently appeared to us – through the idea of "virtuality". We can now vicariously carry out dangerous acts through a computer character! If we can't jump off cliffs, shoot people and drive fast cars, why not experience these "electric" experiences electronically? In the words of Max Frisch, "Technology is a way of understanding the universe without having to experience it ourselves."

In the same way, action films and adventure novels appeal to us – due to the recreation of danger and the thrills of risk. Our favourite heroes and cartoon characters were daring – for example, Odysseus – a gambler, or Superman – a daredevil. Tales of daring exploits always excite the imagination.

However, we have regressed into a society in which too much is provided for – trapped in an urban jungle, we have almost forgotten the thrills that nature can provide. "Progress was alright but it has gone on for too long," said Ogden Nash. Nowadays, we are drifting into dreariness, ignorant and unaware of the escapes or risk. For us, risks include wearing "unstylish clothes" or buying shares (once again – an example of our natural instincts to gamble). For me, our ability to lull into this somnambulant state is the greatest risk of all. Unpredictability and risk enhance all our emotions and provide the greatest excitement possible.

I, therefore, urge you to agree with me that we all need risk and danger in our lives.

Examiner's comments

This is a very **forceful, controlled piece of persuasive writing**. The student has sustained a **convincing oral register** throughout and, in particular, has made good use of **rhetorical questions, examples and quotations to reinforce his arguments**. There is a **consistent awareness of the reader** and vocabulary has been carefully chosen to persuade and convince. There is a **good use of humour** and a very effective **mix of long and short sentences to keep the reader's interest**. The **opening immediately creates interest** and the argument builds up to a **convincing conclusion** which also contains a final reminder that this is a speech and that the audience are being persuaded to agree with its ideas.

OXFORD

AQA
GCSE
Maths

FOUNDATION MODULAR

Dave Capewell
Geoff Fowler
Peter Mullarkey
Katherine Pate

OXFORD
UNIVERSITY PRESS

OXFORD
UNIVERSITY PRESS

Great Clarendon Street, Oxford OX2 6DP

Oxford University Press is a department of the University of Oxford.
It furthers the University's objective of excellence in research,
scholarship, and education by publishing worldwide in

Oxford   New York

Auckland   Cape Town   Dar es Salaam   Hong Kong   Karachi
Kuala Lumpur   Madrid   Melbourne   Mexico City   Nairobi
New Delhi   Shanghai   Taipei   Toronto

With offices in

Argentina   Austria   Brazil   Chile   Czech Republic   France   Greece
Guatemala   Hungary   Italy   Japan   South Korea   Poland   Portugal
Singapore   Switzerland   Thailand   Turkey   Ukraine   Vietnam

Oxford is a registered trade mark of Oxford University Press
in the UK and in certain other countries

British Library Cataloguing in Publication Data

Data available

ISBN 9780199128914

10 9 8 7 6 5 4 3 2 1

Printed in Singapore by KHL Printing Company

Paper used in the production of this book is a natural, recyclable
product made from wood grown in sustainable forests.
The manufacturing process conforms to the environmental
regulations of the country of origin.

Acknowledgements
The Publisher would like to thank the Assessment and Qualifications Alliance for their kind permission to reproduce past exam questions. The
Assessment and Qualifications Alliance accepts no responsibility whatsoever for the accuracy or method of working in the answers given

The Publisher would like to thank the following for permission to reproduce photographs:

Cover: SugaAngel/Shutterstock; **p2-3:** J A Giordano/CORBIS SABA; **p16-17:** Slobodan Djajic/Dreamstime; **p20:** Derek Holloway; **p21:** Monkey Business
Images/Shutterstock; **p32-33:** Harish Tyagi/epa/Corbis; **p40:** OUP; **p46-47:** Science Photo Library; **p48-49:** Kuzma/Shutterstock; **p55:** INTERFOTO/
Alamy; **p64-65:** Juan Fuertes/Shutterstock; **p75:** Konstantin Sutyagin/Dreamstime; **p79:** Justin Case; **p80:** Tim Graham/Alamy; **p84-85:** 4774344sean/
Dreamstime; **p100-101:** Christophe Testi/Dreamstime.com; Andrzej Tokarski/Dreamstime.com; Christopher Elwell/Dreamstime.com; 350jb/Dreamstime.
com; Branislav Senic/Dreamstime.com; Yeko Photo Studio/Shutterstock; Studiotouch/Shutterstock; **p102-103:** Bhe017/Dreamstime; **p104:** OUP;
p116: Sami Sarkis; **p117:** Adisa/Dreamstime; **p126-127:** Elyrae/Dreamstime; **p133:** Russell Kightley/Science Photo Library; **p138-139:** Jeremy Broad/
Dreamstime; **p149:** RIA Novosti/Alamy; **p152-153:** Feng Yu/Dreamstime.com; iStockphoto.com; Christophe Testi/Dreamstime.com; Lobke Peers/
Shutterstock; Sailorr/Dreamstime.com; Zentilia/Dreamstime.com; **p154-155:** The London Art Archive/Alamy; **p159:** Peter Adams Photography/Alamy;
p170-171: Ivan Cholakov/Dreamstime; **p175:** Humanities & Social Sciences Library/New York Public; Library/Science Photo Library; **p190-191:**
Ivan Kmit/Dreamstime; **p201:** hcss5/Shutterstock; **p206-207:** iStockphoto.com; Ben Renard-wiart /Dreamstime.com; Bruce Hempell /Dreamstime.
com; Rider of the Storm/Dreamstime.com; Elifranssens/Dreamstime.com; Ben Renard-wiart/Dreamstime.com; Grondin Julien/Dreamstime.com; Ben
Mcleish/Dreamstime.com; c./Shutterstock; **p208-209:** Gregory Sams/Science Photo Library; **p224-225:** Joggie Botma/Dreamstime; **p244-245:** Jakub
Krechowicz/Dreamstime; **p248:** OUP/Photodisc; **p251:** OUP/Photodisc; **p256-257:** Jim Cooper/Getty Images; Danny De Bruyne/Dreamstime.com; Feng Yu/
Shutterstock; Mike Flippo/Shutterstock; **p258-259:** Dgareri/Dreamstime; **p272-273:** OUP; **p274:** OUP; **p275:** Ivan Vdovin/JAI/Corbis; **p288:** OUP; **p292-
293:** Dennis Hallinan/Alamy; **p299:** OUP; **p308-309:** Feng Yu/Dreamstime.com; Digital Vision/Getty Images; Giraffarte/Dreamstime.com; **p310-311:** OUP;
p312: OUP/Ingram; **p330-331:** Getty Images; **p336:** Inc/Shutterstock; **p342-343:** Doug Steley A/Alamy; **p349:** OUP; **p351:** Elizabeth A Whiting/Corbis;
p354-355: iStockphoto.com; Christophe Testi/Dreamstime.com; Alex Varlakov/Dreamstime.com; Yang Jay/Dreamstime.com; Design56/Dreamstime.
com; Tatiana Popova/Shutterstock; Condor 36/Shutterstock; **p356-357:** Stocktrek Images/Getty Images; **p361:** Dariusz Miszkiel/Dreamstime; **p364:** OUP/
Photodisc; **p370-371:** Ivonne Wierink/Shutterstock; **p384-385:** James Steidl/Dreamstime; **p388:** OUP/Hemera; **p394-395:** Andry A/Alamsyah/Alamy;
Eduardo Miller/Shutterstock; Michael Mcdonald/Dreamstime.com; www.lucypringle.co.uk; Zaznoba/Dreamstime.com; **p396-397:** Soleg1974/Dreamstime;
p410: OUP; **p437:** Araldo de Luca/Corbis; **p446:** Raja Rc/Dreamstime.com

The Publisher would also like to thank Anna Cox for her work in creating the case studies.
The charts on pages 45-46 are reproduced courtesy of the Meteorological Office; the bar chart on page 152 is reproduced courtesy of Defra; the data on
page 250 is reproduced courtesy
of the IAAF.

Figurative artwork is by Peter Donnelly

About this book

This book has been specifically written to help you get your best possible grade in your AQA GCSE Mathematics examinations. It is designed for students who have achieved level 4 or below at Key Stage 3 and are looking to progress to a grade E at GCSE Foundation tier.

The authors are experienced teachers and examiners who have an excellent understanding of the AQA specification and so are well qualified to help you successfully meet your objectives.

The book is made up of chapters that are based on AQA Modular specification 4360, and is organised clearly into the three units that will make up your assessment:

Unit 1	**Statistics and Number**	**pages 2 – 137**
Unit 2	**Number and Algebra**	**pages 138 – 271**
Unit 3	**Geometry and Algebra**	**pages 272 – 407**

Towards the end of the book, the **C Booster** section provides targeted access to grades C and D. References to this section are made throughout the book, so you can skip ahead and improve your grade potential. **Functional maths** and **problem-solving** are flagged in the exercises throughout.

- In particular there are **case studies**, which allow you to apply your GCSE knowledge in a variety of engaging contexts.

- There are also **rich tasks**, which provide an investigative lead-in to the chapter – you may need to study some of the techniques in the chapter in order to be able to complete them properly.

Also built into this book are the new **assessment objectives:**

AO1   recall knowledge of prescribed content
AO2   select and apply mathematical methods in a range of contexts
AO3   interpret and analyse problems and select strategies to solve them
AO2 and AO3 are flagged throughout, particularly in the regular **summary assessments**, as these make up around 50% of your assessment.

Finally, you will notice an icon that looks like this:

This shows opportunities for **Quality of Written Communication**, which you will also be assessed on in your exams.

Best wishes with your GCSE Maths – we hope you enjoy your course and achieve success!

Contents

Finding your way around this book

NUMBER	ALGEBRA	GEOMETRY	DATA

UNIT 1

1 **N1** Properties of number

4 **N2** Integer calculations

7 **N3** Fractions and percentages

2 **D1** Probability

3 **D2** Collecting data

5 **D3** Displaying data

6 **D4** Averages and range

8 **D5** Further probability

UNIT 2

10 **N4** Fractions and decimals

12 **N5** Powers, roots and primes

15 **N6** Ratio and proportion

9 **A1** Expressions

11 **A2** Functions and graphs

13 **A3** Sequences

14 **A4** Formulae and real-life graphs

16 **A5** Equations

UNIT 3

20 **N7** Decimal calculations

23 **A6** Further equations

17 **G1** Measures, length and area

18 **G2** Angles and 2D shapes

19 **G3** 2D and 3D shapes

21 **G4** Transformations

22 **G5** Further transformations

24 **G6** Measuring and constructing

25 **G7** Further geometry

PLUS SECTION C Booster

Introduction

Negative numbers have been the source of great controversy in the history of mathematics. Because negative numbers could not represent real quantities people were reluctant to accept them. The Greeks, who understood equations, called any equation with a negative solution absurd!

What's the point?

In the present day, negative numbers have lots of 'real' meanings such as representing temperatures below zero, indicating losses on the stock market, and showing that something is moving or flowing in the opposite direction to normal.

Check in

1   Write the number three hundred and four in figures.

2   Calculate
    a 7×10 **b** $5 - 17$ **c** $40 \div 8$

3   What is the temperature on this thermometer?

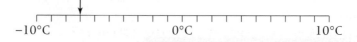

Orientation

What I need to know	What I will learn	What this leads to
Key stage 3 →	■ Understand place value ■ Read scales, dials and timetables ■ Calculate with negative numbers, including in context ■ Round whole numbers and decimals	→ N2 + 5

Rich task

Temperature can be measured in both Centigrade and Fahrenheit.
A temperature of −20 degrees Centigrade is equal to −4 degrees Fahrenheit.
A temperature of +20 degrees Centigrade is equal to +68 degrees Fahrenheit.
How many degrees Centigrade is 41 degrees Fahrenheit?

This spread will show you how to:
- Understand place value and order positive numbers
- Multiply and divide by powers of 10

Keywords
Digit
Order
Place value

- The value of each **digit** in a number depends upon its place in the number. This is called its **place value**.

In the number 4207

Thousands	Hundreds	Tens	Units
4	2	0	7

The digit 4 stands for 4 thousands

The digit 2 stands for 2 hundreds

The digit 7 stands for 7 units

You write this number in words as four thousand, two hundred and seven.

You can compare numbers using a place value table. Compare the place values of the first non-zero digits. If they are the same, compare the second digits. Keep comparing digits until you find a difference.

Example

Put these numbers in **order** from lowest to highest.
17   6300   5993   2330   2426   12 540

Put the numbers in a place value table.

Ten Thousands	Thousands	Hundreds	Tens	Units
			1	7
	6	3	0	0
	5	9	9	3
	2	3	3	0
	2	4	2	6
1	2	5	4	0

Look at the first non-zero digits (in bold).
You can now put all the numbers in order except for 2330 and 2426.

For these two numbers you need to look at the second digit
    2330   2426
In order the numbers are 17, 2330, 2426, 5993, 6300, 12 540.

You can use a place value table to multiply and divide by 10 or 100.

- To multiply a number by 10 all the digits move one place to the left.

- To divide a number by 100 all the digits move two places to the right.

p.196

$37 \times 10 = 370$

Hundreds	Tens	Units
	3	7
3	7	0

$\times 10$

$4850 \div 100 = 48.5$

Thousands	Hundreds	Tens	Units	•	tenths
4	8	5	0	•	
		4	8	•	5

$\div 100$

The **0** holds the digits in place.

1 Write each of these numbers in figures.
  a eighty-seven
  b one hundred and forty-three
  c four hundred and six
  d four hundred and sixty
  e two thousand and fifty-three
  f eight thousand, five hundred and three
  g eight thousand, five hundred and thirty
  h thirty-four thousand, six hundred and forty
  i thirty thousand, four hundred and sixty-four
  j two hundred and six thousand, five hundred and three

2 These are the areas of eight countries in square kilometres.
Write each number in words.

a	Algeria	2 381 741	**b**	Chile	756 950
c	France	543 965	**d**	India	3 166 829
e	China	9 596 960	**f**	United Kingdom	244 100
g	USA	9 368 900	**h**	Australia	7 682 300

3 Put each list of numbers in order, starting with the smallest.
  a 56   34   9   112   178   89   139
  b 2372   1784   2386   1990   3233   3022
  c 40 500   45 045   4555   4005   40 545   44 054
  d 240 440   204 044   24 445   245 004   42 024   242 404

4 Draw a place value table to calculate each of these.
The first one has been started for you.
  a 29×10

Thousands	Hundreds	Tens	Units	•	tenths	hundredths
		2	9	•		
				•		

  b 132×10 **c** $590 \div 10$ **d** 17×100
  e $6400 \div 10$ **f** $73 \div 10$ **g** $345 \div 100$

5 Calculate
  a 12×10 **b** 4×100 **c** $320 \div 10$ **d** $4600 \div 100$
  e 30×10 **f** 4.6×10 **g** $230 \div 100$ **h** $659 \div 10$
  i 34×1000 **j** 3.56×100 **k** $23.6 \div 10$ **l** 0.345×100

This spread will show you how to:

- Represent numbers as positions and transitions on a number line
- Read measurements and information from scales, dials and timetables

Keywords
Estimate
Number line
Scale
Timetable

- Every number can be represented as a position on a **number line**.

Most of the **scales** you read are number lines.

You use a ruler to measure lengths. You use a weighing scale to measure weight or mass. You use a measuring jug to measure a volume of liquid.

Example

Write the reading shown on each scale.

a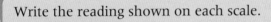
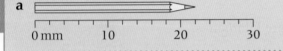

b
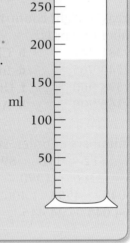

ml

p.276

a The length of the pencil is between 20 and 30 mm.
There are 5 spaces between 20 and 30 mm.
So 5 spaces represent 10 mm.
Each space represents 10 ÷ 5 = 2 mm.
The pencil is 22 mm long.

b The reading is between 150 and 200 ml.
There are 5 spaces between 150 and 200 ml.
So 5 spaces represent 50 ml.
Each space represents 50 ÷ 5 = 10 ml.
The reading is 180 ml.

- You can **estimate** a measurement from a scale.

You need to be able to read **timetables** for buses and trains.

Example

Station	Depart	Depart	Depart
Penrith	08:00	09:00	10:00
Kendal	08:20	09:20	10:20
Lancaster	08:35	09:35	10:35
Preston	08:55	09:55	10:55
Warrington	09:15	10:15	11:15

How long does it take the 09:20 train from Kendal to get to Warrington?

The train leaves Kendal at 09:20 and arrives at Warrington at 10:15.
The journey time is:

40 minutes   15 minutes

09:20 09:30 09:40 09:50 10:00 10:10 10:20

From 09:20 to 10:00 = 40 minutes
From 10:00 to 10:15 = 15 minutes
Total time   = 55 minutes

1 Write the number each of the arrows is pointing to.

a

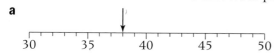

b

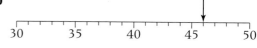

c

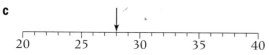

d

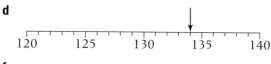

e

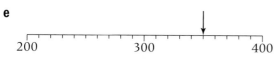

f

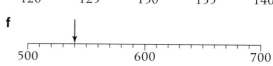

2 Write the reading shown on each scale.

a

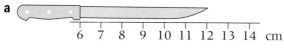

b

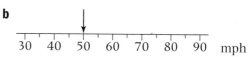

c

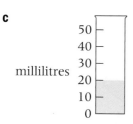

d

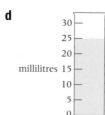

3 Write the readings on each scale.

a

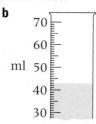

b

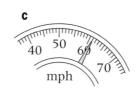

c

d

4

Lancaster–Keswick bus timetable			
Lancaster	12:30	14:20	17:25
Kendal	13:35	15:30	18:35
Windermere	14:03	15:58	19:03
Ambleside	14:18	16:18	19:23
Grasmere	14:36	16:36	19:41
Keswick	14:56	16:56	20:01

a What time does the 12:30 bus from Lancaster arrive in Keswick?

b A bus arrives in Grasmere at 19:41.
At what time did it leave Kendal?

c How many minutes does it take the 13:35 bus from Kendal to get to Ambleside?

d Karen catches the 17:25 bus from Lancaster. How long does it take her to travel to Windermere?

e Pete is travelling from Kendal and needs to be in Keswick by 4:45 pm. What is the latest bus he can catch from Kendal?

Temperature

This spread will show you how to:

- Order temperatures and position them on a number line
- Calculate changes in temperature

Keywords
Degrees Celsius
Negative
Number line
Temperature

- You use **negative** numbers for **temperatures** below 0°C.

These readings show the temperatures in Sydney and Moscow.

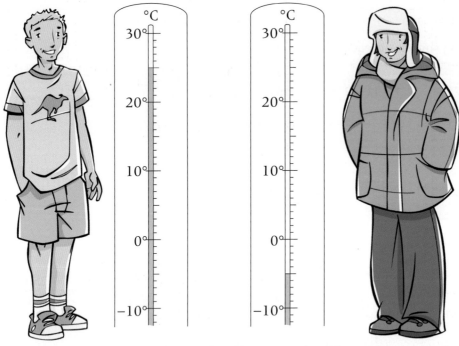

Sydney, Australia   Temperature is 25°C   Temperature is −5°C   Moscow, Russia

The temperature scale is a **number line**.

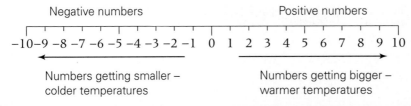

Negative numbers   Positive numbers

−10 −9 −8 −7 −6 −5 −4 −3 −2 −1   0   1   2   3   4   5   6   7   8   9   10

Numbers getting smaller – colder temperatures   Numbers getting bigger – warmer temperatures

Example

The temperature in London is 13 °C. During the night the temperature falls by 18°. What is the night-time temperature in London?

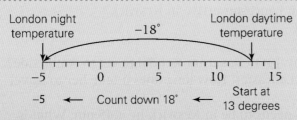

London night temperature   −18°   London daytime temperature

−5   0   5   10   15

−5   ←   Count down 18°   ←   Start at 13 degrees

The night-time temperature in London is −5°C.

1 Write the temperature on each of these thermometers.

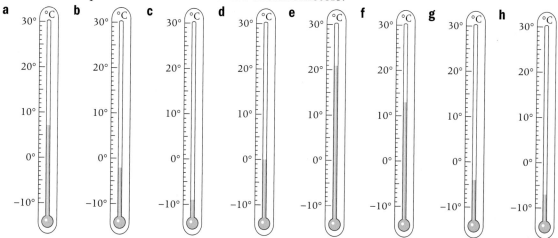

a   b   c   d   e   f   g   h

2 Write the hottest and coldest temperatures in each of these lists.
All the temperatures are in degrees Celsius.

a	−3	−6	0	7	−2	12
b	0	−12	−15	−8	−3	−17
c	12	21	−2	14	9	3
d	−12	15	19	−31	28	8

3 What temperature is
a 5 degrees higher than 7 °C   b 10 degrees higher than 2 °C
c 4 degrees higher than −1 °C   d 12 degrees higher than −15 °C
e 4 degrees lower than 12 °C   f 5 degrees lower than 2 °C
g 8 degrees lower than −3 °C   h 15 degrees lower than 7 °C?

4 This table shows the highest and lowest temperatures, in °C, in
several cities around the world.

City	Perth	Cape Town	Copenhagen	Calgary	Manchester
Highest summer temperature	36	40	21	16	28
Lowest winter temperature	12	15	−12	−25	−2

a Which city had the highest summer temperature?
b Which city had the lowest winter temperature?
c Which city had the biggest difference in temperature between
summer and winter?
d Which city had the smallest difference in temperature between
summer and winter?

This spread will show you how to:

Keywords
Add
Multiply
Negative number
Number line
Subtract

- Order negative numbers and position them on a number line
- Add, subtract and multiply with negative numbers

- You can order negative numbers using a **number line**.

Example

Place these numbers in order, starting with the smallest.

$$-3 \quad -4 \quad 2 \quad -5 \quad -2 \quad 4$$

Using a number line

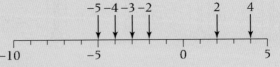

-5 is further away from zero than -4, so it is smaller.

The correct order is $-5, -4, -3, -2, 2, 4$.

You can use a number line to **add** and **subtract negative numbers**. There are two rules to remember.

- Adding a negative number is the same as subtracting a positive number.

- Subtracting a negative number is the same as adding a positive number.

Example

Calculate
a $8 + -3$ **b** $-8 - -3$

a Start at 8 and subtract 3 (move to the left).

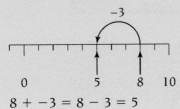

$8 + -3 = 8 - 3 = 5$

b Start at -8 and add 3 (move to the right).

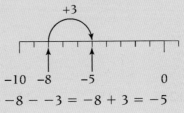

$-8 - -3 = -8 + 3 = -5$

You can **multiply** with negative numbers. There are two rules to remember.

- Negative number $\times$ positive number $=$ negative number

$$-3 \times 4 = -12$$

- Negative number $\times$ negative number $=$ positive number

$$-3 \times -4 = 12$$

1 Copy and complete this table, working out the new temperature in each case.

Start temperature (°C)	Change in temperature	New temperature (°C)
14	−11	
7	−10	
13	−6	
−5	+11	
−8	−5	

2 Calculate

a $3 + 5$ **b** $15 − 12$ **c** $7 − 10$ **d** $4 − 13$ **e** $14 − 17$
f $12 − 9$ **g** $−4 + 8$ **h** $−3 + 12$ **i** $−15 + 11$ **j** $−3 + 7$
k $−8 − 2$ **l** $−3 + 5$ **m** $−2 − 6$ **n** $−9 − 7$ **o** $−3 + 8$
p $−21 + 14$ **q** $21 − 14$ **r** $−21 − 14$ **s** $−13 − 23$ **t** $−16 + 34$

3 Calculate

a $16 + −3$ **b** $8 + −6$ **c** $13 + −5$ **d** $−7 + −3$ **e** $−6 + −7$
f $−4 + −8$ **g** $−8 + −2$ **h** $12 − −7$ **i** $5 − −11$ **j** $−3 − −6$
k $−9 − −2$ **l** $−4 − −2$ **m** $−6 − −10$ **n** $−3 + −2$ **o** $−3 − −2$
p $15 + −11$ **q** $17 − −13$ **r** $14 + −13$ **s** $15 − −11$ **t** $−11 + −14$

4 Calculate

a $3 × 5$ **b** $−3 × 4$ **c** $−2 × 10$ **d** $−3 × 8$ **e** $−4 × 5$
f $−3 × −2$ **g** $−4 × −2$ **h** $−6 × −3$ **i** $−5 × 2$ **j** $−7 × −3$

A03 Problem

5 In these pyramids the brick that sits directly above two bricks is the sum of those two bricks. For example:

Copy and complete these pyramids.

a
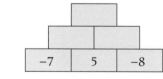

b
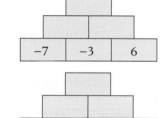

c
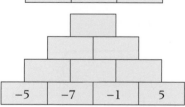

d

This spread will show you how to:

- Round positive whole numbers to the nearest 10, 100 or 1000 and decimals to the nearest whole number
- Estimate the answer to problems

Keywords
Approximate
Estimate
Rounding
Whole number

Rounding gives you the **approximate** size of a number.
When rounding numbers to a given degree of accuracy, look at the next digit.
If it is 5 or more, the number is rounded up.
Otherwise it is rounded down.

You can round a number to the nearest 10, 100 or 1000.

You can round a decimal to the nearest whole number.

Example

a Round 4639 to the nearest 100.
b Round 235.723 to the nearest whole number.

....

a Look at the **tens** digit.

Thousands	Hundreds	Tens	Units
4	6	3	9

4639

4500   4600   4650   4700   4800

The **tens** digit is **3**, so the number is rounded **down** to 4600.

You can say that 4639 ≈ 4600 (to the nearest 100).

b Look at the **tenths** digit.

Hundreds	Tens	Units	•	tenths	hundredths	thousandths
2	3	5	•	7	2	3

235.723

234   235   235.5   236   237

The **tenths** digit is **7**, so the number is rounded **up** to 236.

You can say that 235.723 ≈ 236 (to the nearest whole number).

p.152

This topic is extended on page 408.

- You can estimate the answer to a calculation by rounding the numbers.

Example

John brings 324 tin cans to the recycling centre.
Habib brings 387 tin cans to the recycling centre.
About how many tin cans do the two boys bring to the recycling centre?

....

You can round each number to the nearest 100 to make a good estimate.

324 ≈ 300 (nearest 100)
387 ≈ 400 (nearest 100)

The boys bring about 300 + 400 = 700 tin cans to the recycling centre.

You have to decide whether to round the numbers to the nearest 10, 100 or 1000.

1 Round each of these numbers to the nearest 10.
  a 48   **b** 89   **c** 483   **d** 792   **e** 2638   **f** 6193

2 Round each of these numbers to the nearest 100.
  a 343   **b** 484   **c** 882   **d** 2732   **e** 5678   **f** 16 491

> You could use a number line sketch to help you.

3 Round each of these numbers to the nearest 1000.
  a 3448   **b** 2895   **c** 4683   **d** 36 927   **e** 62 532   **f** 261 932

4 Round each of these numbers to the nearest
  i 1000   **ii** 100   **iii** 10.
  a 3472   **b** 81 382   **c** 1236.4   **d** 283.4   **e** 13 998   **f** 9999

5 Round each of these numbers to the nearest whole number.
  a 4.8   **b** 3.9   **c** 11.6   **d** 25.074   **e** 16.286   **f** 435.972

6 Here are some statistics about eight footballers.

Name	Goals scored in a season	Passes completed in a match	Maximum shot speed (km/h)	Time to run 100 m (s)	Distance run in a match (m)
Peter Beattie	3	23	97.2	10.2	1623
Thierry Angel	26	52	89.6	10.95	12 453
Frank Schmiechal	1	38	69.2	13.7	11 276
Rudi Baros	18	29	93.9	11.03	13 789
Jan van Nistelroo	12	68	92.3	12.37	8673
Milan Dickov	5	15	78.3	16.4	9374
Paul Henry	21	33	83.7	11.06	9898
Phil Lampard	19	46	91.7	12.6	10 372

For each player find
  a the distance run in a match to the nearest 1000 m
  b the maximum shot speed to the nearest 10 km/h
  c the time to run 100 m to the nearest 1 second.
  d Using the data in the table, say who you think is the best player.
    Give reasons for your choice.

7 Use rounding to **estimate** the answer to each of these calculations.
  a 43 + 189   **b** 1563 + 28   **c** 1602 + 2654

Summary

Check out
You should now be able to:

- Understand place value for whole numbers
- Multiply or divide by powers of 10
- Order positive and negative whole numbers
- Add, subtract and multiply negative numbers
- Round whole numbers to the nearest 10, 100 or 1000
- Round decimals to the nearest whole number
- Read and interpret scales, dials and timetables

Worked exam question
Here is a train timetable.

Cleethorpes	0528	0628	0714	0801
Scunthorpe	0600	0700	0745	0832
Doncaster (arr)	0632	0733	0818	0908
Doncaster (dep)	0636	0738	0820	0915
Meadowhall	0701	0805		0941
Sheffield	0710	0814	0852	0950

a How long does the 0528 train from Cleethorpes take
   to travel to Scunthorpe?   (1)

b Anna is travelling from Doncaster to Sheffield.
   She needs to be in Sheffield by half past nine in the morning.

   Which is the latest train from Doncaster she should catch?   (1)

c The 0714 train from Cleethorpes to Sheffield has the shortest
   journey time of these four trains.

   Give a possible reason for this.   (1)

(AQA, 2009)

a
32 minutes

b
Anna must catch the train getting
into Sheffield at 0852. The latest
train is 0820

You should show
your reasoning.

c
Doesn't stop at Meadowhall

Exam questions

1. **a** Write the number 7360 in words. (1)
   b Write 14 390 to the nearest thousand. (1)
   c Write down the value of the 4 in the number 21 840. (1)

2. Write these numbers in order of size.
   Start with the smallest number.
   56   79   28   121   45 (1)

3. The mileage chart shows the distances, in miles, between five cities.

   York
24	Leeds
81	73	Lincoln
184	171	128	Oxford
212	199	142	57	London

   For example, the distance from Leeds to Oxford is 171 miles.
   a What is the distance from York to Lincoln? (1)
   b Which city is the furthest distance from Leeds? (1)
   c Helen travels to work from Oxford to London in the morning.
   In the evening she travels from London back to Oxford.
   She works for five days every week.

   Work out how many miles she travels to and from
   work in a week. (2)
   (AQA, 2008)

4. **a** Jade says that ten million in figures is 1 000 000.

   Explain why Jade is wrong. (1)

   b Hassan says 500 010 is five thousand and ten.

   Is Hassan correct?
   You **must** explain your answer. (1)
   (AQA, 2008)

A02
5. Music videos cost £1.79 to download.
   Rehan downloads 21 videos.
   Estimate how much money Rehan pays.
   Show your working clearly. (3)

Introduction

There are many things in life which are uncertain. Will it be sunny tomorrow? Will my football team win the Premier League? Will I be able to afford a house in the future? The mathematics used to deal with uncertainty is called probability.

What's the point?

When the Met Office gives a weather forecast, they use a complex mathematical model to predict the probability of sunshine in a particular region.

Check in

1 Order these decimals in size, smallest first.

  a 0.25   0.2   0.3

  b 0.7   0.8   0.75

  c 0.85   0.8   1

2 State the shaded part of each diagram as a fraction.

  a   **b**

3 Work out each of these fraction calculations.

  a $\frac{1}{3} + \frac{2}{3}$ **b** $\frac{3}{10} + \frac{7}{10}$

  c $1 - \frac{9}{10}$ **d** $1 - \frac{4}{5}$

  e $1 - \frac{3}{4}$

4 Work out each of these decimal calculations.

  a $1 - 0.2$ **b** $1 - 0.7$

  c $1 - 0.9$

What I need to know	What I will learn	What this leads to
Key stage 3 →	■ Understand and use the vocabulary of probability ■ Understand and use the probability scale ■ List all outcomes for events systematically ■ Calculate probabilities	→ D5

Two people can play an old game called Rock, Paper, Scissors.
In the game,
- rock is a closed fist
- paper is palm on palm,
- and scissors is the number two horizontally.

The players reveal their 'hand' simultaneously.
A rock beats scissors.
Paper beats rock, and scissors beats paper.

Is the game fair?

This spread will show you how to:

• Understand and use the vocabulary of probability

Keywords
Certain
Chance
Even chance
Event
Impossible
Outcome

• The **outcomes** of spinning a coin are a Head and a Tail.
• An **event** is one or more outcomes. A Head is an event, when spinning a coin.
• The **chance** of an event happening can be measured using words, for example, likely, certain, impossible.

The event may be

impossible   possible   certain

Choosing a   Choosing a   Choosing a
blue ball   blue ball   blue ball

• You can use words to describe how likely it is that an event will happen.

more and more likely to happen

impossible   **unlikely**   **even**   **likely**   **certain**
                      or   **chance**   or
                 poor chance   good chance

| The event will never happen | | The event has the same chance of happening as not happening | | The event will definitely happen |

Example

Use impossible, unlikely, even chance, likely or certain to describe these events.

a You get a Head when you spin a coin.
b A baby will be born tomorrow.
c It will snow on the Costa del Sol in Spain next winter. (It did in 2005!)

· ·

a Even chance
b Likely
c Unlikely

1

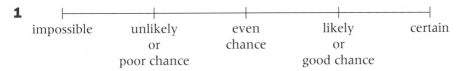

impossible | unlikely or poor chance | even chance | likely or good chance | certain

Use impossible, unlikely, even chance, likely or certain to describe these events.

a The day after Christmas Eve is Christmas Day.
b The day after Thursday is Wednesday.
c The sun will rise tomorrow.
d You get a Tail when you spin a coin.
e You are dealt a red card from a shuffled pack of cards.
f It will rain sometime next year.
g You will climb to the top of Mount Everest tomorrow.
h You will roll a 7 on an ordinary dice.
i You will roll an even number on a dice.
j You will roll a 6 on a dice.
k You will pick a red ball from a bag that contains 8 red balls and 2 blue balls.
l You will pick a blue ball from a bag that contains 8 red balls and 2 blue balls.

> Hint for **e**:
> In a pack of normal playing cards there are 26 red cards and 26 black cards.

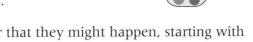

2 Put these events in the order that they might happen, starting with impossible and finishing with certain.

A	**B**	**C**	**D**	**E**
Picking a red ball	Picking a red ball	Picking a red ball	Picking a red ball	Picking a red ball

3 Five different spinners are shown. For each spinner, state which colour is the most likely. Give a reason for your answers.

a **b** **c** **d**

e

Probability scale

This spread will show you how to:

● Understand and use the probability scale

Keywords
Probability
Probability scale

You can use words to describe how likely it is that an event will happen.

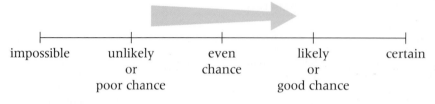

more and more likely to happen

| impossible | unlikely
or
poor chance | even
chance | likely
or
good chance | certain |

There are gaps in the scale.

You can use a number scale to be more accurate.

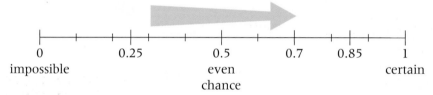

more and more likely to happen

| 0 | 0.25 | 0.5 | 0.7 | 0.85 | 1 |
| impossible | | even
chance | | | certain |

0 means impossible.
1 means certain.

This number is called the **probability**.
The probability measures how likely it is that an event will happen.

● All probabilities have a value between 0 and 1 and can be marked on a **probability scale**.

You can use fractions, decimals or percentages on the probability scale.

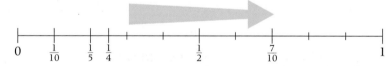

more and more likely to happen

| 0 | $\frac{1}{10}$ | $\frac{1}{5}$ | $\frac{1}{4}$ | $\frac{1}{2}$ | $\frac{7}{10}$ | 1 |

$\frac{1}{2} = 0.5$
$\frac{7}{10} = 0.7$

Example

Mark the position of these events on a probability scale.

a The sun setting today.
b An even number when you roll a dice.
c A glass breaking if dropped onto a stone floor.

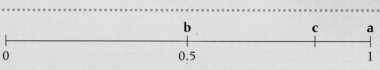

| | | **b** | | **c** | **a** | |
| 0 | | 0.5 | | | 1 | |

c is an approximate answer.

1. Draw a 10 cm line. Put a mark at every centimetre.
   Label the marks 0, 0.1, 0.2, ..., 0.8, 0.9, 1 as shown.

   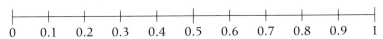

   On your probability scale, mark the position of
   a an impossible event
   b a certain event.

2. Draw a probability scale. Label it 0, 0.5 and 1.
   Mark the points **a**, **b** and **c** on the scale to show the probability of
   these events.
   a You get a Tail when you spin a coin.
   b Tomorrow will be Friday.
   c You will eat tomorrow.

3. Draw a probability scale as in question **2**.
   Mark these probabilities on your scale.
   a You roll a 7 on a dice.
   b You roll a number 6 or less.
   c You roll an odd number.

   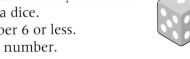

4. Draw a probability scale as in question **2**.
   Mark these probabilities on your scale.
   a You will be absent from school tomorrow.
   b You will get wet on your way home today.
   c You will watch television tonight.

   DID YOU KNOW?

   In 2008, the average
   television viewer in
   the US watched more
   than 151 hours of
   television per month,
   according to Nielson
   Media Research.

5. Draw a probability scale as in question **2**.
   Mark these probabilities on your scale.
   a The sun will shine in Spain this summer.
   b The bottom card of a shuffled pack of playing cards is Red.
   c You roll a 6 on a dice.

6. Wayne says that the probability that he will go to school tomorrow is
   1.2. Explain why the number 1.2 must be wrong.

7. A bag contains 1 green and 2 red balls. One ball is picked out.
   Draw a probability scale. Label it 0, 0.5 and 1. Mark the points **a**,
   b and **c** on the scale to show the probability of these events.
   a a blue ball   **b** a green ball   **c** a red ball.

This spread will show you how to:

- List all outcomes for single events in a systematic way
- Understand and use estimates or measures of probability including equally likely outcomes

Keywords
Equally likely
Event
Outcome
Probability
Systematically

When rolling a dice, the possible **outcomes** are 1, 2, 3, 4, 5 and 6.

The six outcomes are shown in order or **systematically.**

Each outcome is **equally likely** as the faces of the dice are identical in size and shape.

- The **probability** is a number that measures how likely it is that an event will happen.

You can calculate the probability using this formula.

An event is one or more outcomes.

- Probability of an event happening $= \dfrac{\text{number of favourable outcomes}}{\text{total number of all possible outcomes}}$

 p.124

0 means impossible.
1 means certain.

All probabilities have a value between 0 and 1.

Example

A counter is taken out of the bucket.

a List the possible outcomes.
b Find the probability that a blue counter is taken out.
c Find the probability that a red counter is taken out.
d Find the probability that a green counter is taken out.

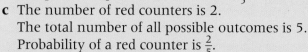

a Blue, Blue, Blue, Red, Red
b The number of blue counters is 3.
   The total number of all possible outcomes is 5.
   The probability of a blue counter is $\frac{3}{5}$.
c The number of red counters is 2.
   The total number of all possible outcomes is 5.
   Probability of a red counter is $\frac{2}{5}$.
d The number of green counters is 0.
   The total number of all possible outcomes is 5.
   Probability of a green counter is $\frac{0}{5} = 0$.

1 List all the possible outcomes when
   a spinning a coin
   b spinning this spinner
   c rolling an ordinary dice
   d trying to catch a ball
   e picking a letter from

2 List the three possible outcomes when a ball is taken from the bag.

3 List the three possible outcomes when a ball is taken from the bag.

4 List the three possible outcomes when a ball is taken from the bag.

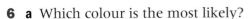

5 List the possible outcomes when the spinner is spun.

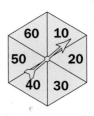

For the questions **6–10**, the outcomes are equally likely.

6 **a** Which colour is the most likely?
   b Calculate the probability of spinning orange.
   c Calculate the probability of spinning pink.

7 Calculate the probability of spinning a Head with a coin.

8 An ordinary dice is rolled. Calculate the probability of rolling
   a a 3   **b** an even number   **c** a 7.

9 Some children cannot decide whether to go swimming, skating or bowling. Three cards are put into a tin. One card is taken out to decide the activity.
Calculate the probability that the children go bowling.

10 A tetrahedron dice has only four faces.
The four outcomes are 1, 2, 3 or 4.
Calculate the probability that the score is
   a a 3   **b** an even number   **c** an odd number   **d** a 5.

23

Calculating probabilities

This spread will show you how to:

- Calculate probabilities
- Understand and use the probability scale

Keywords

Probability
Probability scale

You can measure how likely it is that an event will happen by using a number between 0 and 1 called the **probability**.

The probability can be represented on a **probability scale**.

0 means
impossible.
1 means certain.

```
0.0   0.1   0.2   0.3   0.4   0.5   0.6   0.7   0.8   0.9   1.0
 ├─────┼─────┼─────┼─────┼─────┼─────┼─────┼─────┼─────┼─────┤
 0    1/10   1/5              1/2         7/10              1
```

You can use
decimals or
fractions.

You can calculate the probability using this formula.

- Probability of an event happening = $\dfrac{\text{number of favourable outcomes}}{\text{total number of all possible outcomes}}$

The probability of an event can be written as P(event).

Example

The numbers 1 to 10 are put into a bag.

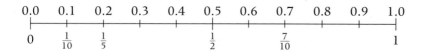

Karen picks one number out of the bag without looking.
Calculate the probability she picks

a the number 6
b a number greater than 7
c a multiple of 4
d a square number.

....

a There are 10 possible outcomes.
There is one 6.
P(6) = $\frac{1}{10}$
b There are three numbers greater than 7.
P(greater than 7) = $\frac{3}{10}$
c There are two numbers that are multiples of 4 (4, 8).
P(multiple of 4) = $\frac{2}{10}$ = $\frac{1}{5}$
d There are three square numbers (1, 4, 9).
P(square number) = $\frac{3}{10}$

7 is not included
in 'greater than 7'

For the following questions, the outcomes are equally likely.

1 A bag contains one yellow ball and four red balls. One ball is taken out of the bag. Calculate the probability that the ball is
   a red   **b** yellow   **c** blue.

2 A bag contains five red balls. One ball is taken out of the bag. Calculate the probability that the ball is
   a red   **b** blue.

3 A bag contains three red and two yellow balls. One ball is taken out of the bag. Calculate the probability that the ball is
   a red   **b** yellow   **c** blue.

4 This spinner is spun. Calculate the probability that the arrow lands on
   a a 2   **b** an odd number
   c a square number   **d** a prime number
   e a number 3 or less.

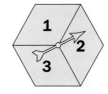

5 If one letter is chosen at random from the word ISOSCELES, what is the probability that the letter is
   a a C   **b** an E   **c** an S
   d a vowel   **e** a consonant?

6 If one letter is chosen at random from the word PARALLELOGRAM, what is the probability that the letter is
   a an O   **b** an A   **c** an L
   d a vowel   **e** a consonant?

7 These shapes are drawn on six cards.
One card is picked at random.
What is the probability that the shape on the card
   a is an isosceles triangle   **b** is a triangle
   c is a quadrilateral   **d** is a square
   e is an octagon   **f** has more than four sides
   g has all of its sides equal   **h** is a regular shape?

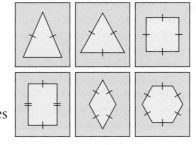

8 There are 14 boys and 16 girls in a class.
If one student is chosen at random, what is the probability that the student is
   a a boy   **b** a girl?

Probably not

This spread will show you how to:

- Identify different mutually exclusive outcomes and know the sum of the probabilities of all these outcomes is 1
- Understand and use the probability scale

Keywords
Event
Mutually exclusive
Outcome

A ball is picked from a box.

The possible **outcomes** are Green, Green and Red.

Probability of picking a green ball $= \frac{2}{3}$

Probability of picking a red ball $= \frac{1}{3}$

The probabilities of the events add up to 1.

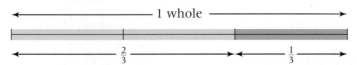

1 whole

$\frac{2}{3}$ $\frac{1}{3}$

$\frac{2}{3} + \frac{1}{3} = 1$

- The probabilities of all possible outcomes of an event add up to 1.

Probability of picking a green ball $= \frac{2}{3}$.

Probability of **not** picking a green ball $= 1 - \frac{2}{3} = \frac{1}{3}$.

- Probability of an event not happening $= 1 -$ Probability of the event happening

Example

The probability that Emma does her homework is $\frac{7}{10}$.

Calculate the probability that she does not do her homework.

$$1 - \frac{7}{10} = \frac{3}{10}$$

Probability she does not do her homework $= \frac{3}{10}$.

These outcomes are **mutually exclusive** because if you get one outcome you cannot get the other one.

This topic is extended to calculating mutually exclusive outcomes on page 438.

- Mutually exclusive outcomes cannot occur at the same time.

Example

Which of these outcomes are mutually exclusive?

A	**B**	**C**
Spinning a coin: Head, Tail	Pressing a light switch: Light on, light off	Eating breakfast: Cornflakes, muesli

A, **B**.

C is not mutually exclusive as you could choose both cornflakes and muesli.

1 A bag contains one blue and four red balls. One ball is taken out.
 a Calculate the probability that the ball is blue.
 b Calculate the probability that the ball is red.
 c Calculate the sum of these answers.

2 A bag contains three blue and seven green balls. One ball is taken out.
 a Calculate the probability that the ball is blue.
 b Calculate the probability that the ball is green.
 c Calculate the sum of these answers.

3 An ordinary dice is rolled.
 a Calculate the probability of rolling
   i a 1　**ii** a 2　**iii** a 3　**iv** a 4　**v** a 5　**vi** a 6.
 b Calculate the sum of the answers.

4 A box contains many red and blue counters.
 One counter is taken out. The probability that a red counter is taken out is 0.4.
 Calculate the probability that a blue counter is taken out.

5 The probability of winning a raffle is 0.1.
 Calculate the probability of not winning the raffle.

6 A spinner is made from blue, green, yellow and pink triangles.
 a Calculate the probability of spinning blue.
 b Calculate the probability of not spinning blue.

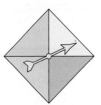

7 A drawing pin is dropped. The probability that the pin lands point up is $\frac{4}{5}$.
 What is the probability that the pin does not land point up?

8 The probability of rain at Styhead Tarn in the Lake District is $\frac{7}{10}$.
 Calculate the probability of it not raining at Styhead Tarn.

9 The letters of the word EQUILATERAL are put in a bag. One letter is taken out.
 a Calculate the probability of choosing an E.
 b Calculate the probability of not choosing an E.

This spread will show you how to:

- Use and interpret two-way tables for discrete data

Keywords
Equally likely
Random
Two-way table

When someone or something is chosen at **random**, each person or item must be **equally likely** to be chosen.

For example, picking counters from a bag, provided the counters are replaced and the bag is well shaken.

- A **two-way table** links two types of information.

p.42

100 students were asked whether they preferred swimming or running for exercise.

	Boys	Girls
Swimming	9	28
Running	31	32

9 boys preferred swimming.

32 girls preferred running.

$9 + 28 = 37$ students preferred swimming.
$31 + 32 = 63$ students preferred running.
$9 + 31 = 40$ students were boys.
$28 + 32 = 60$ students were girls.

You can calculate the probability of randomly selecting the different groups of students using the two-way table.

Example

The two-way table gives the number of males/females and adults/children in a room.
One person is selected at random.

	Adults	Children
Male	18	5
Female	15	12

Calculate the probability that the person selected is

a a female
b a child
c an adult male.

....

a $15 + 12 = 27$ female
   $P(\text{female}) = \frac{27}{50}$
b $5 + 12 = 17$ children
   $P(\text{child}) = \frac{17}{50}$
c There are 18 adult males.
   $P(\text{adult male}) = \frac{18}{50} = \frac{9}{25}$

The total number of people is
$18 + 5 + 15 + 12 = 50.$

1 The speeds of vehicles passing a school are measured.
The first 50 vehicles are shown in the table.
Calculate the probability that a vehicle passing
the school is travelling at

  a 30 mph or under

  b over 30 mph.

The speed limit outside the school is 30 mph.

  c What is the probability that a vehicle passing the
school is breaking the law?

	Number of vehicles
30 mph or under	15
Over 30 mph	35

2 The numbers of students in a class who are
right-handed or left-handed are shown in the
two-way table.

  a How many students are in the class altogether?

A student is chosen at random.
What is the probability that the student is

  b a right-handed boy

  c a right-handed girl

  d a left-handed boy

  e a left-handed girl?

	Boys	Girls
Right-handed	12	13
Left-handed	3	2

3 A building set consists of red and yellow bricks.
Each brick is either a cube or a cuboid.
The two-way table shows the number of
each type of brick in the set.

	Cubes	Cuboids
Red	8	5
Yellow	1	6

  a How many bricks are in the building set altogether?

  b How many yellow bricks are in the building set altogether?

  c How many cubes are in the building set altogether?

A brick is selected at random. Calculate the probability
that the brick is

  d yellow

  e a cube.

4 The numbers of people in a library are
shown in the two-way table.

  a How many people are in the library altogether?

  b How many males are in the library?

  c How many under 18s are in the library?

One person is selected at random. Calculate the
probability that the person is

  d a male

  e an under 18

  f a female who is under 18.

	Males	Females
Under 18	5	10
18 or over	20	15

Summary

Check out
You should now be able to:

- Understand and use the vocabulary of probability
- Understand and use the probability scale
- List all outcomes for single events in a systematic way
- Understand and use estimates or measures of probability
- Identify mutually exclusive events and know that the sum of the probabilities of these outcomes is 1
- Use and interpret two-way tables and use them to calculate probabilities

Worked exam question

1. A fair spinner has eight equal sections.
Four sections are white (W).
Three sections are red (R).
One section is green (G).
Here are four statements about the spinner.
For each student, write 'True', 'false', or 'Cannot say.'

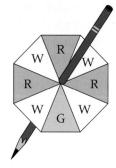

a It is most likely to land on red.

b It is unlikely to land on green.

c It has an even chance of landing on white.

d It is impossible to land on green three times in a row. (4)

(AQA, 2008)

- -

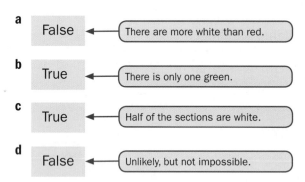

a False ← There are more white than red.

b True ← There is only one green.

c True ← Half of the sections are white.

d False ← Unlikely, but not impossible.

Exam questions

1 **a** Toni has ten coloured cards.
Eight cards are blue and two are red.
Toni picks a card at random.

Choose a word from this list to describe each of the following events.

impossible   unlikely   evens   likely   certain

  a **i** The card picked is blue. (1)
    ii The card picked is yellow. (1)
    iii The card picked is blue or red. (1)

  b Jay has a different set of ten coloured cards.
He has an even chance of picking a blue card.

How many blue cards are there in this set? (1)

(AQA, 2008)

2 **a** On a copy of the probability scale below, mark with a cross (×) the probability
that you will see a rainbow in the sky at least once next year.

(1)

  b On a copy of the probability scale below, mark with a cross (×) the
probability that you will get a 7 when you roll an ordinary 6-sided dice.

(1)

3 The two-way table shows some information about the colours of Vauxhall
cars and of BMW cars in a car park. Some of the information is missing.

	black	blue	red	Total
Vauxhall	8	9		
BMW				22
Total	12		14	40

One of the cars is to be picked at random.
Work out the probability that this car will be blue. (3)

Introduction

In the run up to a general election, opinion polls are taken to find out which political party people are likely to vote for. The results of just a thousand people's voting intentions are taken very seriously by the media and the politicians.

What's the point?

Surveys allow statisticians to analyse manageable amounts of data, without having to gauge the opinion of everyone in the country. The results are quicker, less costly, and still meaningful.

Check in

1 Put these numbers in order of size, smallest first.
   a 37, 42, 17, 6, 30, 19, 26, 29
   b 118, 135, 106, 121, 130, 115
   c 156, 145, 154, 165, 166, 155, 144

2 Calculate
   a 63 + 58   **b** 48 + 96
   c 73 + 95 + 84   **d** 138 + 275
   e 63 + 5   **f** 38 − 15
   g 96 − 47   **h** 136 − 54
   i 258 − 69   **j** 432 − 166

3 The table shows the average times of sunset and sunrise for 6 months of the year.

	Sunrise	Sunset
January	07:53	16:20
March	06:06	18:17
May	05:00	20:45
July	04:58	21:04
September	06:35	19:00
November	07:23	15:58

What time does the sun
   a rise in July   **b** set in May?

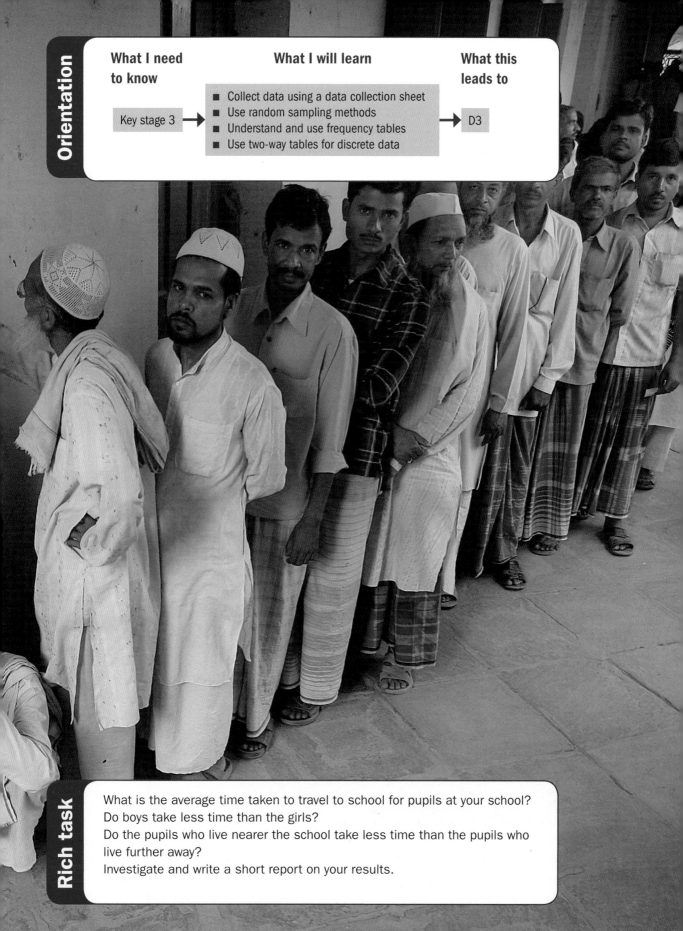

What I need to know

What I will learn

What this leads to

Key stage 3 →

- Collect data using a data collection sheet
- Use random sampling methods
- Understand and use frequency tables
- Use two-way tables for discrete data

→ D3

Rich task

What is the average time taken to travel to school for pupils at your school?
Do boys take less time than the girls?
Do the pupils who live nearer the school take less time than the pupils who live further away?
Investigate and write a short report on your results.

Data collection sheets

This spread will show you how to:
- Use data collection sheets for discrete data
- Understand and use frequency tables to show data

Keywords

Data
Data collection
  sheet
Frequency table
Tally chart

Before this headline could be written, information called **data** was collected.

You can collect data using a **data collection sheet** (This one is a **tally chart**).

Colour	Tally	Frequency
Red	|||| |||| |||	13
Blue	|||| ||	7
White	|||| ||||		11

|||| = 5

The data can also be shown using a **frequency table**.

Colour	Frequency
Red	13
Blue	7
White	11

← 7 people chose Blue

Example

The students in a Year 10 class were asked to name their favourite season. Use the data collection sheet to tally the data. Calculate the frequencies.

Season	Tally	Frequency
Spring		
Summer		
Autumn		
Winter		

Winter	Summer	Spring	Spring	Winter	Autumn	Summer
Spring	Autumn	Summer	Winter	Winter	Summer	Summer
Spring	Summer	Summer	Summer	Spring	Spring	

Season	Tally	Frequency
Spring	||||		6
Summer	|||| |||	8
Autumn	||	2
Winter	||||	4

A02 Functional Maths · **Unit 1**

1 Tickets to see an Irish band cost £5, £10, £15 or £20.
These price tickets are sold one morning:

These values are all in pounds (£).

15	10	10	5	5	5	5	5	10	20
20	5	5	5	5	10	5	10	5	15
15	20	20	5	5	10	10	10	10	5
5	5	10	5	10	15	20	20	20	20

a Copy and complete the tally chart.
b How many £5 tickets were sold?
c How many tickets were sold altogether?

Price	Tally	Number of tickets
£5		
£10		
£15		
£20		

2 The vowels in a paragraph on the front page of a newspaper are

a	e	i	a	e	o	u	e	i	a
e	o	a	i	e	u	e	o	i	o
u	o	u	i	e	e	o	i	a	e
a	o	e	i	o	e	e	i	o	u
a	a	e	e	o	i	u	e	o	e

Britain's Best Rag   56p
ECHO
TAX CUTS OR UP?
The Prime Minister was involved in a new controversy yesterday as the Chancellor changed his mind without asking.

a Copy and complete the data collection sheet to show the vowels in the paragraph.
b Which vowel occurred the most?

Vowel	Tally	Frequency
a		
e		
i		
o		
u		

3 A tetrahedron dice is numbered 1, 2, 3, 4.
a Copy and complete the data collection sheet to show these scores.

4	2	1	3	1	3	4	2
3	3	2	2	2	3	4	4
2	4	1	1	2	4	1	2
1	2	1	3	2	1	4	3
2	3	1	4	4	2	3	1

b State the number of times a 3 was rolled.

Score	Tally	Frequency
1		
2		
3		
4		

A02 Functional Maths

4 A class of students are asked to give the month of their birthday.

Mar	May	Apr	Jun	Sep	Mar	Jun	Feb
Sep	Dec	Nov	Nov	Apr	Mar	Jul	Aug
Aug	Mar	Apr	Feb	Jan	Sep	Jun	Jun
Sep	Nov	Oct	Jan	Jun	Dec	Oct	Feb

a Draw and complete a tally chart to show this information.
b Calculate the number of students in the class.
c In which month were most students born?

Observation, controlled experiment and sampling

This spread will show you how to:

- Collect data using various methods including observation and controlled experiment
- Calculate total frequency from a discrete frequency table
- Use random sampling methods, taking steps to minimise bias

Keywords

Biased
Controlled experiment
Data collection sheet
Observation
Random sample

- You can collect data by **observation**.
  For example, to find how many people use the dodgem ride at the fair, you would have to watch and count the people on the ride.
- You can collect data by a **controlled experiment**.

This topic is extended to random sampling of databases on page 446.

Example

Simon throws a dice 50 times. He thinks 'lucky' 6 will happen more often than the other numbers. The results are shown.

3	1	4	3	5	2	6	2	1	3
4	2	2	6	3	1	1	2	3	4
5	6	1	2	1	4	3	5	6	2
1	4	6	3	2	2	1	5	5	6
2	4	3	2	5	6	4	4	6	3

Complete the **data collection sheet** to show the dice scores for this controlled experiment.

Score	Tally	Freq.
1		
2		
3		
4		
5		
6		

Score	Tally	Freq.
1	ЖⅢ	8
2	Ж Ж Ⅰ	11
3	Ж ⅢⅠ	9
4	Ж Ⅲ	8
5	Ж Ⅰ	6
6	Ж Ⅲ	8
		50

Check the frequencies add to 50.

Sometimes it is impossible to collect data from all the population and so a **random sample** is used.

Instead of asking every student in your school, you could choose a random sample of 50 students. The students are chosen so that the sample is not **biased**.

- The larger the sample, the more accurate the data will be.

1 Decide whether each of these data collections is an observation or a controlled experiment.

a Rolling a dice
b Spinning a coin
c Whether people walk under a ladder
d The colour of vehicles
e Spinning a spinner
f The number of birds in a garden
g The punctuality of trains
h The choices of a school meal
i Choosing chocolates out of a selection box
j The ages of teachers at a school

A02 **Functional Maths**

2 The number of passengers in passing cars are counted.
The results are shown.

| 1 | 0 | 2 | 0 | 1 | 0 | 1 | 3 | 1 | 0 | 3 | 2 |
| 0 | 1 | 0 | 0 | 2 | 1 | 0 | 0 | 0 | 1 | 2 |

a Is this data collection an observation or a controlled experiment?
b Copy and complete the data collection sheet to show this information.
c Calculate the total number of cars that passed.

Number of passengers	Tally	Number of cars
0		
1		
2		
3		

3 A spinner, labelled A to E, is spun and the letter is recorded.
The results are shown.

C	B	E	D	E	A	B	D	A	E
B	C	D	A	E	B	C	B	A	E
A	E	D	E	B	C	B	A	D	E
E	C	B	D	A	B	A	C	D	C

a Is this data collection an observation or a controlled experiment?
b Copy and complete the frequency table to show the results.
c How many times was the spinner spun altogether?
d Do you think the spinner is biased? Explain your answer.
e How could you improve the reliability of your answer?

Letter	Tally	Frequency
A		
B		
C		
D		
E		

Surveys

This spread will show you how to:

- Collect data using various methods including questionnaires and surveys

Surveys are used to find people's views and opinions.

> 2 out of 3 boys like chocolate but only

- You can collect data with a survey using
  - a data collection sheet
  - a questionnaire.

You can collect all the data on one **data collection sheet**.

Age group under 16/16 +	M/F	Like chocolate?
16+	F	no
under 16	F	yes
16+	M	yes

You will need one **questionnaire** for each person in your survey.

Chocolate questionnaire

Age group

Under 16 ☐   16 or more ☐

Gender   Do you like chocolate?

M ☐ F ☐   Y ☐   N ☐

Any other comments?

- You must be careful what questions you ask in a survey.
  - Never ask a personal question.   For example, did you brush your teeth yesterday? What is your age?
  - Never ask a leading question.   For example, what do you think of this beautiful wood being chopped down to build a noisy road?
  - Never ask a vague question.   For example, how often do you eat meat?
  - Never ask a question that will give too many answers.   For example, what did you eat yesterday?

Example

One question in a questionnaire is

How often do you do homework?

Sometimes ☐   Occasionally ☐   Regularly ☐

Explain why the suggested answers are not satisfactory.

....

1 Always/never are not given.
2 Sometimes/occasionally mean the same.
3 Regularly could mean every day, every week or every month.

1 James uses a data collection sheet for a survey to find his class's favourite soup.
He limits the choice to Tomato (T), Vegetable (V), Fish (F) or Other (O).
His completed sheet is

T	T	T	V	F	V	V	T	T	V
F	O	T	V	O	O	T	V	T	F
O	T	V	O	T	V	O	O	O	O

a Copy and complete the tally
chart to show the data.

b Calculate the number of
students in James's class.

c State the most favourite soup.

Type of soup	Tally	Number of students
Tomato (T)		
Vegetable (V)		
Fish (F)		
Other (O)		

2 Andrew uses a questionnaire for a survey about
eating habits.
His questionnaire is shown.
He stops people in the street and asks them to
answer the questions.

Name:

Age:

What is your favourite meal?

The first response from an elderly lady is
shown.
Write three criticisms of Andrew's
questionnaire.

Name: Anonymous

Age: Older than you!

What is your favourite meal?

Prawn cocktail, soup, meat and two
veg, dumplings, gravy, chocolate
gateau with ice cream, cheese and
                                    PTO

3 These questions appeared on a questionnaire.
Write one criticism of each question.
a What is your favourite sweet?
b How often do you use a computer?
c How much pocket money/allowance are you given?
d Did you have a shower this morning?
e These buses are always late. What do you think of the bus service?
f How much do you spend on clothes?
g How tall are you?
h Do you like shopping?
i Where do you live?
j How many DVDs do you own?   loads   a lot   many

This spread will show you how to:

- Understand the difference between primary and secondary data
- Understand and use frequency tables to show data
- Identify which primary data you need to collect and in what format, including grouped data, considering equal class intervals

Keywords

Class interval
Group
Primary data
Secondary data

- **Primary data** is data you collect yourself, for example, you count the number of heads when spinning a coin.
- **Secondary data** is data someone else has already collected, for example, National Census, information from newspapers or the internet.

Some surveys produce data with too many different values. For example, 36, 44, 18, 27, 23, 6, 73, 25, 19, 31, 80, 46, 51, 55, 65 could be the exam marks for 15 students.

A data collection sheet or a frequency table would have too many categories.

- You can **group** the data into **class intervals** to avoid this.

Example

The number of cars in a car park was recorded every day for one month. The results are shown.

8	34	10	15	24	49	0	13	25	19
23	31	45	0	15	3	21	22	27	47
0	9	24	36	17	19	45	0	18	5

Complete the grouped frequency table.

Number of cars	Tally	Freq.
0 to 9		
10 to 19		
20 to 29		
30 to 39		
40 to 49		

class intervals

Number of cars	Tally	Freq.
0 to 9 |卌 |||	8
10 to 19	卌 |||	8
20 to 29	卌 ||	7
30 to 39	|||	3
40 to 49	||||	4
		30

卌 = 5

← Check that the frequencies add to 30.

1 Decide whether these data collection methods give primary data or secondary data.

a The times of the goals in football matches from a newspaper
b Measuring heights of students in your class
c The rainfall each month in Paris from the internet
d The number of Heads when spinning a coin
e The results of an experiment you do in a science lesson
f The number of telephone calls your class made yesterday evening
g The number of people who went to the theatre in 2005 from information on the internet
h The population of Switzerland from a book
i The reaction times of students in your class by an experiment
j The times of low and high tides from a leaflet.

2 a Copy and complete the frequency table using these weights of people, in kilograms.

67	40	56	65	57	42	45
56	66	69	42	51	58	63
65	69	61	44	67	55	43
58	63	68	54	57	49	48
47	42					

Weight (kg)	Tally	Number of people
40 to 44		
45 to 49		
50 to 54		
55 to 59		
60 to 64		
65 to 69		

b Calculate the number of people shown in the frequency table.

3 a Copy and complete the frequency table using these exam marks.

45	36	34	56	71	38	55
63	72	80	14	25	44	37
51	58	35	47	22	10	33
37	54	61	77	24	27	29
31	35	27	28	32	36	52
58	59	60	50	35	29	18
66	55	32	35	21	53	67
79						

Exam mark	Tally	Frequency
1 to 10		
11 to 20		
21 to 30		
31 to 40		
41 to 50		
51 to 60		
61 to 70		
71 to 80		

b Calculate the number of people who took the exam.

Functional Maths

A02

4 The heights, in centimetres, of students are shown.

148	143	148	152	155	160	171	144
132	133	161	172	133	149	150	164
168	170	153	150	138	139	144	151
163	165	180	180	155	160	165	155
145	133	138	161	168	136	147	145

a Draw and complete a frequency table, using suitable class intervals.
b Calculate the total number of students in the frequency table.
c What can you say about the heights of students in this sample?

Two-way tables and surveys

This spread will show you how to:
- Use two-way tables for discrete and grouped data
- Collect data using various methods

Keywords
Column
Frequency table
Row
Total
Two-way table

You can summarise data in a **frequency table**.
This table shows the preferred takeway food of a sample of people.

Food	Number of people
Pizza	8
Burger	7
Curry	5

7 people prefer a burger.

You can show more detail in a **two-way table**.

p.28
A two-way table links two types of information, for example, food and gender.

	Men	Women
Pizza	3	5
Burger	4	3
Curry	5	2

3 women prefer a burger.

You can extend the two-way table by adding
– an extra **row** to give the total of men, women and people
– an extra **column** to give the total of each food.
The extra row and column headings are **totals**.

	Men	Women	Totals
Pizza	3	5	8
Burger	4	3	7
Curry	3	2	5
Totals	10	10	20

3 + 5 = 8
10 + 10 = 20
3 + 4 + 3 = 10

Example

Some children are asked, 'Do you ever eat fruit?'
The results of a survey are shown in the two-way table.
a How many girls never eat fruit?
b How many boys eat fruit?
c How many children answered the survey?

Do you ever eat fruit?

	Yes	No
Boys	6	8
Girls	9	7

....

a 7 girls
b 6 boys
c 6 + 8 + 9 + 7 = 30 children

1 The results of an eye colour survey are shown.
Use the two-way table to find the number of
 a blue-eyed boys
 b brown-eyed girls
 c boys
 d girls
 e blue-eyed children
 f brown-eyed children.

	Eye colour		
	Blue	**Brown**	**Other**
Boys	35	24	14
Girls	47	36	4

2 At a local school, students have the opportunity
to study French and Spanish.
The table shows the choice for all Year 10 students.
Find the number of students that study
 a French and Spanish
 b French but not Spanish
 c neither French nor Spanish
 d Spanish
 e French.

	Spanish	**Not Spanish**
French	16	55
Not French	51	14

3 There are two cinemas in a Cinecomplex.
The number of people in each cinema is shown
in the two-way table.
Calculate the number of
 a adults in the Cinecomplex
 b children in the Cinecomplex
 c people in Cinema 1
 d people in Cinema 2
 e people in the whole Cinecomplex.

	Cinema	
	1	**2**
Adult	31	47
Child	12	8

4 In a traffic survey, the colour and speed of 100 cars are recorded.
The results are summarised in the two-way table.
 a State the number of cars that are
  i red and over the speed limit
  ii not speeding and not red.
 b Calculate the number of cars that are
  i red   **ii** over the speed limit.

	Not speeding	**Over the speed limit**
Red	5	55
Not red	10	30

 c Calculate, as a simplified fraction, the number of cars that are
  i not speeding   **ii** not red.
 d Maria claims that drivers of red cars tend to break speed limits.
  Use the two-way table to decide whether you agree with Maria.

D2

Summary

Check out
You should now be able to:

- Use data collection sheets for discrete and grouped data
- Understand and use frequency tables
- Collect data using a variety of methods
- Collect data from a variety of sources
- Identify possible sources of bias
- Use two-way tables for discrete data

Worked exam question

Monan asks some friends to choose their favourite sport from a list.
Here are the results.

rugby	football	football	cricket	rugby
football	rugby	cricket	basketball	cricket
rugby	football	football	rugby	football
cricket	football	cricket	basketball	football

a Complete the tally chart and frequency column to
show these results. (2)

Sport	Tally	Frequency
basketball		
cricket		
football		
rugby		

b Which sport is the mode? (1)

(AQA, 2009)

....

a

Sport	Tally	Frequency
basketball	||	2
cricket	||||	5
football	|||| |||	8
rugby	||||	5

b

Football ← Football has the highest frequency.

Exam questions

1 A doctor wants to encourage her patients to take more exercise.
The doctor has approximately 500 patients.
She decides to do a survey about what exercise her patients take.

a This is a question in the survey.

> **Q** Do you exercise?
>
> **A** Tick a box
>
> Yes ☐ No ☐ Sometimes ☐ Everyday ☐

   i Give a criticism of the question. (1)
  ii Give a criticism of the response section. (1)

b This is another question in the survey.

> **Q** How many miles did you walk last week?

Give a suitable response section for this question. (1)

c **i** The doctor decides to use one of three methods to do the survey.

Method 1   Give the survey to the first 50 patients seen in a week
Method 2   Choose 50 patients at random
Method 3   Choose 26 patients, picking one whose surname begins with
               each letter of the alphabet

Give a reason why method 3 is **not** suitable. (1)

 ii Which of the other two methods for doing the survey will give the most
reliable results?
Give a reason for your choice. (1)

(AQA, specimen)

Functional Maths 1: Weather

Before creating a weather forecast, data is collected from all over the world to give information about the current conditions. A supercomputer and knowledge about the atmosphere, the Earth's surface and the oceans are then used to create the forecast.

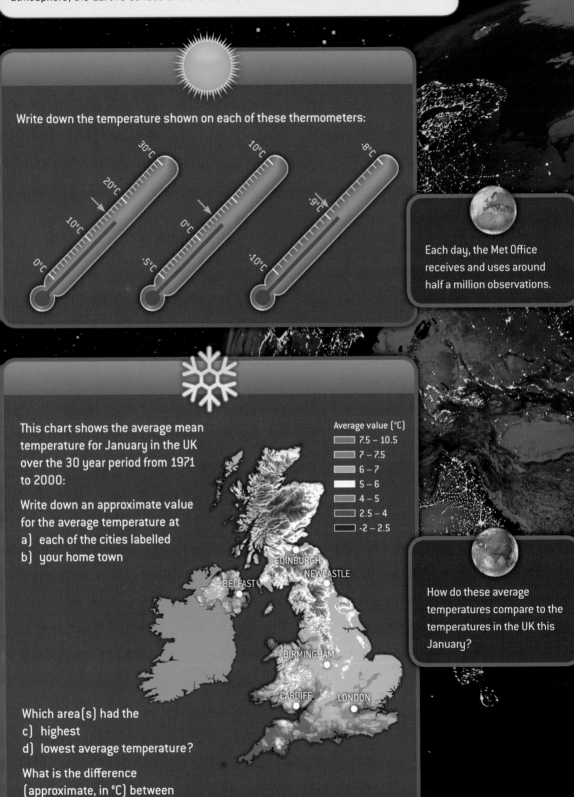

Write down the temperature shown on each of these thermometers:

Each day, the Met Office receives and uses around half a million observations.

This chart shows the average mean temperature for January in the UK over the 30 year period from 1971 to 2000:

Write down an approximate value for the average temperature at
a) each of the cities labelled
b) your home town

Average value (°C)
- 7.5 – 10.5
- 7 – 7.5
- 6 – 7
- 5 – 6
- 4 – 5
- 2.5 – 4
- -2 – 2.5

EDINBURGH
NEWCASTLE
BELFAST
BIRMINGHAM
CARDIFF
LONDON

How do these average temperatures compare to the temperatures in the UK this January?

Which area(s) had the
c) highest
d) lowest average temperature?

What is the difference (approximate, in °C) between these temperatures?

Wind direction is measured in tens of degrees relative to true North and is always given from where the wind is blowing. In the UK, wind speed is measured in knots, where 1knot = 1.15mph, or in terms of the Beaufort Scale.

Research the Beaufort Scale using the internet.

Easterly wind, 090°

Describe the wind speed (in knots) and direction (in tens of degrees and in words) shown by each of these arrows:

15 knots	30 knots	13.5 mph
	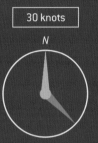	

Observed data can be used to make predictions, but there is always some level of uncertainty. This graph shows the range of uncertainty in temperature in Exeter with some indication of the most probable values:

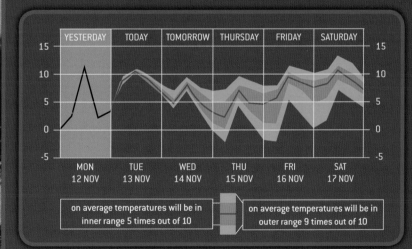

What predictions do you think a weather forecaster would have made about the temperature in Exeter during the week shown?

Justify your response by referring to the graph.

Introduction

In many professions it is vital to perform mental checks on answers that have been calculated. These include doctors working out the dose of medicine to give a patient, pilots checking the fuel required for a flight, or civil engineers calculating the amount of material required to construct a building.

What's the point?

If doctors, pilots and engineers don't check that their answers are sensible, things could go badly wrong and it will affect other people.

Check in

1 Round 2916 to the nearest
   a 1000   **b** 100   **c** 10

2 Calculate
   a 95 − 47   **b** 76 + 29
   c 576 + 239   **d** 914 − 685

3 Calculate
   a 5 × 6   **b** 48 ÷ 8
   c 12 × 6   **d** 282 ÷ 2
   e 12 × 14   **f** 91 ÷ 7

Rich task

The numbers 3 and 6 are multiplied together and then the answer is doubled. This gives 36 (a 2-digit number made from the two original numbers).

Find two 2-digit numbers that when multiplied together and doubled give a 4-digit number.

This spread will show you how to:

- Use a range of mental methods for addition and subtraction of whole numbers

Keywords
Compensation
Mental methods
Partitioning

Partitioning

Split the numbers into parts (hundreds, tens and units).
Then add or subtract the parts.

Example

Calculate   **a** $37 + 78$ **b** $95 - 43$

a $37 + 78 = 30 + 7 + 70 + 8$
$= 70 + 30 + 15$
$= 100 + 15$
$= 115$

b $95 - 43 = 95 - 40 - 3$
$= 55 - 3$
$= 52$

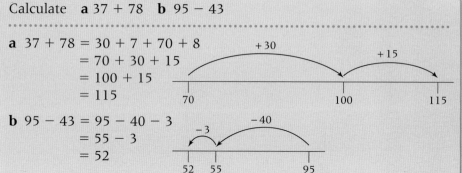

Strategies to help you work out additions and subtractions in your head are called **mental methods**.

p.160

Compensation

When the number you are adding or subtracting is nearly a multiple of 10 or a multiple of 100, round the number up or down.

Example

Calculate   **a** $63 + 29$ **b** $174 - 39$

a $63 + 29 = 63 + 30 - 1$
$= 93 - 1$
$= 92$

b $174 - 39 = 174 - 40 + 1$
$= 134 + 1$
$= 135$

Remember to add or subtract to finish your calculation.

You can also count up from the smallest number to the largest number.

Example

Gerta earns £408 a week. She spends £187 a week on her mortgage. How much money does she have left?

£408 − £187

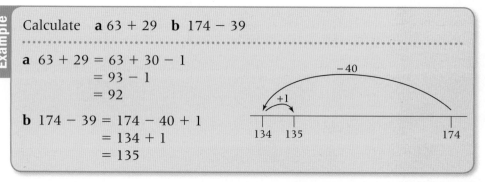

Count up from 187 to the next 100 (that is, 200).
Count up from 200 to the next 100 below 408 (that is, 400).
Count up from 40 to 408.

Add together the counts you have made (that is, $13 + 200 + 8$).

£408 − £187 = 13 + 200 + 8 = £221

This is called shopkeeper's subtraction. Use a number line to help you.

You can extend these techniques to decimals.

1 Write the answers to each of these calculations.
   a 17 + 13   **b** 17 − 8   **c** 16 + 17
   d 18 − 9   **e** 19 + 19   **f** 27 − 14

2 Find the missing number in each of these calculations.
   a 63 + ? = 100   **b** ? + 43 = 100
   c 31 + ? = 100   **d** 53 + ? = 100

3 Use a mental method for each of these calculations.
   a 27 + 43   **b** 48 + 12   **c** 27 + 23
   d 26 + 52   **e** 34 + 23   **f** 61 + 28

 4 Use a mental method for each of these calculations.
   Write the method you have used.
   a 25 + 36   **b** 46 + 31   **c** 72 − 19
   d 48 + 49   **e** 56 + 38   **f** 123 + 39

AO2 Functional Maths

5 Use a mental method of calculation to solve each of these
   problems.
   a Liam spends 43p on a can of cola and 39p on a packet of
   crisps. How much money has he spent?
   b Brad scores 29 points in a game of rugby. In the next game he
   scores 23 points. What is his total score of points for the two
   games?
   c Laura looks after 29 horses. Emma looks after 37 horses.
   How many horses do the girls look after altogether?
   d Thomas owns 56 CDs. He sells 39 of his CDs. How many CDs
   does he have left?

6 Use a mental method to calculate
   a 134 + 29   **b** 245 + 85   **c** 313 + 63
   d 278 + 75   **e** 378 + 208   **f** 512 − 369

AO3 Problem

7 **a** Using each of the digits 1, 2, 3, 4 and 5 only once, what is the
   largest answer for an addition calculation that you can make?

 + ☐☐

   b Using each of the digits 1, 2, 3, 4 and 5 only once, what is the
   smallest answer for a subtraction calculation that you can make?

☐☐☐ − ☐☐

 8 Use a mental method.
   Write the method you have used.

   a Decrease 132 by 64.
   b How many less than 156 is 79?
   c 234 + ☐ = 507. What is the value of ☐?
   d 638 subtract 199.
   e What is the total of 259 and 325?

9 Use a mental method for each of
   these decimal calculations.

   a £1.82 + £0.25
   b £2.93 + £1.58
   c £4.12 − £2.35
   d 19.7 − 13.4

Written addition and subtraction

This spread will show you how to:

- Use a range of written methods for addition and subtraction of whole numbers
- Estimate the answers to problems

Keywords
Addition
Subtraction
Written method

- There is a standard **written method** for addition.

To calculate $3518 + 765$:

Set out the calculation in columns:

Add the units:

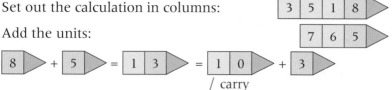

carry
1 ten

Add the tens:

Add the hundreds:

carry
1 thousand

Add the thousands:

So $3518 + 765 = 4000 + 200 + 80 + 3$.

p.164

This is based on the **partitioning** mental method.

You should always estimate the answer.
$3518 + 765$
$\approx 3500 + 800$
$= 4300$

You could set out the calculation like this:

```
    3  5  1  8
+      7  6  5
   4  2  8  3
      1     1
```

- There is a standard written method for subtraction that is based upon the partitioning mental method.

Example

Calculate $3518 - 765$.

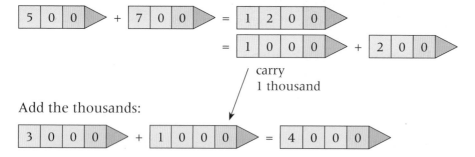

²3̸	¹⁴3̸	¹1	8	Set out the calculation in columns
−		7 6 5		
	2 7	5 3		Subtract the units

Subtract the units $8 - 5 = \mathbf{3}$

Subtract the tens   10 − 60 is not possible!
Move 1 hundred into the tens column $110 - 60 = \mathbf{50}$

Subtract the hundreds   400 − 700 is not possible!
Move 1 thousand into the hundreds column $1400 - 700 = \mathbf{700}$

Subtract the thousands $2000 - 0 = \mathbf{2000}$

You can use this technique with decimals as well.

1 Use a written method to work out these calculations.
   a 234 + 133   **b** 342 + 445   **c** 437 + 261   **d** 487 + 311

2 Use a written method to work out these calculations.
   a 356 − 234   **b** 769 − 436   **c** 786 − 472   **d** 167 − 35

3 Use a written method to work out these additions.
   a 432 + 549   **b** 537 + 249   **c** 345 + 273
   d 487 + 432   **e** 472 + 715   **f** 654 + 533

> In questions 3–6, you may need to carry.

4 Use a written method for each of these additions.
   a 368 + 725   **b** 793 + 432   **c** 527 + 395
   d 438 + 287   **e** 383 + 769   **f** 783 + 978

5 Use a written method for each of these subtractions.
   a 562 − 417   **b** 837 − 618   **c** 748 − 563   **d** 865 − 472

6 Use a written method for each of these subtractions.
   a 584 − 378   **b** 738 − 568   **c** 483 − 277   **d** 407 − 321

7 Use a written method for each of these calculations.
   a 265 + 846   **b** 371 + 686   **c** 831 − 488
   d 1345 + 874   **e** 2576 − 784   **f** 4762 − 1875

8 A battery costs 83p.
   Saima has £5. She buys as many batteries as she can.
   Work out the amount of change Saima should get from £5.

9 Yvonne is planning a holiday. She has a maximum budget of £1800.
   There are three parts to her holiday: transport, accommodation and
   spending money. She can choose various options for each part of
   her holiday:

Transport		Accommodation		Spending money
Flights	£378	Villa	£637	£800
Train	£289	Hotel	£892	£700
Car	£278	Camping	£278	£600

   For example   car + villa + spending money
                  £278 + £637 + £800 = £1715

   Write three choices she could make which would
   be within her budget of £1800.

10 Use a written method for each of these decimal calculations.
    a 2.4 + 3.1   **b** 1.5 + 4.4   **c** 5.9 + 2.3   **d** 3.82 + 4.16
    e 4.5 − 2.2   **f** 3.7 − 1.8   **g** 9.36 − 6.28   **h** 3.4 − 1.52

This spread will show you how to:
- Use a range of mental methods for multiplication and division of whole numbers

Keywords
Divisibility
Factor
Mental method
Multiple
Partitioning

There are lots of strategies you can use to help you work out multiplications and divisions in your head.

Partitioning
Split the numbers into parts (hundreds, tens and units).
Then multiply or divide each part separately.

Example

Calculate   **a** 16×7 **b** $342 \div 3$

a $16 = 10 + 6$

$16 \times 7 = (10 \times 7) + (6 \times 7)$

$\qquad = 70 + 42$

$\qquad = 112$

b $342 = 300 + 42$

$342 \div 3 = (300 \div 3) \div (42 \div 3)$

$\qquad = 100 + 14$

$\qquad = 114$

Remember
To multiply a number by 10, all the digits move one place to the left of the decimal point, for example,
$10 \times 7 = 70$.

Compensation
Use this method when the number you are multiplying by is nearly a **multiple** of 10 or a multiple of 100.

Example

Calculate 14×9

$9 = 10 - 1$

$14 \times 9 = (14 \times 10) - (14 \times 1)$

$\qquad = 140 - 14$

$\qquad = 126$

Here are some other methods you can use.

1 $23 \times 20 = 23 \times 2 \times 10$

$\quad 23 \times 2 = 46$
$\quad 46 \times 10 = 460$

$\quad 23 \times 20 = 460$

Think of multiply by 20 as multiply by 2, followed by multiply by 10

2 $84 \div 6 = 84 \div 2 \div 3$

$\quad 84 \div 2 = 42$
$\quad 42 \div 3 = 14$

$\quad 84 \div 6 = 14$

$6 = 2 \times 3$ so
$84 \div 6$ is the same as
$84 \div (2 \times 3)$.
This means you can divide by 2 and then by 3.

Doubling and halving
Double one of the numbers and halve the other before you multiply.

$12 \times 15 = 6 \times 30$
$\qquad = 180$

Doubling
Double both of the numbers before you divide.

$80 \div 5 = 160 \div 10$
$\qquad = 16$

1 Calculate
  a 4 × 7   **b** 120 ÷ 10   **c** 2 × 34   **d** 78 ÷ 2
  e 5 × 6   **f** 340 ÷ 10   **g** 93 × 2   **h** 5 × 9

2 Use the mental method of partitioning to calculate these.
  Show the method you have used.
  a 6 × 11   **b** 13 × 6   **c** 7 × 13   **d** 11 × 9
  e 16 × 6   **f** 12 × 6

3 Use the mental method of partitioning to calculate these.
  Show the method you have used.
  a 36 ÷ 3   **b** 48 ÷ 4   **c** 88 ÷ 8   **d** 69 ÷ 3
  e 65 ÷ 5   **f** 48 ÷ 3

4 Use the mental method of compensation to calculate each of these.
  Show the method you have used.
  a 7 × 9   **b** 12 × 9   **c** 13 × 11   **d** 11 × 19
  e 14 × 11   **f** 21 × 6

5 Use the mental method of factors to calculate each of these.
  Show the method you have used.
  a 13 × 20   **b** 48 ÷ 6   **c** 23 × 4   **d** 7 × 8
  e 132 ÷ 6   **f** 17 × 4

6 Use the mental method of halving and doubling to calculate each
  of these. Show the method you have used.
  a 4 × 27   **b** 3 × 14   **c** 33 × 4   **d** 14 × 15

7 Use an appropriate mental method to calculate each of these.
  a 7 × 12   **b** 8 × 9   **c** 54 ÷ 6   **d** 11 × 16
  e 12 × 12   **f** 124 ÷ 4

A02 Functional Maths

8 Use an appropriate mental method to solve
  each of these problems.
  a Harry buys 13 CDs at £9 each.
     How much does he spend?
  b Kelvin shares £76 between his four
     grandchildren.
     How much does each child receive?
  c Hope runs every 20 metres in six seconds.
     How long will it take her to run 400 metres?
  d Pens are packed into boxes of six.
     How many boxes will be needed for 78 pens?
  e Trent pays for nine bars of chocolate.
     Each bar of chocolate costs 26p.
     How much money does he spend?

DID YOU KNOW?

The world's first music CD went on sale in 1982. It was an album called The Visitors by the Swedish pop group Abba. Since then, more than 200 billion CDs have been sold worldwide.

This spread will show you how to:
- Use a range of written methods for multiplication and division of whole numbers
- Estimate the answers to problems

Keywords
Dividend
Divisor
Estimate
Grid method
Standard method
Whole number

You can use the **grid method** to multiply whole numbers.

Example

Calculate 312×42

$42 \times 312 \approx 40 \times 300$
$\qquad\quad = 12\ 000$

×	300	10	2
40	$40 \times 300 = 12\ 000$	$40 \times 10 = 400$	$40 \times 2 = 80$
2	$2 \times 300 = 600$	$2 \times 10 = 20$	$2 \times 2 = 4$

Add the totals: $12\ 000 + 400 + 80 + 600 + 20 + 4 = 13\ 104$
So $312 \times 42 = 13\ 104$

You should always **estimate** the answer first.

The calculation is split into four simpler calculations.

p.166

You can use written methods for multiplication and division to solve problems.

Example

Ali buys 16 chocolate bars. Each bar costs 14p.
How much does he spend?

Estimate: $16 \times 14 \approx 20 \times 10 = 200$ pence

$$
\begin{array}{r}
16 \\
\times\ 14 \\
\hline
\end{array}
$$

16×10 $\qquad$ 160
16×4 $\qquad$ $+64$
$\qquad\qquad\quad \overline{224}$ $\qquad$ Ali spends 16×14 pence $= 224$ pence
$\qquad\qquad\qquad\qquad\qquad\qquad\qquad\qquad\qquad\qquad = £2.24.$

This is the **standard method** for multiplication.

Example

Karen shares £85 between her five children. How much will each child get?

Estimate: $85 \div 5 \approx 100 \div 5 = £20$

$$
\begin{array}{r}
5)85 \\
-50 \\
\hline
35 \\
-25 \\
\hline
10 \\
-10 \\
\hline
0
\end{array}
$$

5×10
5×5
$5 \times \dfrac{2}{17}$

So each child receives £17.

$85 \div 5 = 17$

This is the informal 'chunking' method for division.

You subtract 5 (the **divisor**) a total of 17 times from 85 (the **dividend**).

1 Copy and complete these multiplications. Use the same method with parts **c** and **d**.

a 14×8

×	8
10	$10 \times 8 = 80$
4	$4 \times 8 =$

$14 \times 8 = 80 +$ ____
$=$

b 12×9

×	9
10	$=$
2	$=$

$12 \times 9 =$ ____ $+$ ____
$=$

c 14×9 **d** 17×8

2 Copy and complete these multiplications using the grid method.
Remember to do a mental approximation first.

a 12×13

×	10	3
10	$10 \times 10 = 100$	$10 \times 3 = 30$
2	$2 \times 10 =$	$2 \times 3 =$

$12 \times 13 = 100 + 30 +$ ____ $+$ ____
$=$

b 15×16

×	10	6
10	$10 \times 10 =$	$10 \times 6 =$
5	$=$	$=$

$15 \times 16 =$ ____ $+$ ____ $+$ ____ $+$ ____
$=$

c 15×18

×	10	8
10	$=$	$=$
5	$=$	$=$

$15 \times 18 =$ ____ $+$ ____ $+$ ____ $+$ ____
$=$

3 Use an appropriate method of calculation to work out each of these multiplications.

a 13×124 **b** 17×183 **c** 13×167 **d** 23×143 **e** 62×158
f 83×176 **g** 36×254 **h** 53×271 **i** 83×512

4 Use an appropriate method of calculation to work out each of these divisions.

a $138 \div 6$ **b** $176 \div 8$ **c** $140 \div 5$ **d** $217 \div 7$
e $297 \div 9$ **f** $448 \div 8$ **g** $112 \div 8$ **h** $126 \div 7$

5 Use an appropriate method to solve each of these problems.
  a Ian uses 19 text messages. Each message costs 7p.
  What is the total cost of the text messages?
  b Samira buys 17 fruit bushes at a cost of £7 per bush.
  What is the total cost of the 17 fruit bushes?
  c Mika has 14 packets of sweets. Each packet contains 14 sweets.
  How many sweets does he have altogether?
  d Albert buys 13 chocolate bars. Each bar costs 16 pence.
  How much does he spend?

This spread will show you how to:

- Know and use the order of operations, including brackets

Keywords
Brackets
Index
Order of
  operations
Power

Eve and Sarah are working out this calculation.

2 + 3 × 4

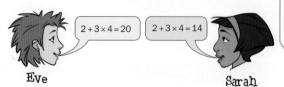

To find out who is correct, use the **order of operations**.

Brackets
First work out the contents of any brackets.

Powers or indices
Then work out any powers or roots.

Multiplication and division
Then work out any multiplications and divisions.

Addition and subtraction
Finally work out any additions and subtractions.

$2 + 3 \times 4$

$= 2 + 12$
$= 14$

Sarah is correct because she has followed the order of operations.

Example

Put brackets into this expression to make the answer correct.

2 × 3 + 4 − 5 = 9

By inserting a pair of brackets

$2 \times (3 + 4) - 5 = 2 \times 7 - 5$ (work out the multiplication)
$= 14 - 5$ (work out the subtraction)
$= 9$ ✓ the correct answer

For lots of additions and subtractions (or multiplications and divisions), work them out from left to right.

Calculations involving brackets need to be interpreted carefully.

Example

Calculate each of these amounts.

a $\dfrac{160}{5 + 11}$ **b** $21 + 2(8 + 7)$

a $\dfrac{160}{5 + 11} = \dfrac{160}{(5 + 11)}$ **b** $21 + 2(8 + 7) = 21 + 2 \times 15$
$= 160 \div (5 + 11)$ $= 21 + 30$
$= 160 \div 16$ $= 51$
$= 10$

Rewrite division calculations using brackets, like part a.

1 Match each of these calculations with one that gives the same answer.

A	$7 + 3$	**1**	$7 - 4$
B	$2 + 3 \times 4$	**2**	$33 - 9$
C	$18 \div 6$	**3**	$6 \times 3 - 4$
D	6×4	**4**	$15 - 5$

2 Calculate these using the order of operations.

a $2 + 6 \times 3$ **b** $2 \times 12 - 7$ **c** $8 + 20 \div 4$ **d** $2 \times 3 + 4 \times 2$
e $14 \div 2 + 3$ **f** $2 + 7 \times 5$ **g** $2 + 3 \times 3 - 4$ **h** $4 \times 3 + 2 \times 6$

3 Calculate these using the order of operations.

a $(2 + 6) \times 3$ **b** $2 \times (12 - 7)$
c $(8 + 20) \div 4$ **d** $2 \times (3 + 4) \times 2$
e $15 \div (2 + 3)$ **f** $(2 + 7) \times 5$
g $(2 + 3) \times 3 - 4$ **h** $4 \times (3 + 2) \times 6$

Note: You can use a calculator to work with brackets.

p.334

4 Calculate these using the order of operations.

a $2 + 3^2 \times 4$ **b** $2^2 \times 3 - 7$
c $4^2 + 20 \div 4$ **d** $2 \times 3^2 + 4 \times 2$
e $16 \div 2^2 + 3$ **f** $2 + 7 \times 5^2$

5 Calculate these using the order of operations.

a $(2 + 6) \times 3^2$ **b** $2^2 \times (12 - 7)$
c $(8^2 - 20) \div 4$ **d** $2 \times (3^2 + 4)$
e $33 \div (2 + 3^2)$ **f** $(2^2 + 7) \times 5$

6 Copy these calculations. Insert brackets where necessary to make each of them correct.

a $3 \times 2 + 1 = 9$ **b** $5 \times 3 - 1 = 10$
c $3 + 5 \div 2 = 4$ **d** $2 + 3^2 \times 4 = 44$
e $4^2 \div 5 + 3 = 2$ **f** $4 \times 5 + 5 \times 6 = 240$

7 Calculate each of these amounts.

a $\dfrac{3 + 7}{5}$ **b** $\dfrac{14 - 8}{2 + 1}$ **c** $\dfrac{5 \times 4}{2 \times 5}$

d $\dfrac{2 \times 3 + 4}{5}$ **e** $\dfrac{24}{2 + 3 \times 5}$

8 Calculate these amounts.

a $3(2 + 5)$ **b** $4(2 + 6)$ **c** $5 + 4(7 - 3)$ **d** $3^2 + 2(7 - 4)$

9 Use the numbers 3, 4, 5, 7 and 8 to make as many of the numbers as you can from 10 to 40.
You may use each digit only once in each calculation.

Number	Calculation	Number	Calculation
10	$= 3 + 7$	26	=
11	$= 4 + 7$	27	$= (4 + 5) \times 3$
12	=	28	=
13	$= 8 - 7 + 3 \times 4$	29	$= 3 \times 7 + 8$

Use the correct order of operations for each calculation.
Copy and complete this table to show all your results.

Calculator methods 1

This spread will show you how to:
- Carry out more complex calculations using the functions of a calculator
- Give an answer to a given degree of accuracy

You can use a scientific calculator to carry out more complex calculations that involve decimals.

Example

Use your calculator to work out this calculation
$$3.46 + 2.9 \times 4.8$$
Give your answer to one decimal place.

....

Estimate
$3.46 + 2.9 \times 4.8 \approx 3 + 3 \times 5$ (using the order of operations)
$= 3 + 15 = 18$

You type [3] [.] [4] [6] [+] [2] [.] [9] [×] [4] [.] [8] [=]

The calculator should display
$$\boxed{\begin{array}{l} 3.46+2.9\times4.8 \\ \quad\quad 17.38 \end{array}}$$

So the answer is $17.38 = 17.4$ (1 decimal place)

A scientific calculator has algebraic logic, which means that it understands the **order of operations**.

In this case the calculator automatically works out the multiplication before the addition.

A scientific calculator has **bracket** keys.

Example

a Use your calculator to work out $(3.9 + 2.2)^2 \times 2.17$.
Write all the figures on your calculator display.
b Put brackets in this expression so that its value is 16.26.
$$1.4 + 3.9 \times 2.2 + 4.6$$

....

a Estimate
$(3.9 + 2.2)^2 \times 2.17 \approx (4 + 2)^2 \times 2$ (using the order of operations)
$= 6^2 \times 2$
$= 36 \times 2$
$= 72$

You type [(] [3] [.] [9] [+] [2] [.] [2] [)] [x^2] [×] [2] [.] [1] [7] [=]

The calculator should display $\boxed{\begin{array}{l}(3.9+2.2)^2\times2.17 \\ \quad 80.7457\end{array}}$ = 80.7457

a $(1.4 + 3.9) \times 2.2 + 4.6$

The calculator should display $\boxed{\begin{array}{l}(1.4+3.9)\times2.2+4.6 \\ \quad 16.26\end{array}}$

$= 16.26$ ✓ the correct answer

---

1 Use your calculator to work out these.
In each case, first write an estimate for your answer.
Write the answer from your calculator to one decimal place.
a $3.4 + 6.2 \times 2.7$

Estimate　　　　$3.4 + 6.2 \times 2.7 \approx 3 + 6 \times 3$
　　　　　　　　　　　　　　　　　　$= 3 + 18$
　　　　　　　　　　　　　　　　　　$=$ ____
Using the calculator　$3.4 + 6.2 \times 2.7 =$ _____

b $1.98 \times 11.7 - 4.6$
d $2.09 \times 2.87 + 3.25 \times 1.17$
f $1.2 + 3.7 \times 0.5$

c $7.8 + 19.3 \div 4.12$
e $13.67 \div 1.75 + 3.24$

2 Use your calculator to work out each of these calculations.
Write all the figures on your calculator display.
a $(2.3 + 5.6) \times 3^2$
c $(2.8^2 - 2.04) \div 2.79$
e $11.33 \div (6.2 + 8.3^2)$
b $2.3^2 \times (12.3 - 6.7)$
d $7.2 \times (4.3^2 + 7.4)$
f $(2.5^2 + 1.37) \times 2.5$

3 Calculate each of these, giving your answer to one decimal place.
a $\dfrac{5.4 + 3.8}{4.5 - 2.9}$
b $\dfrac{3.8 - 1.67}{4.3 - 2.68}$
c $\dfrac{12.4 + 5.8}{14.5 - 3.9}$
d $\dfrac{13.08 - 2.67}{2.13 + 2.68}$

Hint for part **a**:
Type the
calculation as
$(5.4 + 3.8) \div$
$(4.5 - 2.9) =$

4 Put brackets into each of these expressions to make them correct.
a $3.4 \times 2.3 + 1.6 = 13.26$
c $2.6 + 6.5 \div 1.3 = 7$
e $2.4^2 \div 1.8 \times 3.2 + 1.6 = 15.36$
b $3.5 \times 2.3 - 1.04 = 4.41$
d $1.4^2 - 1.2 \times 2.3 = 1.748$
f $3.2 + 5.3 \times 2.4 - 1.2 = 10.2$

5 Use your calculator to work out each of these. Write all the figures
on your calculator display.
a $\dfrac{462.3 \times 30.4}{(0.7 + 4.8)^2}$
b $\dfrac{13.58 \times (18.4 - 9.73)}{(37.2 + 24.6) \times 4.2}$

6 Here is a mathematical calculation.
$$\dfrac{50.1 + 29.8}{50.1 - 29.8}$$

a Write **approximate** values for 50.1 and 29.8 that you could use
to estimate the value of the mathematical expression.
b Work out an estimate for the mathematical calculation.
c Use your calculator to work out the value of the calculation.
Write all the figures on your calculator display.

Summary

Check out

You should now be able to:

- Use mental and written methods for addition and subtraction of whole numbers
- Use mental and written methods for multiplication and division of whole numbers
- Know and use the order of operations, including brackets

Worked exam question

Calculate $\dfrac{5.6 \times 7.8}{4.3 - 2.1}$

a Write down your full calculator display. (1)

b Write your answer to part **a** to one decimal place. (1)

c Write your answer to part **a** to the nearest hundredth. (1)

d Insert brackets in

$$5.6 \times 7.8 \div 4.3 - 2.1$$

so that it is equal to $\dfrac{5.6 \times 7.8}{4.3 - 2.1}$ (1)

(AQA, 2008)

a $\dfrac{5.6 \times 7.8}{4.3 - 2.1} = 19.85454545$

b 19.9

c 19.85 ← The second decimal place is hundredths.

d $(5.6 \times 7.8) \div (4.3 - 2.1)$ ← Brackets take priority in the order of operations.

Exam questions

1 A bakery sells cakes in boxes of six.
   One box costs £2.76
   a Vic buys eight boxes for a party.
      i Work out the cost of eight boxes. (2)
      ii Nine of the cakes were **not** eaten at the party.

        How many cakes were eaten at the party? (2)

   (AQA, 2008)

2 **a** Round 272 to the nearest 10. (1)
   b Round 272 to the nearest 100. (1)
   c Manish is thinking of a number.

   To the nearest 10 my number is 400.
   My number is **not** 400.

   Manish is correct.
   What could his number be? (1)

   (AQA, 2008)

3 Ticket prices for a theme park are shown.

Single tickets		Family tickets	
Adult	£12.50	1 Adult and 2 children	£25
Child	£8	1 Adult and 3 children	£30
		2 Adults and 2 children	£35
		2 Adults and 3 children	£40

Mr and Mrs Shah and their two children visit the theme park.
They buy a family ticket.

How much money is saved compared to the total cost of single tickets?
You **must** show your working. (4)

(AQA, 2008)

Introduction

Over 30% of the numbers in everyday use begin with the digit 1.
'Benford's law', as it is called, makes it possible to detect when a list of numbers has been falsified. This is particularly useful in fraud investigations for detecting 'made-up' entries on claim forms and expense accounts, and it was also used in investigating the 2009 Iranian elections.

What's the point?

Recognising patterns in numbers and measures helps us to understand them, and also helps us to make sense of a world that is increasingly swamped with data.

Check in

1 Calculate each of these divisions.
  a 360 ÷ 2   **b** 360 ÷ 4   **c** 360 ÷ 10   **d** 360 ÷ 5
  e 360 ÷ 6   **f** 360 ÷ 12   **g** 360 ÷ 180   **h** 360 ÷ 90

2 Put these numbers in order of size, smallest first.
  a 31, 43, 25, 29, 36, 41, 49, 30
  b 243, 342, 324, 234, 432, 423
  c 21.3, 23.1, 31.2, 13.2, 12.3, 32.1

3 Find the value of the angle x.

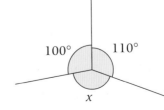

Orientation

What I need to know	What I will learn	What this leads to
D2 →	■ Use pictograms, bar charts and pie charts to display data in categories ■ Use stem-and-leaf diagrams to display numerical data ■ Draw line graphs for numerical data	→ D4

Rich task

Here are some statements about young people:

'They eat too many sweets'

'They've all got mobile phones and iPods'

'They stay up too late'

'They don't do any homework'

Investigate if these statements are true.

This spread will show you how to:
* Draw and produce pictograms for data in **categories**

Keywords
Category
Pictogram
Represents

* You can use a **pictogram** to display data.

Pictograms use symbols to give an eye-catching picture of the size of each category.

A pictogram shows
- how each **category** compares with the others
- all the data, but in categories.

You may have to use part of a symbol to **represent** some quantities.

Number of bottles of milk sold

Monday	🍶 🍶
Tuesday	🍶 🍶
Wednesday	
Thursday	🍶 🍶
Friday	🍶 🍶 🍶 🍶 🍶

Key: 🍶 represents 2 bottles

🍶 represents 2 bottles

🍶 represents 1 bottle

Always give a key.

Example

The number of cars that a car salesman sells is given in the table.

Week	Cars sold
1	4
2	6
3	12
4	10

a Draw a pictogram to illustrate this information.
   Use 🚗 to represent 4 cars.

b In which week did he sell most cars?

a So 🚗 represents 2 cars.

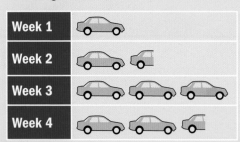

Week 1	🚗 🚗
Week 2	🚗 🚗 🚗
Week 3	🚗 🚗 🚗
Week 4	🚗 🚗 🚗

Key: 🚗 represents 4 cars

b In week 3.

$4 + 2 = 6$

$4 + 4 + 2 = 10$

Don't forget the key.

1 The number of people who eat different take-away food is shown in the pictogram.
   Copy and complete the pictogram to show six people eating Chinese and five people eating Indian.

Key:
☨ represents one person

Italian	☨ ☨ ☨ ☨ ☨
English	☨ ☨
Chinese	
Indian	

2 The colours of flowers in a garden are shown in the pictogram.
   Copy and complete the pictogram with this information.

Key:
✿ represents 5 flowers

Red	Yellow	Blue	White	Other
5	20	10	15	25

Red	✿
Yellow	✿ ✿ ✿ ✿
Blue	
White	
Other	

3 The pictogram shows where people use the internet the most.
   Copy the pictogram and represent this information on your diagram:

Library 6   School 9   Work 17

Key:
⌨ represents 2 people

Home	⌨ ⌨ ⌨ ⌨
Internet cafe	⌨ ⌨ ⌨
Library	
School	
Work	

4 This data is from a newspaper survey.
   Draw a pictogram using to represent 10 people.

Daily paper A	40
Daily paper B	50
Daily paper C	35
Daily paper D	25
Other	15

5 The results of a survey about people's favourite hot drink are given in the table.

   Letting 🥤 represent 20 people, draw a pictogram for this data.

Tea	80
Coffee	60
Hot chocolate	50
Soup	30
Other	20

Bar charts

This spread will show you how to:
- Draw and produce bar charts for data in categories
- Draw bar-line charts

Keywords

Bar chart
Bar-line chart
Frequency
Horizontal
Vertical

You can use a **bar chart** to display data.

Bar charts use bars to give a visual picture of the size of each category.

- A bar chart shows
  - how each category compares with the others
  - all the data, but in categories.

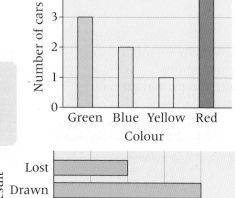

Vertical bars

Note the equal gaps between the bars.

The bars can be horizontal or vertical.

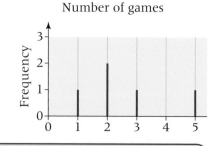

Horizontal bars

- **Bar-line charts** are a good way to display (discrete) numerical data.

Lines are drawn instead of bars.

Example

A class are asked to name one favourite pet. The results are shown.

Pet	Dog	Cat	Guinea pig	Other
Frequency	16	9	12	3

Draw a bar chart to show this information.

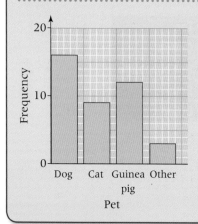

1 The cost of renting a car for a day in different countries is shown.
Copy and complete the bar chart.

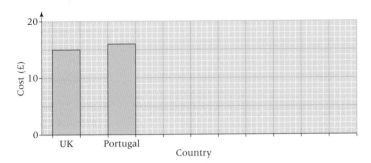

Country	Cost
UK	£15
Portugal	£16
Ireland	£21
Germany	£19
France	£17
USA	£16

2 The number of concerts held at various venues is given.
Copy and complete the bar chart.

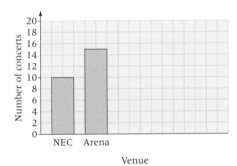

Venue	Number of concerts
NEC	10
Arena	15
MEN	20
NIA	18
Wembley	9

3 The numbers of packets of crisps in a shop are shown in the frequency table.
Draw a vertical bar chart to show this information.

Flavour	Number of packets
Plain	5
Salt'n'Vinegar	3
Cheese & Onion	4
Smokey Bacon	1
Other	8

4 The number of Bank Holidays in different countries is shown.
Draw a bar chart to show this information.

Country	Number of Bank Holidays
UK	8
Italy	16
Iceland	15
Spain	14

5 The cost to fly to certain resorts is given in the frequency table.
Draw a bar chart to show this information.

Resort	Cost (£)
Lisbon	90
Crete	100
Malta	80
Menorca	70
Cyprus	110

Interpreting pictograms and bar charts

This spread will show you how to:

- Understand the difference between discrete and continuous data
- Interpret data from pictograms and bar charts
- Calculate the modal category of a data set

Keywords
Bar chart
Category
Discrete
Modal
Pictogram

- **Discrete** data can only take exact values (usually collected by counting). For example, the number of pets in a home.
- You can interpret information on **categories** and discrete data from a **pictogram** or a **bar chart**. The size of each category gives the frequency.
- **Qualitative** data is information that is not numerical, for example types of sweets or days of the week.
- **Quantitative** data is information that is numerical; it can be counted (**discrete**) or measured (**continuous**).

Continuous data can have any value, for example, your height.

Example

The pictogram shows the number of students attending school in a week.
The class has 20 students.

Monday	◯◯◯◯
Tuesday	◯◯◖
Wednesday	◯◯◯
Thursday	◯◗
Friday	◯◯◹

Key: ◯ represents 4 students

Calculate
a the number of students that attended on Tuesday
b the number of students that were absent on Thursday.

....

a 4 + 4 + 2 = 10 students
b 20 − (4 + 3) = 20 − 7 = 13 students

Example

The bar chart shows the types of sweets in an assorted box.
Calculate
a the number of chocolate sweets
b the total number of sweets in the box.
c Find the **modal** type of sweet.

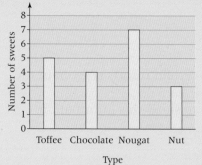

Modal means the most frequent type.

....

a 4   **b** 5 + 4 + 7 + 3 = 19 sweets   **c** Nougat

A02 Functional Maths

1 The numbers of buses that stop at a village through the week are shown on the bar chart.
  a How many buses stop at the village on Thursday?
  b On which days is there no bus service?
  c Calculate the total number of buses that stop at the village throughout the week.

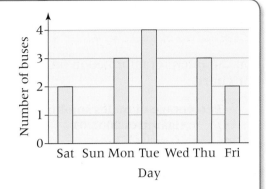

2 The number of foreign language teachers at a school is shown in the pictogram.
  a Which subject has only one teacher?
  b How many French teachers teach at the school?
  c Calculate the total number of foreign language teachers at the school.

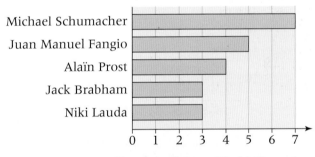

Key: 🏃 represents 2 teachers

3 The number of times each racing driver has been the Formula 1 World Champion is shown on the bar chart.
  a Who has been the F1 World Champion the most times?
  b How many times has Alaïn Prost been the F1 World Champion?

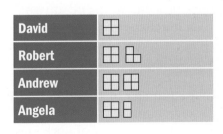

Number of times World Champion

4 Four friends played a series of games. The number of wins for each person is shown in the pictogram.
Angela won six games.
  a What does ⊞ represent?
  b How many games did Robert win?
  c Who won the most games and how many did that person win?
  d Who won the least games and how many did that person win?
  e Calculate the total number of games played.

David	⊞
Robert	⊞ ⊟
Andrew	⊞ ⊞
Angela	⊞ ⊟

Key: ⊞ represents ?

Dual bar charts

This spread will show you how to:

• Use the shape of dual bar charts to compare two data sets

Keywords
Bar chart
Dual bar chart

You can interpret information on categories and discrete data from a **bar chart**.

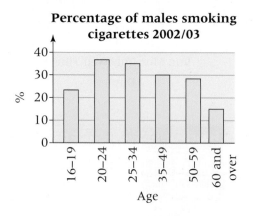

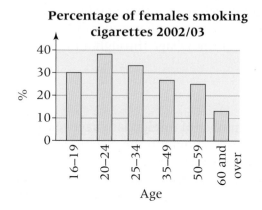

• You can combine two bar charts to create a **dual bar chart**, which helps you to compare two sets of data.

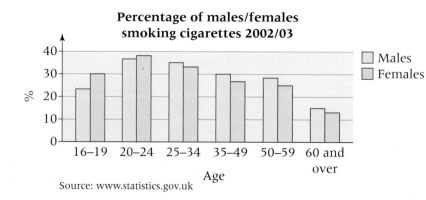

Source: www.statistics.gov.uk

The sets of data you compare must be the same type, for example Boy/Girl.

Example

The chart shows the sales of pork pies one weekend at two rival butchers.

Calculate

a the number of pork pies that Billy sold on Sunday

b the total number of pork pies that were sold by both butchers.

....

a 7 pork pies

b 5 + 7 + 6 + 5 = 23 pork pies

1 The number of letters delivered
one week to No 10 and No 12 on
the same street is shown on the
bar chart.
  a State the number of letters
   that were delivered to
     i No 10 on Tuesday
     ii No 12 on Friday.
  b Which day did
     i No 12 receive no letters
     ii No 10 receive 2 letters?
  c Which was the only day that No 12 received more post than No 10?
  d Calculate the total number of letters delivered in the week to
     i No 10   **ii** No 12.
  e Which day did the postman deliver the most letters to No 10 and
   No 12 combined?

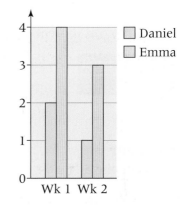

2 The number of visits to the swimming baths over two
weeks for Daniel and Emma is shown on the bar chart.
  a State the number of visits for
     i Emma in Week 1
     ii Daniel in Week 2.
  b Calculate the total number of visits for
     i Daniel
     ii Emma.

3 The bar chart shows the number and
flavour of milkshakes that Mark and Peter
drank.
  a State the number of
     i banana milkshakes drunk by Mark
     ii orange milkshakes drunk by Peter.
  b Which flavour milkshake was not drunk
   by Mark?
  c Which flavour milkshake did Mark and
   Peter drink the same number of?
  d Calculate the total number of milkshakes
   drunk by
     i Mark
     ii Peter.

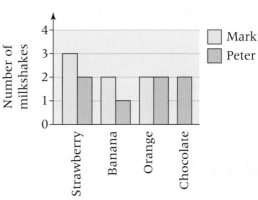

This spread will show you how to:
● Draw and produce pie charts for data in categories

Keywords
Angle
Category
Pie chart
Proportion
Sector

You can use a **pie chart** to display data.

Pie charts use a circle to give a quick visual picture of all the data.
The size of each **angle** shows the size of each **category**.

● A pie chart shows
  – the **proportion** or fraction of each category
    compared to the whole circle
  – all the data, but in categories.

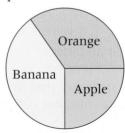

Apple is a quarter of all the data.

Banana is the biggest **sector**.

All the data must be included.

Example

A group of 12 students were asked how they travelled to school that day.
The results are shown.

Method of travel	Walked	Bus	Car	Other
Frequency	6	2	3	1

Draw a pie chart to illustrate this information.

Method 1
Calculate the angle for one person:
360° ÷ 12 = 30°
Divide the circle into sectors of 30°.
Colour and label the sectors.

The angles at a point add to 360°.

Method 2
Calculate the angle for one person:
360° ÷ 12 = 30°
Calculate the angles for each category

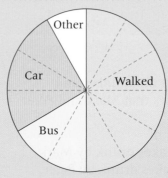

Walked	6 × 30° = 180°
Bus	2 × 30° = 60°
Car	3 × 30° = 90°
Other	1 × 30° = 30°
	Add to check: 360°

Measure, colour and label the sectors.

Check by adding the angles of the sectors.

In the above example, Method 1 is time-consuming and inaccurate.
It is better to use Method 2.

1 Alvin makes eight sandwiches:
   1 tuna
   2 cheese and tomato
   3 chicken
   2 corned beef

   Draw a pie chart to show this information.

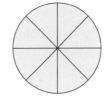

2 Sophie spends £6 on her hobby of painting:
   £1 on paper
   £2 on paint brushes
   £3 on paint

   Draw a pie chart to show this information.

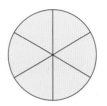

3 A survey question asks 'Do you think smoking should be banned in public places?'
   The results are:

Yes	5
No	4

   a Calculate the number of people who were asked the question.
   b Calculate the angle one person represents in a pie chart.
   c Calculate the angles to represent Yes and No.
   d Draw a pie chart to show the results of the survey.

DID YOU KNOW?

In 2007, the proportion of smokers in the UK fell to 21%, down from 45% in 1974.

4 Seven boys and five girls attend an after-school homework club.
   a Calculate the total number of students.
   b Calculate the angle one student represents in a pie chart.
   c Calculate the angles to represent boys and girls.
   d Draw a pie chart to show the information.

5 A school fete is open from 10 am to 4 pm.
   a Calculate the number of minutes the school fete is open.

   A teacher has offered to help.
   She spends these times on each stall.

   b Draw a pie chart to show this information.

Stall	Time
Bat the Rat	30 mins
Hook a Duck	25 mins
Smash a Plate	35 mins
Roll a Coin	80 mins
Tombola	70 mins
Break 1	60 mins
Break 2	60 mins

6 In one week, 180 letters were delivered to a business.
   The letters were delivered in this pattern.

   Draw a pie chart to show this information.

Mon	45
Tues	30
Wed	25
Thurs	20
Fri	50
Sat	10
Sun	0

Interpreting pie charts

This spread will show you how to:

- Interpret data from a pie chart
- Calculate the modal category of a data set

Keywords
Category
Modal
Pie chart
Proportion
Sector

- You can interpret data from a **pie chart**.

A pie chart does not show the actual number of items in each **category**.

A pie chart does show the size of each category compared to the total number of items.

Drinks sold at a machine

Cappuccino is the biggest **sector**.

The pie chart shows the **proportion** of drinks bought at a vending machine.
More cappuccinos were sold compared to the other categories, but we do not know how many drinks were sold.

Example

60 vehicles are shown on the pie chart.

a Calculate the numbers of cars, vans, buses and lorries.

b State the modal type of vehicle.

Vehicles parked in the High St.

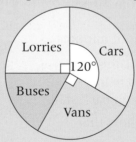

---

a 60 vehicles = 360°
1 vehicle = 6°
The angle for Buses is 360° − (90° + 90° + 120°) = 60°
  Cars 120 ÷ 6 = 20 cars
  Vans 90 ÷ 6 = 15 vans
  Buses 60 ÷ 6 = 10 buses
  Lorries 90 ÷ 6 = 15 lorries
 Check: 20 + 15 + 10 + 15 = 60 vehicles

b The modal type of vehicle is Car.

The angles at a point add to 360°.

Modal means the most frequent type.

1 The survey results for the favourite band of
100 people are shown.
  a What fraction of the circle represents
    i Kasabian **ii** The Prodigy **iii** Glasvegas?
  b Calculate the number of people who voted for
    i Kasabian **ii** The Prodigy **iii** Glasvegas.
  c State the modal band.

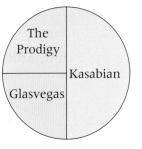

2 Six drinks of soup are represented on the pie chart.
  a Copy and complete   6 drinks = 360°
                             1 drink = ___°

  b Calculate the number of drinks that are
    i tomato **ii** chicken **iii** beef.
  c State the modal type of drink.

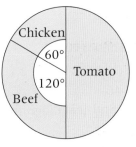

3 A shop sells 12 loaves of three different types: organic,
wholegrain and white.
  a Copy and complete   12 loaves = 360°
                             1 loaf = ___°

  b Calculate the number of loaves that are
    i organic **ii** wholegrain **iii** white.
  c State the modal type of loaf.

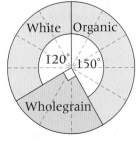

4 Nine newspapers delivered on a street are shown on
the pie chart.
  a Copy and complete   9 newspapers = 360°
                             1 newspaper = ___°

  b Calculate the number of newspapers delivered that are
    i the Planet **ii** the News **iii** the Daily Rag.
  c State the modal newspaper.

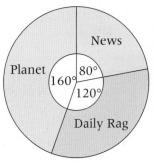

5 A car dealer sells 18 cars in one week of three different
types: diesel, petrol and electric.
  a Calculate the angle that represents one car.
  b Calculate the number of cars sold that are
    i diesel **ii** petrol **iii** electric.
  c State the modal type of car sold.

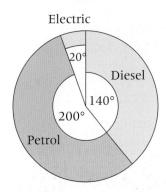

This spread will show you how to:

● Draw and produce stem-and-leaf diagrams

You can use a **stem-and-leaf diagram** to display numerical data.

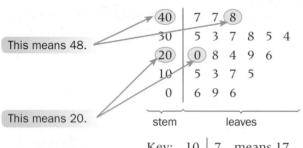

This means 48.

This means 20.

stem   leaves

Key: 10 │ 7   means 17

This stem-and-leaf diagram is **unordered**.

It works by partitioning each number into two parts.

Always give the key.

A stem-and-leaf diagram is quick and easy to construct.

● A stem-and-leaf diagram shows
  – the shape of the distribution
  – each individual value of the data.

Gives a 'feel' for the data.

No loss of detail of the data.

This stem-and-leaf diagram is **ordered**, as the data is in numerical order.

A stem-and-leaf diagram is like a bar chart, but with more detail.

```
40 │ 7  7  8
30 │ 3  4  5  5  7  8
20 │ 0  4  6  8  9
10 │ 3  5  5  7
 0 │ 6  6  9
```
stem   leaves

Key: 10 │ 7   means 17

Example

The heights, in centimetres, of 10 students are shown.

    168   154   172   167   156
    154   163   160   165   158

Show the heights in an ordered stem-and-leaf diagram.

p.96

```
150 │
160 │
170 │
```

```
150 │ 4  6  4  8              150 │ 4  4  6  8
160 │ 8  7  3  0  5   order   160 │ 0  3  5  7  8
170 │ 2              ──────▶   170 │ 2
```

Key: 150 │ 4   means 154 cm   Key: 150 │ 4   means 154 cm

You can order the data before you draw the diagram if you want.

1 The numbers of houses on each street of a town are shown.

    12   5 25 27   7 35 15 10 22 18
    34 30 14 19 20 28 32   4 25 36

a Copy and complete the stem-and-leaf diagram.

```
 0 | 4  4  6  8
10 | 0  3  5  7  8     Key:  10 | 8  means 18 houses
20 | 2
30 |
```

b Redraw the table to give an ordered stem-and-leaf diagram.

2 The weights, in kilograms, of 30 students are shown.

    48 47 48 53 61 70 45 56 57 60
    42 46 44 55 63 65 49 50 55 65
    70 53 64 61 46 47 56 40 41 54

Draw an ordered stem-and-leaf diagram using stems of 40, 50, 60, 70.
Remember to give the key.

3 The exam marks of 40 students are shown.

    33 48 18 63 51 66 52 19 55 43
    50 35 52 66 43 48 32 18 17 26
     5 15 10 25 36 51 61 48 58 68
    38 67 11 18 27 30 40 60 46 55

Draw an ordered stem-and-leaf diagram using stems of 0, 10, 20, 30, 40, 50, 60.
Remember to give the key.

4 The attempted heights, in centimetres, during a High Jump event are shown.

    214 204 225 230 244
    210 207 209 240 232
    230 216 242 233 238
    206 217 236 216 211
    208 230 209 237 241

Draw an ordered stem-and-leaf diagram using stems of 200, 210, 220, 230, 240.

5 The times, in seconds, taken for 24 athletes to run 200 metres are given.

    24.5 20.1 20.3 21.4 22.1 22.0 24.8 21.0
    25.1 21.5 22.6 23.5 20.9 21.6 23.5 24.0
    25.0 21.8 21.8 22.1 21.0 23.5 24.6 21.5

Copy and complete an ordered stem-and-leaf diagram to show this data.

```
20 | 4  4  6  8
21 | 0  3  5  7  8     Key:  20 | 9  means 20.9 seconds
22 | 2
23 |
24 |
25 |
```

Time series graphs

This spread will show you how to:

● Draw and produce line graphs for time series data

Keywords

Horizontal
Line graph
Time series
 graph
Trend

You can use a **line graph** to show how data changes as time passes.

The temperature in Belfast is measured every hour from 8 am to 4 pm.

The graph shows the data.

Time is always the **horizontal** axis.

These line graphs are called **time series graphs**.

● A time series graph shows
  – how the data changes, or the **trend**
  – each individual value of the data.

Example

The number of Christmas cards Britney received are shown in the table.

Date in December	12	13	14	15	16	17	18	19	20	21	22	23	24
Number of cards	1	2	4	0	3	3	4	3	2	4	7	8	5

Draw a line graph to show this information.

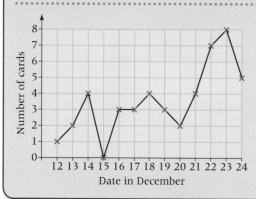

1 The number of photographs taken each day during a 7-day holiday is given.

Sunday	Monday	Tuesday	Wednesday	Thursday	Friday	Saturday
8	12	11	16	19	2	13

Copy and complete the line graph to show this information.

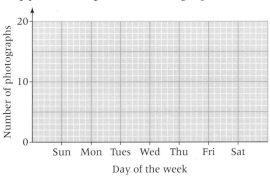

2 The number of sunny days in each month is given.

Jan	Feb	Mar	Apr	May	Jun	Jul	Aug	Sep	Oct	Nov	Dec
9	8	10	15	19	20	21	25	24	18	17	11

Copy and complete the line graph, choosing a suitable vertical scale.

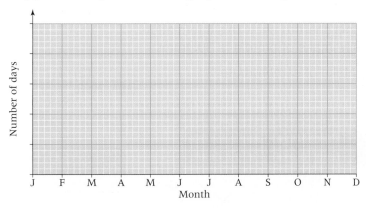

3 The number of points gained by the winners of the football Premiership is shown from 1993–2005.

Year	1993	1994	1995	1996	1997	1998
Points	84	92	89	82	75	78
Winner	Man Utd	Man Utd	Blackburn	Man Utd	Man Utd	Arsenal

Year	1999	2000	2001	2002	2003	2004	2005
Points	79	91	80	87	83	90	95
Winner	Man Utd	Man Utd	Man Utd	Arsenal	Man Utd	Arsenal	Chelsea

Draw a line graph to show this information.

Check out

You should now be able to:

- Produce pictograms, vertical and horizontal bar charts, bar-line charts, line graphs and pie charts to display data
- Draw and use stem-and-leaf diagrams
- Interpret graphs and charts, including line graphs
- Look at data to find patterns and exceptions

Worked exam question

Josh's percentage daily intake of different food types is shown in the table.

Food type	Percentage daily intake	Angle for use in pie chart
Carbohydrate (C)	50%	
Protein (P)	10%	
Other (O)		

a   **i**   Complete the table.   (3)

    ii   Draw a fully labelled pie chart to show this information.

b   Josh knows that his daily intake of protein is 90 grams.

    Calculate Josh's daily intake of carbohydrate.   (2)

           (AQA, 2008)

....

a   **i**

Food type	Percentage daily intake	Angle for use in pie chart
Carbohydrate (C)	50%	180°
Protein (P)	10%	36°
Other (O)	40%	144°

> 50% of 360° is 180°.
> 10% is 36°, so 40% must be 4 × 36° = 144°

> The percentages need to add up to 100%.

    ii

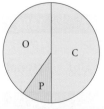

b

10% is 90 g

So 50% is 5 × 90 g = 450 g

Exam questions

1 The dual bar chart shows the sales of monthly magazines in a newsagents. The data is collected over one month.

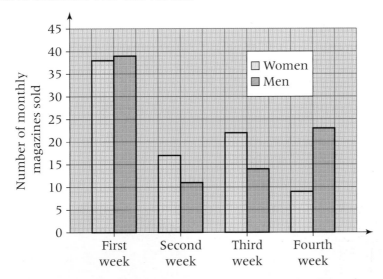

a Give a reason why the sales of monthly magazines are greatest in the first week of the month. (1)

b The shopkeeper thinks that more women than men buy monthly magazines.

Does the data support this?
Show working to justify your answer. (3)

(AQA, specimen)

2 A school is raising money to buy sports equipment.
The pictogram shows the amount of money raised during some events.

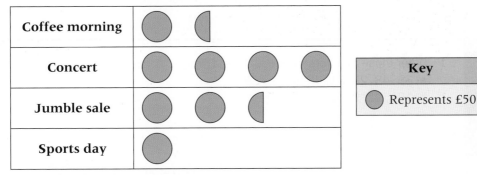

a Which event raised the most money? (1)
b How much money did the concert raise? (1)
c How much more money did the Jumble sale raise than the Sports day? (1)
d The school needs to raise £500 in total.
How much more money do they need to raise to meet their target? (3)

Introduction

Statistics are vital in medicine as they are used to test the safety and performance of new drugs. Tests are performed on large groups of people and the analysis of the results is used to evaluate the safety and reliability of the new drug.

What's the point?

When data is analysed it is essential for that analysis to be correct. Statisticians use a range of techniques to analyse and compare large data sets. It is the use of statistical techniques that ensures a drug is safe to be on sale to the general public.

Check in

1 Order these numbers in size, smallest first.

   a 35, 48, 26, 31, 40, 41, 29, 36

   b 101, 92, 91, 102, 98

   c 6, $4\frac{1}{2}$, 8, 4, $7\frac{1}{2}$

2 Write out the 10 numbers shown in each frequency table.

a

Number	Frequency
80	3
81	0
82	1
83	2
84	4

b

Number	Frequency
45	2
46	1
47	0
48	4
49	3

Orientation

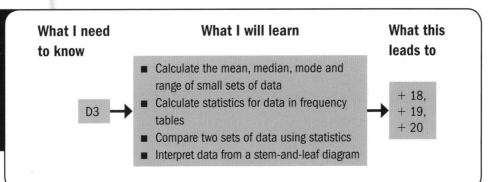

What I need to know	What I will learn	What this leads to
D3 →	■ Calculate the mean, median, mode and range of small sets of data ■ Calculate statistics for data in frequency tables ■ Compare two sets of data using statistics ■ Interpret data from a stem-and-leaf diagram	→ + 18, + 19, + 20

Rich task

What is the most likely time during a football game for a team to score a goal?

It is frequently stated by football commentators that teams are most likely to concede a goal within five minutes of scoring a goal themselves. Is this true?

Investigate and write a report on your results.

This spread will show you how to:

- Calculate the mean of small sets of data

The **average** 15-year-old girl in the UK is 164 cm tall.

This does not suggest that every girl's height is 164 cm, but that 164 cm can be used to represent the height of all the 15-year-old girls in the UK.

You can use one value to represent a set of data.
One **representative value** is called the **mean**.

- Mean $= \dfrac{\text{total sum of the values}}{\text{number of values}}$

Example

Five students measured their pulse rates.
The beats per minute for the students were

64   73   75   78   68

Calculate the mean pulse rate.

. . . .

$$\begin{aligned}
\text{Mean} &= \frac{\text{total sum of the values}}{\text{number of values}} \\
&= \frac{64 + 73 + 75 + 78 + 68}{5} \\
&= \frac{358}{5} \\
&= 71.6 \text{ beats per minute}
\end{aligned}$$

Notice that the mean does not have to be one of the values.

71.6 is between the lowest value (64) and the highest value (78).

1 a Calculate the mean of these five numbers.

      1, 1, 2, 4, 7

  b Copy the diagram to illustrate the five numbers.

  c Mark the mean on your diagram with a horizontal line.

  d Show how the parts of bars above the mean can be moved to give five equal numbers.

2 a Calculate the mean of these six numbers.

      1, 2, 2, 6, 6, 7

  b Draw a diagram to illustrate the six numbers.

  c Mark the mean on your diagram.

  d Show how seven parts of bars can be moved to give six equal numbers.

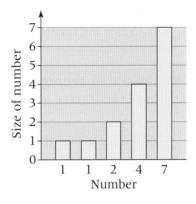

3 The times taken for Pete to travel to work are

Monday	Tuesday	Wednesday	Thursday	Friday
24 mins	18 mins	21 mins	17 mins	15 mins

Calculate his mean time taken.

4 Calculate the mean for each set of numbers.

  a 4, 9, 7, 12   **b** 8, 11, 8

  c 3, 2, 2, 3, 0   **d** 1, 9, 8, 6

  e 2, 2, 4, 1, 0, 3   **f** 23, 22, 25, 26

  g 17, 19, 19, 20, 18, 17, 16   **h** 103, 104, 105

  i 14, 10, 24, 12   **j** 4, 6, 7, 6, 4, 4, 3, 7, 3, 6

5 Calculate the mean for each set of numbers.

  a 3, 2, 1, 4, 2   **b** 8, 7, 6, 5

  c 3, 2, 2, 5, 1, 2   **d** 14, 15, 15, 13, 18, 15, 16, 18

  e 108, 107, 110, 101

6 The numbers of matches in five different matchboxes are shown on the diagram.

Calculate the mean number of matches in a box.

7 The mean of these three numbers is 8.

Calculate the missing number.

  (6) (9) (?)

8 Find two numbers with a mean of 3.5.

The median

This spread will show you how to:

- Calculate the median of small sets of data

Keywords
Average
Median
Representative
value

You can use an **average** to represent a set of data.
One **representative value** is called the median.

- The **median** is the middle value when the data are arranged in order of size.

The data must be in numerical order.

Example

Lisa catches a bus each day.
The number of minutes that the bus is late is shown.

1, 3, 1, 4, 0, 2, 2

Calculate the median number of minutes late.

First arrange the data in numerical order.

0, 1, 1, 2, 2, 3, 4

middle value

Median = 2 minutes

- When there are two middle numbers, the median is the number that is halfway between these two middle numbers.

Example

The numbers of passengers in 10 cars were counted. The results were

2 0 1 0 3 2 0 0 4 0

Calculate the median number of passengers.

First arrange the data in numerical order.

0 0 0 0 ⓪ ① 2 2 3 4

two middle values

Median = (0 + 1) ÷ 2

= 0.5 passengers

For an even number of data items, there will be two middle values.

1 a Write these numbers in order, smallest first.
  i 7, 8, 8, 5, 4, 3, 3   **ii** 11, 12, 10, 9, 9
  iii 38, 35, 30, 37, 34   **iv** 101, 98, 103, 97, 99, 97, 95
  v 3, 2, 0, 0, 1, 2, 1, 2, 3
  b Use your answers to find the median of each set of numbers.

2 The weights of five boys are given on the right.
  a Arrange the weights in order, smallest first.
  b Find the median weight.
  c Which boy has the median weight?

Tony	71 kg
Tom	64 kg
Tim	61 kg
Tariq	70 kg
Thomas	66 kg

3 Eleven students were asked how many hours of television they had watched yesterday. The results were
  4, $3\frac{1}{2}$, 0, 1, $\frac{1}{2}$, 5, 2, $2\frac{1}{2}$, 10, 1, $1\frac{1}{2}$
  Find the median number of hours of television watched.

4 The numbers of tomatoes on each of seven plants in a greenhouse are
  12, 6, 9, 15, 10, 9, 7
  Find the median number of tomatoes on the plants.

5 The ages, in years, of eight children in a creche are:
  2, 4, 2, 3, 5, 1, 3, 4
  Find the median age for the children.

6 Ten students were asked to estimate a minute.
  Their attempts, in seconds, were
  65, 71, 57, 41, 56, 68, 85, 42, 58, 60
  Calculate the median time in seconds.

7 The numbers of passengers in 20 cars are recorded.
  The numbers are
  1, 0, 0, 1, 2, 3, 5, 0, 1, 2, 1, 1, 2, 0, 0, 0, 4, 2, 1, 1
  Calculate the median number of passengers.

A03 Problem

8 Explain why these statements are wrong.
  a The median of 3, 2, 1, 5, 6 is 1.
  b The median of 1, 1, 2, 3 is 1 or 2.
  c You cannot find the median of 8, 8, 9, 10 because there is no middle number.

The mode and range

This spread will show you how to:

● Calculate the mode and range of small sets of data

Keywords
Average
Modal
Mode
Range
Representative
  value
Spread

You can use an **average** to represent a set of data.
One **representative value** is called the mode.

● The **mode** is the value that occurs most often.

Example

In the last ten football matches, Matlock Town scored 2, 5, 2, 3, 4, 1, 3, 1, 1, 1 goals. Calculate the modal number of goals.

1 goal occurred most often.
Mode = 1 goal
You can represent the goals on a diagram.

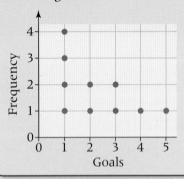

The mode is also called the **modal** value.

The modal number of goals scored is 1.

● You can measure the **spread** of the numbers by calculating the range.

● The **range** is the highest value minus the lowest value.

The range measures the spread of the data.

Example

Find

a the range
b the mode of these numbers of goals.

1, 1, 1, 1, 2, 2, 3, 3, 4, 5, 3, 3

a Range = highest value − lowest value
      = 5 − 1
      = 4 goals
b There are 2 modes: 1 and 3

1 The shop Tops4U sells 25 tops in one day.
The sizes sold are

L   M   L   M   XL   L   M   M   XL   M
M   XL   XL   L   M   M   L   L   M   L
L   L   XL   M   M

M = Medium
L = Large
XL = Extra large

a Copy and complete the frequency table for the tops.

Size	Tally	Frequency
Medium (M)		
Large (L)		
Extra large (XL)		

b State the modal size.

2 Calculate the mode and range of each set of numbers.

a 0, 0, 1, 1, 1, 1, 2, 2, 2, 3, 3, 4, 4   **b** 5, 5, 6, 6, 6, 7, 7, 7, 7, 8, 8, 8, 8, 8

c 10, 11, 11, 11, 12, 12, 13, 14   **d** 21, 22, 23, 24, 24, 25, 25, 25, 26

e 8, 8, 8, 9, 9, 10, 11   **f** 4, 3, 5, 5, 6, 6, 4, 3, 4, 5, 6, 5, 3

3 Calculate the mode and range of these sets of numbers.

a
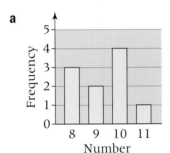

b
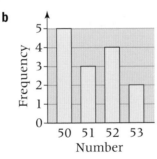

c
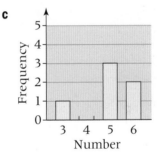

4 The mean monthly temperature, in °F, is shown for Leeds.

Average temperature

	Jan	Feb	Mar	Apr	May	Jun	Jul	Aug	Sep	Oct	Nov	Dec
°F	41	41	44	46	54	58	62	61	56	52	45	44

Source: www.weatherbase.com

Calculate the range of the temperatures.

5 The range of five weights is 18 kg.
The five weights in order are 35 kg, 42 kg, 43 kg, 51 kg, ? kg.
Calculate the value of the unknown weight.

6 The mode of these five numbers is 4.
Find the missing number and calculate the range.

AO3 | Problem

Frequency tables

This spread will show you how to:
- Calculate the mean, mode, median and range of sets of data

Keywords
Frequency table
Mean
Median
Mode
Range
Spread

- You can calculate
  - the **mean**
  - the **mode**
  - the **median**
  - the **range**

  from a **frequency table**.

Example

A dice was thrown ten times. The scores were

6, 1, 4, 1, 1, 5, 5, 1, 1, 6

Complete the frequency table and calculate the mean, mode, median and range of the ten scores.

Score	Tally	Frequency
1		
2		

This topic is extended to finding the mean from a frequency table on page 442.

Score	Tally	Frequency
1	IIII	5	← 1 was thrown on five occasions.
2		0
3		0
4	I	1
5	II	2
6	II	2	← 6 was thrown on two occasions.
		10

The results can be written in numerical order

1, 1, 1, 1, 1, 4, 5, 5, 6, 6

Mean = total of scores ÷ number of throws
= $\frac{31}{10}$
= 3.1

Mode = 1 as 1 occurs the most often.

Median = (1 + 4) ÷ 2
= 2.5 as there are two middle scores.

Range = highest value − lowest value
= 6 − 1
= 5

The mean, mode and median must be between 1 and 6 inclusive.

The range measures the **spread** of the results.

1 The numbers of days that 20 students were absent from school in a week were

1	2	1	0	5	0	5	3	3	1
2	1	1	5	1	2	4	0	0	1

a Copy and complete the frequency table.
b Calculate the mean, mode, median and range of the 20 numbers.

Number of days	Tally	Frequency
0		
1		
2		
3		
4		
5		

2 The numbers of shots taken for each hole for a round of golf were

3	4	3	2	3	4	3	4	3
4	3	2	4	6	3	4	4	4

a Copy and complete the frequency table.

Number of shorts	Tally	Frequency
2		
3		
4		
5		
6		

b Calculate the mean, mode, median and range of the 18 scores.

3 Twenty people are asked 'How many televisions do you have in your home?' The results are

1	2	0	2	3	2	1	1	1	2
1	3	3	1	4	2	1	2	1	1

a Copy and complete the frequency table.
b Calculate the mean, mode, median and range of the 20 numbers.

Number of TVs	Tally	Frequency
0		
1		
2		
3		
4		

4 Ten people are asked to choose a number from

| 1 | or | 2 | or | 3 | or | 4 |

The results are shown in the bar chart.
a Write the ten numbers in order of size, smallest first.
b Calculate the mean, mode, median and range of the ten numbers.

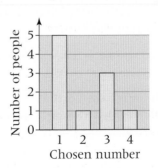

This spread will show you how to:

- Compare two sets of data using mean, mode, median and range
- Draw and interpret diagrams to represent data

Keywords
Compare
Mean
Median
Mode
Range
Spread

The **mean**, **mode** and **median** each give one typical value to represent the data. The **range** is a number that measures the **spread** of the data.

- You can **compare** two sets of data using
  - any of the mean, mode and median
  - the range.

Example

The results of a test are shown in the diagrams.

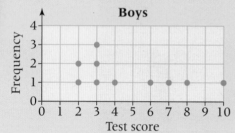
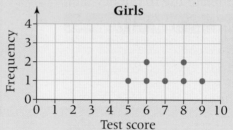

a Calculate the mean and median for each set of data.
b Compare the sets of data using the mean and median.
c Calculate the range for each set of data.
d Compare the sets of data using the range.

....

a Boys' mean = (2 + 2 + 3 + 3 + 3 + 4 + 6 + 7 + 8 + 10) ÷ 10
= 48 ÷ 10 = 4.8
Boys' median = (3 + 4) ÷ 2 = 3.5 (the mean of the 5th and 6th test scores)
Girls' mean = (5 + 6 + 6 + 7 + 8 + 8 + 9) ÷ 7
= 49 ÷ 7 = 7
Girls' median = 7   (the 4th test score)

b The mean and median show on average the girls did better in the test than the boys.

Use the words 'on average'.

c Boys' range = 10 − 2 = 8
Girls' range = 9 − 5 = 4

d The range shows that the boys' results are more spread out than the girls' results. The girls' results are more consistent.

- When you compare data, you should use
  - a measure of average
  - a measure of spread.

1 The numbers of people who live in each house in Windermere
   Street are

      1, 1, 1, 1, 2, 2, 2, 4, 4

   a Calculate the mean, mode and median of these numbers.
   The numbers of people who live in each house in Coniston
   Road are

      3, 3, 3, 3, 4, 6, 6

   b Calculate the mean, mode and median of these numbers.
   c Use your answers to compare the average number of people in
   each house for the two streets.

2 John throws three darts. He scores 40, 20, 20.
   Jim throws three darts. He scores 1, 5, 60.
   a Calculate the range of the scores for John
   and Jim.
   b Who is more consistent?

3 The ages of ten teachers are
   25, 22, 51, 34, 28, 45, 37, 28, 33, 50.
   a Calculate the range of these ages.
   b All the Year 11 students are either 15 or 16 years old.
   Calculate the range of the Year 11 ages.
   c Explain the meaning of these two answers.

Functional Maths

A02

4 The highest recorded monthly temperatures for St Tropez in
   France and for Wick in Scotland are shown.

   Highest recorded temperature (°C)

	Jan	Feb	Mar	Apr	May	Jun	Jul	Aug	Sep	Oct	Nov	Dec
St Tropez	17	22	22	24	27	30	34	33	29	26	20	19
Wick	13	13	16	19	22	24	23	23	21	19	15	13

   a List the temperatures for St Tropez and for Wick in order, smallest first.
   b Calculate the median temperature for St Tropez and for Wick.
   c Using the answers for the median, compare the two sets of data.
   d Calculate the range of the temperatures for St Tropez and for Wick.
   e Using the answers for the range, compare the two sets of data.
   f A temperature of 27°C is recorded in September. Which place is this more likely
   to have been recorded in: St. Tropez or Wick? Give a reason for your answer.

This spread will show you how to:
- Interpret data from a stem-and-leaf diagram
- Calculate the mean, mode, median and range from a stem-and-leaf diagram

Keywords
Ordered
Stem-and-leaf diagram

- You can interpret numerical data from a **stem-and-leaf diagram**.

Hannah recorded the lengths in mm of the leaves that fell off an oak tree one October day.

The numbers in her stem-and-leaf diagram are

104, 105, 108, 112, 112, 114, 115, 120, 124, 127, 132, 138, 141, 142, 147.

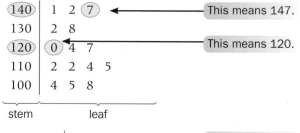

140	1 2 ⑦	← This means 147.
130	2 8	
120	⓪ 4 7	← This means 120.
110	2 2 4 5	
100	4 5 8	

stem   leaf

Key: 110 | 4 means 114 mm

Always give the key.

Her stem-and-leaf diagram is **ordered** as the data is in numerical order.

- You can calculate the mean, mode, median and range from the stem-and-leaf diagram.

Example

The ages of nine people in a judo club are shown in the diagram.

40	6
30	2 4 5 5
20	7 8
10	1 3

Key: 20 | 7 means 27

Calculate
a the mean
b the mode
c the median
d the range.

....

a Mean = (11 + 13 + 27 + 28 + 32 + 34 + 35 + 35 + 46) ÷ 9
        = 261 ÷ 9 = 29
b Mode = 35, the most common age
c Median = 32, the middle age when arranged in order
d Range = 46 − 11 = 35 years (highest age minus lowest age)

1 Emma takes a spelling test every week. Her marks are shown in the stem-and-leaf diagram.

```
 0 | 9
10 | 1  2  3  3  4  4  5  7  7     Key:   10 | 5   means 15 marks
20 | 0  0  0
```

  a Write out her 13 scores in numerical order, smallest first.
  b Calculate
    i the mean   **ii** the mode
    iii the median **iv** the range.

2 The cost, in pence, of various types of sweets are
  38 44 48 20 29 37 29 39 40
  a Copy and complete the stem-and-leaf diagram.

```
20 | 4  6  4  8
30 | 8  7  3  0  5     Key:   20 | 9   means 29p
40 | 2
```

  b Redraw your table to give an ordered stem-and-leaf diagram.
  c Calculate
    i the mean   **ii** the mode
    iii the median **iv** the range.

3 The weights, in kilograms, of seven students are shown in the stem-and-leaf diagram.

```
40 | 3  5  5
50 | 0  6                Key:   40 | 3   means 43 kg
60 | 3  9
```

Calculate
a the mean   **b** the mode
c the median   **d** the range.

4 The reaction times, in seconds, for 15 people are shown in the stem-and-leaf diagram.

```
 9 | 9
10 | 0  1  1  1  2  3  5  7     Key:   10 | 5   means 10.5 seconds
11 | 8  9
12 | 0  7  7
```

Calculate
a the mean   **b** the mode
c the median   **d** the range.

Summary

Check out

You should now be able to:

- Calculate the mean, mode, median, range and modal class
- Compare sets of data using mean, mode, median and range
- Interpret diagrams and draw conclusions

Worked exam question

Donna asks ten classmates how many days they were absent from school last term.
The results are

2 0 3 7 8 0 1 11 6 4

a Calculate the mean number of days absent.   (3)
b Donna says that the mean should be 3.5
   She is **not** correct.

   Which average has the value 3.5?
   Give a reason for your answer.   (2)

(AQA, 2009)

a
$$2 + 0 + 3 + 7 + 8 + 0 + 1 + 11 + 6 + 4 = 42$$
$$42 \div 10 = 4.2$$

> Add up all the numbers and divide by how many there are.

b
In numerical order;
0 0 1 2 3 4 6 7 8 11
The median is between the 5th and 6th values:
$$\frac{3 + 4}{2} = 3.5$$
The median is 3.5

> Add up the two middle values and divide by 2.

Exam questions

1 A hospital manager asks 11 people how many weeks they had to wait for an operation.
Here are his results.

5	4	17	14	17	15
24	11	8	17	11	

   a How many people waited more than ten weeks? (1)
   b Write down the mode. (1)
   c Work out the range. (1)
   d Calculate the mean. (3)
   e The hospital manager uses the mean to show the average waiting time.
      Give a reason for his choice. (1)

(AQA, 2009)

2 The bar chart shows the number of driving tests that learner drivers had to take before they passed.

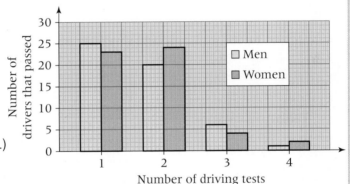

   a Write down how many men passed on their third attempt. (1)
   b Work out how many more men than women passed at their first attempt. (2)
   c None of the women took more than 4 attempts to pass.
      How many women in total did **not** pass at their first attempt? (2)
   d The number of lessons taken by 11 drivers is shown.

25	33	41	50	21	43
54	37	42	18	24	

     i Complete an ordered stem-and-leaf diagram to show this data.
       Remember to complete the key. (3)
     ii One of these 11 drivers is chosen at random.
       Write down the probability that this driver had fewer than 30 lessons. (1)

(AQA, 2009)

3 Mr. Jones kept a record of the number of absences in his class for two weeks.
Here are his results.

3	0	5	4	9	2	0	1	0	3

Using measures of average and the range, comment on the absences in Mr. Jones's class. (4)

Functional Maths 2: Sandwich shop

The manager of a catering company can use data about customer numbers in order to spot trends in customer behaviour and to plan for the future.

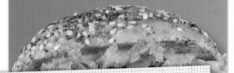

Simply Sandwiches

Simply Sandwiches

iches, paninis, baguettes and salads

Simply Sandwiches

Customer numbers at 'Simply sandwiches' takeaway over a given two-week period were:

Day	Number of Customers	
	Week 1	Week 2
Monday	50	54
Tuesday	68	60
Wednesday	47	53
Thursday	58	57
Friday	52	56
Saturday	76	70
Total		

Simply Sandwiches

Use the data in the table to construct a bar chart to show how many customers visit the sandwich shop on each day during this two-week period.

Copy and complete the table.

During this two-week period,

a) which is the busiest day at the sandwich shop

b) what is the range of daily customer numbers?

This bar chart shows customer behaviour over a different two-week period. Compare the two sets of data, including reference to the quietest/busiest days and the spread of the data. Give possible explanations and justify your response with reference to the data.

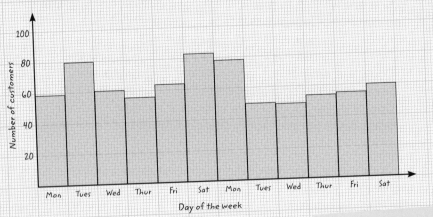

Is data collected over a two-week period enough to be able to estimate customer numbers for any given week? Justify your answer referring to the information.

A manager can use data about customer numbers to help estimate how much stock to order each week. In reality, limitations due to space and the shelf life of products also apply.

In the second week of the two-week period at 'Simply sandwiches', sales of the different varieties of sandwiches were:

Variety	Mon	Tues	Weds	Thurs	Fri	Sat	Total	Average
Ham	14	16	13	14	17	18		
Cheese	9	11	12	10	8	12		
Hummus	6	5	7	4	6	8		
Tuna	7	6	6	8	6	9		
Chicken	18	22	15	21	19	23		
Total								

Copy the table and fill in the missing values.

The manager does a weekly stocktake every Sunday before placing the order for the following week.

The stocktake figures for this week were:

Product	Stock (packs)	Portions per pack	Portions left	Stock needed	Amount to order
Bread	6	20			
Ham	2.5	10			
Cheese	3	10			
Hummus	2	14			
Tuna	1.5	8			
Chicken	1	10			

Copy and complete the table to show an estimate of how much of each product the manager should order to last for the following week.

The stock will be delivered on Wednesday morning.

Estimate how much (if any) of each product the manager will have in stock when the order arrives.

Comment on how well the manager estimated the order for the previous week.

Justify your answers by referring to the data.

Simply Sandwiches

Sandwiches, paninis, baguettes and salads

Fractions and percentages

Introduction

In modern society, people often want to buy their own house, own a new car or go to university. To do these things they often need to borrow money from a bank or building society. These organisations lend the money but charge an amount (called 'interest') that is calculated as a percentage or fraction of the amount borrowed.

What's the point?

Being able to solve problems involving percentages gives people greater control of their finances. It allows them to budget properly and be aware of the risks involved in borrowing too much money, which can lead to debt and bankruptcy.

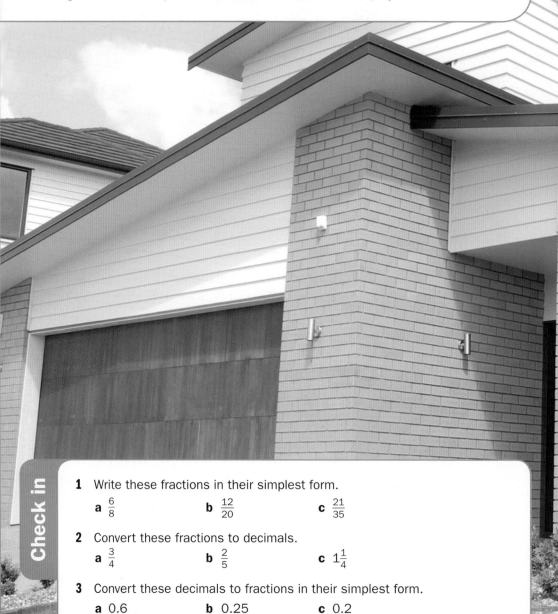

Check in

1 Write these fractions in their simplest form.

   a $\frac{6}{8}$ **b** $\frac{12}{20}$ **c** $\frac{21}{35}$

2 Convert these fractions to decimals.

   a $\frac{3}{4}$ **b** $\frac{2}{5}$ **c** $1\frac{1}{4}$

3 Convert these decimals to fractions in their simplest form.

   a 0.6   **b** 0.25   **c** 0.2

Orientation

What I need to know	What I will learn	What this leads to
Key stage 3 →	■ Convert between fractions, decimals and percentages ■ Calculate a fraction of an amount ■ Calculate a percentage of an amount ■ Calculate percentage increase and decrease ■ Use percentages in real-life problems	→ N4

Look ahead to: +4 (page 414)

Rich task

Marie invests some money in a building society at 5% simple interest per year.

At the end of one year she earns £25 interest.

How much did Marie originally invest?

(**Note:** you will learn more about simple interest on page 336).

This spread will show you how to:

- Use fraction notation and vocabulary
- Calculate a given fraction of a given quantity
- Express a given number as a fraction of another

Keywords

Denominator
Equal
Fraction
Numerator

In real life you don't just use whole numbers.

When a pizza is divided into 8 equal slices

When you measure someone's height

$1\frac{1}{2}$ m

When you read the petrol gauge in a car

Each slice is part of the whole pizza.
One slice is $\frac{1}{8}$ of the whole pizza.

This person is one whole metre and half of another metre.

This car is about $\frac{3}{4}$ full with petrol.

- You can use a **fraction** to describe a part of a whole. To use a fraction the whole must be divided into **equal** sized parts.

Numerator: the top number shows how many parts you have.

5 out of the 9 equal sections are shaded.

Fraction shaded $= \dfrac{5}{9}$

Denominator: the bottom number shows how many equal sized parts the whole has been divided into.

Example

In a class there are 30 students. 19 of the students are girls.
What fraction of the class are girls?

....

19 out of the 30 students are girls.
Fraction of girls $= \frac{19}{30}$

The whole is the entire class of 30.

Example

Here is a fuel gauge from a car. How full is the petrol tank?
Give your answer as a fraction.

Empty   Full

....

The fuel gauge is divided into five equal sections.
Three of the sections are coloured, and showing fuel.
The car is $\frac{3}{5}$ full.

1 Write the fraction of each of these shapes that is shaded.

a

b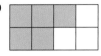

c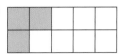

d

e

f

2 a There are 28 students in a class. 15 are boys and 13 are girls. What fraction of the class are
  i boys   **ii** girls?

  b Tyrone has eight pairs of brown shoes and seven pairs of black shoes. What fraction of his shoes are
  i brown   **ii** black?

  c Wesley earns £300 a week. He pays £91 of his money each week in tax. He saves £60 each week. What fraction of his weekly wage does Wesley
  i pay in tax   **ii** save?

  d A teacher works for eight hours at school and three hours at home. What fraction of the day does the teacher work
  i at school   **ii** at home?

  e Rory has a collection of 13 CDs, 15 DVDs and nine computer games. What fraction of his collection is
  i CDs   **ii** DVDs   **iii** computer games?

  f Irene has 38 hardback books and 77 paperback books. What fraction of her books are
  i hardbacks   **ii** paperbacks?

3 Write the fraction indicated by each of the pointers.

a

```
      A          B  C         D      E
      ↓          ↓  ↓         ↓      ↓
   ├──┼──┼──┼──┼──┼──┼──┼──┼──┼──┤
   0                          1
```

b

```
                F      G             H
                ↓      ↓             ↓
   ├────┼────┼────┼────┼────┼────┼────┤
   0                   1
```

c

```
            I         J         K
            ↓         ↓         ↓
   ├┬┬┬┬┼┬┬┬┬┼┬┬┬┬┼┬┬┬┬┼┬┬┬┬┼┬┬┬┬┤
   4         5         6         7
```

> Some of these fractions are greater than 1. You write $1\frac{1}{4}$.

This spread will show you how to:

- Simplify fractions by cancelling common factors
- Recognise and find equivalent fractions
- Add and subtract simple fractions

The same fraction of each rectangle is shaded.

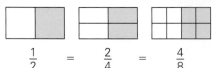

$$\frac{1}{2} \quad = \quad \frac{2}{4} \quad = \quad \frac{4}{8}$$

These fractions are called **equivalent** fractions.

Equivalent fractions are assessed in all three units.

- You can find equivalent fractions by multiplying the numerator and denominator by the same number.

This topic is extended to adding and subtracting fractions on page 410.

Example

Find two equivalent fractions for $\frac{4}{7}$.

$$\overset{\times 3}{\frac{4}{7} = \frac{12}{21}} \qquad \overset{\times 5}{\frac{4}{7} = \frac{20}{35}}$$
$$\underset{\times 3}{} \qquad\qquad \underset{\times 5}{}$$

So $\frac{12}{21} = \frac{4}{7}$ and $\frac{20}{35} = \frac{4}{7}$

- You can simplify a fraction by dividing the numerator and denominator by the same number. This process is called **cancelling**.

Example

Write each of these fractions in its **simplest form**.

a $\frac{15}{20}$ **b** $\frac{24}{30}$

a $\overset{\div 5}{\frac{15}{20} = \frac{3}{4}}$ **b** $\overset{\div 2}{\frac{24}{30} = \frac{12}{15}} \overset{\div 3}{= \frac{4}{5}}$
$\underset{\div 5}{}$ $\underset{\div 2}{} \quad \underset{\div 3}{}$

- You can add or subtract fractions with the same denominator.

$$\frac{3}{5} + \frac{1}{5} = \frac{4}{5}$$

When the denominators are the same, you can add or subtract fractions by simply adding or subtracting the numerators.

1 Write the fraction of each of these shapes that is shaded.
Give your answer in its simplest form.

a   **b**   **c**

d   **e**

2 Copy and complete each of these equivalent fraction families.

a $\frac{1}{2} = \frac{2}{4} = \frac{?}{10} = \frac{?}{16}$

b $\frac{3}{10} = \frac{6}{20} = \frac{?}{30} = \frac{15}{?} = \frac{30}{?}$

c $\frac{4}{5} = \frac{?}{10} = \frac{12}{?} = \frac{?}{25} = \frac{?}{100}$

d $\frac{5}{8} = \frac{10}{?} = \frac{?}{24} = \frac{?}{80} = \frac{75}{?}$

e $\frac{2}{9} = \frac{?}{18} = \frac{6}{?} = \frac{10}{?} = \frac{?}{81}$

f $\frac{7}{4} = \frac{?}{8} = \frac{?}{12} = \frac{?}{40} = \frac{77}{?}$

3 Find the missing number in each of these pairs of equivalent fractions.

a $\frac{2}{3} = \frac{?}{9}$

b $\frac{4}{5} = \frac{12}{?}$

c $\frac{3}{4} = \frac{?}{20}$

d $\frac{1}{8} = \frac{?}{40}$

e $\frac{5}{7} = \frac{30}{?}$

f $\frac{4}{9} = \frac{?}{63}$

g $\frac{7}{8} = \frac{?}{48}$

h $\frac{7}{10} = \frac{?}{100}$

i $\frac{12}{15} = \frac{?}{5}$

j $\frac{18}{24} = \frac{3}{?}$

k $\frac{30}{35} = \frac{?}{7}$

l $\frac{14}{35} = \frac{2}{?}$

m $\frac{?}{3} = \frac{16}{24}$

n $\frac{4}{?} = \frac{20}{55}$

o $\frac{?}{10} = \frac{56}{80}$

p $\frac{9}{13} = \frac{?}{65}$

4 Cancel down each of these fractions into their simplest form.

a $\frac{4}{8}$

b $\frac{3}{9}$

c $\frac{4}{6}$

d $\frac{8}{10}$

e $\frac{9}{12}$

f $\frac{10}{15}$

g $\frac{3}{15}$

h $\frac{12}{16}$

i $\frac{14}{16}$

j $\frac{13}{16}$

k $\frac{12}{18}$

l $\frac{8}{20}$

m $\frac{16}{24}$

n $\frac{21}{28}$

o $\frac{20}{25}$

p $\frac{18}{30}$

q $\frac{12}{36}$

r $\frac{24}{40}$

s $\frac{14}{42}$

t $\frac{27}{63}$

5 Find an equivalent fraction for each fraction. Both of your fractions
should have the same denominator.

a $\frac{1}{2}$ and $\frac{1}{3}$

b $\frac{1}{5}$ and $\frac{1}{3}$

c $\frac{1}{2}$ and $\frac{1}{5}$

d $\frac{2}{3}$ and $\frac{1}{4}$

e $\frac{3}{10}$ and $\frac{1}{3}$

f $\frac{4}{5}$ and $\frac{1}{4}$

g $\frac{1}{3}$ and $\frac{3}{7}$

h $\frac{5}{6}$ and $\frac{3}{4}$

6 Calculate each of these. Give your answer in its simplest form.

> You will need to
> be able to add
> and subtract
> fractions for
> Unit 2.

a $\frac{1}{3} + \frac{1}{3}$

b $\frac{2}{5} + \frac{1}{5}$

c $\frac{3}{10} + \frac{7}{10}$

d $\frac{4}{9} + \frac{2}{9}$

e $\frac{7}{8} + \frac{5}{8}$

f $\frac{13}{7} - \frac{6}{7}$

g $\frac{5}{16} - \frac{1}{16}$

h $\frac{13}{18} - \frac{5}{18}$

i $\frac{12}{15} + \frac{8}{15}$

j $\frac{19}{16} - \frac{7}{16}$

k $\frac{12}{35} + \frac{8}{35}$

l $\frac{23}{30} - \frac{7}{30}$

This spread will show you how to:

- Understand and interpret percentages
- Convert fractions into percentages
- Convert percentages into fractions

Keywords
Equivalent
Fraction
Percentage

- A **percentage** is a fraction of something. It is written as the number of parts per hundred.

40% is the fraction $\frac{40}{100}$.

40% of this line is shaded. The line is divided into 100 parts and 40 of them are shaded.

- To change a percentage into a **fraction** you write it as a fraction out of a 100 and then simplify.

Some useful equivalents to remember.

$10\% = \frac{10}{100} = \frac{1}{10}$

$20\% = \frac{20}{100} = \frac{1}{5}$

$25\% = \frac{25}{100} = \frac{1}{4}$

$50\% = \frac{50}{100} = \frac{1}{2}$

$75\% = \frac{75}{100} = \frac{3}{4}$

Example

Write these percentages as fractions in their simplest form.

a 60% **b** 45%

a $60\% = \frac{60}{100}$

$$\overset{\div 10 \qquad \div 2}{\frac{60}{100} = \frac{6}{10} = \frac{3}{5}} \quad 60\% = \frac{3}{5}$$
$$\underset{\div 10 \qquad \div 2}{}$$

b $45\% = \frac{45}{100}$

$$\overset{\div 5}{\frac{45}{100} = \frac{9}{20}} \quad 45\% = \frac{9}{20}$$
$$\underset{\div 5}{}$$

To simplify a fraction, divide the numerator and denominator by the same number.
Equivalent fractions are also assessed in Unit 2.

- To change a fraction into a percentage you write it as an equivalent fraction out of 100 and then change it into a percentage.

Example

Change these fractions into percentages.

a $\frac{7}{10}$ **b** $\frac{7}{25}$

a

$$\overset{\times 10}{\frac{7}{10} = \frac{70}{100}} \quad \frac{70}{100} = 70\%$$
$$\underset{\times 10}{}$$

b

$$\overset{\times 4}{\frac{7}{25} = \frac{28}{100}} \quad \frac{28}{100} = 28\%$$
$$\underset{\times 4}{}$$

You can express something as the percentage of a whole by first finding the fraction of the whole.

Example

What percentage of this shape is shaded?

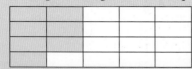

There are 20 equal parts. 7 of the parts are shaded. The fraction shaded is $\frac{7}{20}$.
Converting to a percentage:
% shaded $= \frac{7}{20} = \frac{35}{100} = 35\%$

1 This rectangle has been divided into 100 parts.

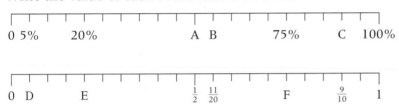

    a What percentage of the rectangle is shaded yellow?
    b What percentage of the rectangle is shaded green?
    c What percentage of the rectangle is not shaded green?

2 Write these percentages as fractions out of 100.
    a 35%   **b** 10%   **c** 67%   **d** 43%
    e 95%   **f** 56%   **g** 140%   **h** 135%

3 Write the value of each of the letters on these number lines.

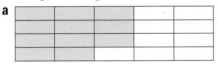

4 Write these percentages as fractions in their simplest form.
    a 50%   **b** 80%   **c** 15%   **d** 85%
    e 28%   **f** 6%   **g** 150%   **h** 115%

5 Write each of these fractions as a percentage.
    a $\frac{27}{100}$ **b** $\frac{1}{2}$ **c** $\frac{7}{10}$ **d** $\frac{11}{25}$ **e** $\frac{3}{4}$
    f $\frac{34}{200}$ **g** $\frac{6}{5}$ **h** $\frac{21}{20}$ **i** $\frac{26}{40}$ **j** $\frac{33}{75}$

6 What percentage of each of these shapes is shaded?

7 A shirt is 65% polyester and 35% cotton.
Write 35% as a fraction.
Give your answer in its simplest form.

8 How would you write $17\frac{1}{2}$% as a fraction in
its simplest form?
Show all your working out.

This spread will show you how to:

● Convert between fractions, decimals and percentages
● Order fractions, decimals and percentages

Keywords
Decimal
Equivalent
Fraction
Order
Percentage

You can change between fractions, decimals and percentages.

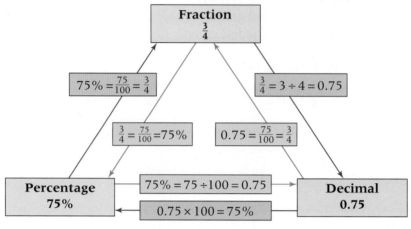

p.156

p.166

You can compare the size of fractions by placing them on a number line.

Example

Which is bigger, $\frac{3}{5}$ or $\frac{5}{8}$?

....

Divide a line into five equal pieces and shade three of them.
This is $\frac{3}{5}$ of the line.

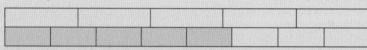

Divide a second line of the same length into eight equal pieces and shade five of them. This is $\frac{5}{8}$ of the line.

$\frac{5}{8}$ is greater than $\frac{3}{5}$.

This topic is extended to comparing fractions on page 410.

● You can **order fractions**, decimals and percentages by converting them into decimals.

Example

Write these numbers in order of size. Start with the smallest number.

    0.85   72% $\frac{7}{8}$ $\frac{4}{5}$

....

$72\% = \frac{72}{100} \div 100 = 0.72$

$\frac{7}{8} = 7 \div 8 = 0.875$

$\frac{4}{5} = 4 \div 5 = 0.8$

Placing the decimals in order   0.72   0.8   0.85   0.875

So the order is   72% $\frac{4}{5}$ 0.85 $\frac{7}{8}$

1 Write these percentages as decimals.
   a 67%   **b** 78%   **c** 99%   **d** 70%   **e** 39%
   f 88%   **g** 150%   **h** 125%   **i** 99.9%   **j** 110%

2 Write these decimals as percentages.
   a 0.32   **b** 0.22   **c** 0.85   **d** 0.03   **e** 0.54
   f 0.63   **g** 0.38   **h** 0.375   **i** 0.333   **j** 1.25

3 Write these decimals as fractions in their simplest form.
   a 0.8   **b** 0.28   **c** 0.325   **d** 0.05   **e** 0.12

4 Change these fractions to decimals. Give your answers to two
  decimal places as appropriate.

   a $\frac{3}{10}$ **b** $\frac{7}{25}$ **c** $\frac{7}{12}$ **d** $\frac{9}{15}$ **e** $\frac{15}{7}$

5 Write these percentages as fractions in their simplest form.
   a 25%   **b** 40%   **c** 65%   **d** 15%   **e** 145%

6 A shirt is 65% polyester and 35% cotton.
  Write 65% as a decimal.

7 Write each of these fractions as percentages.
  Give your answers to one decimal place as appropriate.

   a $\frac{48}{100}$ **b** $\frac{6}{25}$ **c** $\frac{17}{10}$ **d** $\frac{8}{15}$ **e** $\frac{11}{16}$

   > Try converting the fraction into a decimal first.

8 Copy and complete this table. Use the most effective method to
  convert between fractions, decimals and percentages.

Fraction (in its simplest form)		$\frac{5}{9}$		$\frac{13}{5}$	
Decimal (to 3 dp)	0.76			0.125	
Percentage (to 1 dp)			85%		17.5

   > dp means decimal places.

9 For each pair of fractions, write which is the larger fraction.

   a $\frac{3}{4}$ and $\frac{2}{3}$ (draw a number line 12 cm long)

   b $\frac{4}{5}$ and $\frac{3}{4}$ (draw a number line 20 cm long)

   c $\frac{4}{5}$ and $\frac{5}{6}$ (draw a number line 30 cm long)

   d $\frac{2}{3}$ and $\frac{3}{5}$ (draw a number line 15 cm long)

   e $\frac{4}{7}$ and $\frac{2}{5}$ (draw a number line 35 cm long)

   > Draw a number line and mark each fraction on the number line.

10 Put these lists of numbers in order, starting with the smallest.

   a 0.4   43% $\frac{3}{8}$ 0.35

   b $\frac{3}{5}$ 0.56   61% $\frac{4}{7}$

   c $\frac{3}{4}$ $\frac{2}{3}$ 70%   0.715

This spread will show you how to:

- Express one number as a fraction of another number
- Calculate a given fraction of an amount
- Use mental, written and calculator methods to calculate with fractions

Keywords

Fraction

You can express one number as a **fraction** of another number.

Example

In a class there are 30 students. 18 of the students are boys. What fraction of the class are boys? Give your answer in its simplest form.

 p.120

There are 30 students in the class altogether (the **whole**).
18 of the students are boys.
Fraction of the class who are boys $= \frac{18}{30} = \frac{3}{5}$

You can calculate a fraction of a number or quantity in several ways.

Example

Calculate using a mental method.

a $\frac{1}{4}$ of £20   **b** $\frac{3}{5}$ of €200

a $\frac{1}{4}$ of £20 = 20 ÷ 4 = £5

b $\frac{1}{5}$ of €200 = 200 ÷ 5 = €40

$\frac{3}{5}$ of €200 = 3 × 40 = €120

Finding $\frac{1}{5}$ of something is the same as dividing by 5.

Example

Calculate $\frac{3}{8}$ of 56 kg using a written method.

$\frac{3}{8}$ of 56 kg $= \frac{3}{8} \times 56$ kg   To work out a fraction of an amount,
multiply the fraction by the amount.

$= 3 \times \frac{1}{8} \times 56$ kg

$= \frac{3 \times 56}{8}$

$= \frac{168}{8} = 21$ kg

Multiplying by $\frac{1}{8}$ is the same as dividing by 8.

You could also work out
$3 \times (56 \div 8) = 3 \times 7$
                    $= 21$

Example

Calculate $\frac{7}{8}$ of £93 using a calculator.

Decimal equivalent for $\frac{7}{8} = 7 \div 8 = 0.875$

$\frac{7}{8}$ of £93 $= \frac{7}{8} \times £93 = 0.875 \times 93$
                      $= 81.375 = £81.38$

---

1 Write the fraction of each of these shapes that is shaded, leaving your answer as a fraction in its simplest form.

a   **b**   **c** 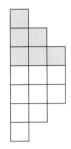 **d**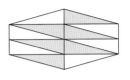

2 Use a mental method to calculate each of these amounts.

a $\frac{1}{2}$ of 40 sheep   **b** $\frac{1}{3}$ of 15 apples   **c** $\frac{1}{5}$ of 25 shops   **d** $\frac{1}{4}$ of 48 marks

3 For each answer state the fraction in its simplest form.
  a There are 30 students in a class. 20 are boys and 10 are girls. What fraction of the class are
    i boys   **ii** girls?
  b Horace earns £500 a week. He pays £150 of his money each week in tax. He saves £120 each week. What fraction of his weekly wage does Horace
    i pay in tax   **ii** save?
  c Michael and Shafique share £200. Michael has £80 and Shafique has £120. What fraction of the £200 belongs
    i to Michael   **ii** to Shafique?

4 Use a mental or written method to work out these.

a $\frac{8}{10}$ of €200

$\frac{1}{10}$ of €200 = 200 ÷ 10 = _____

$\frac{8}{10}$ of €200 = 8 × _____ = _____

b $\frac{2}{5}$ of £40   **c** $\frac{3}{4}$ of 60 minutes   **d** $\frac{4}{7}$ of 77 pencils

e $\frac{3}{10}$ of £84   **f** $\frac{5}{6}$ of 42 apples   **g** $\frac{7}{12}$ of 36p

5 Use a suitable method to calculate each of these. Where appropriate round your answer to two decimal places.

a $\frac{7}{15}$ of 375   **b** $\frac{9}{10}$ of $450   **c** $\frac{4}{7}$ of 800 kg

d $\frac{5}{9}$ of 234 m   **e** $\frac{17}{18}$ of 400 tonnes   **f** $\frac{4}{5}$ of 360°

g $\frac{12}{25}$ of 750 marbles   **h** $\frac{11}{15}$ of £255   **i** $\frac{4}{15}$ of £345

j $\frac{1}{6}$ of 546 hours

Percentage of a quantity

This spread will show you how to:

- Use percentage as an operator
- Calculate a percentage of an amount using mental and written methods

Percentages, fractions and decimals are ways of writing the same thing.

$$25\% = \frac{25}{100} = \frac{1}{4} = 0.25$$

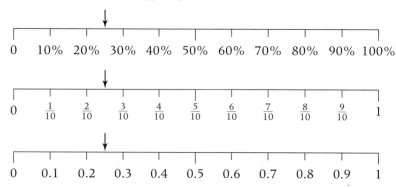

Some useful equivalents to remember.

$1\% = \frac{1}{100} = 0.01$

$10\% = \frac{10}{100} = \frac{1}{10} = 0.1$

$20\% = \frac{20}{100} = \frac{1}{5} = 0.2$

$25\% = \frac{25}{100} = \frac{1}{4} = 0.25$

$50\% = \frac{50}{100} = \frac{1}{2} = 0.5$

You can calculate simple percentages of amounts in your head using equivalent fractions.

Example

Calculate
a 10% of £41 **b** 50% of 84 m

a $\frac{1}{10}$ of £41 $\left(10\% = \frac{1}{10}\right)$

$= \frac{1}{10} \times £41$

$= £41 \div 10$

$= £4.10$

b $\frac{1}{2}$ of 84 m $\left(50\% = \frac{1}{2}\right)$

$= \frac{1}{2} \times 84$ m

$= 84$ m $\div 2$

$= 42$ m

- To calculate a percentage of an amount using a written method, change the percentage to its equivalent fraction and multiply by the amount.

Example

Calculate 15% of £80.

15% of £80 $= \frac{15}{100} \times £80$

$= 15 \times £80 \times \frac{1}{100}$

$= \frac{15 \times £80}{100}$

$= \frac{£1200}{100}$

$= £12$

Alternatively you could use a mental method:

10% of £80 $= \frac{1}{10}$ of 80

$= 80 \div 10 = 8$

So 5% of 80 $= 8 \div 2 = 4$

So 15% of 80 $= 8 + 4 = 12$

15% of £80 is £12.

$15\% = 10\% + 5\%$

1 a What fraction of this shape is shaded?

  b What percentage of the shape is shaded?
  c Copy the shape and shade in more squares so that 70% of the shape is shaded.

2 Calculate these percentages without using a calculator.
  a 50% of £60 **b** 50% of 40   **c** 50% of 272p   **d** 10% of 40
  e 10% of 370p **f** 1% of £700   **g** 50% of 12 kg   **h** 50% of £31
  i 1% of 200   **j** 1% of 420 m

3 Calculate these percentages using a mental method.
  a 10% of £40 **b** 10% of £340   **c** 5% of £120   **d** 20% of 210 km
  e 20% of $530 **f** 25% of £300   **g** 20% of £32   **h** 5% of 28 m

4 Calculate these percentages using a mental method.
  The first one is started for you.

  a 60% of 40

$$50\% \text{ of } 40 = \tfrac{1}{2} \text{ of } 40 = 20$$
$$\underline{10\% \text{ of } 40 = \tfrac{1}{10} \text{ of } 40 = ?}$$
$$60\% \text{ of } 40 \qquad\qquad = ?$$

> Use percentages which you can work out quickly in your head.

  b 60% of £70   **c** 40% of £30   **d** 40% of 45 m
  e 2.5% of £80   **f** 70% of 150 m   **g** 15% of 120 kg
  h 35% of 400 mm **i** 7.5% of 300 km

5 Write how you would use a mental method to calculate
  a 15% of anything   **b** 5% of anything   **c** 20% of anything
  d 90% of anything   **e** 11% of anything   **f** 17.5% of anything.

6 Calculate these percentages using a mental or written method. Show all the steps of your working out.
  a 11% of £18   **b** 60% of 7300 km   **c** 8% of £30
  d 2% of €3000   **e** 7% of 60 m   **f** 13% of 40 cm
  g 75% of 48 m   **h** 3% of £70

7 Rearrange these cards to make three correct statements.

25% of	£450	= £128
30% of	£640	= £130
20% of	£520	= £135

This spread will show you how to:

- Calculate a percentage of an amount
- Calculate percentage increase and decrease

Keywords

Decrease
Increase
Percentage

You can already calculate a **percentage** of an amount.

> **Calculate**
> **a** 12% of £50 **b** 12.6% of 320 m
>
> **a** 12% of £50 $= \frac{12}{100} \times £50$
> $= \frac{12 \times £50}{100}$
> $= \frac{£600}{100}$
> $= £6$
>
> **b** 12.6% of 320 m $= \frac{12.6}{100} \times 320$
> $= 0.126 \times 320$
> $= 40.32$ m

This topic is extended to harder percentage increase and decrease on page 414.

Percentages are used in real life to show how much an amount has increased or decreased.

- To calculate a percentage **increase**, work out the increase and add it to the original amount.

- To calculate a percentage **decrease**, work out the decrease and subtract it from the original amount.

> **a** Karen is paid £800 a month. Her employer increases her wage by 6%. Calculate the new wage Karen is paid each month.
> **b** In January a car costs £3400. In February the price is reduced by 17%. What is the new price of the car?
>
> **a** Increase in wage $= 6\%$ of £800 $= \frac{6}{100} \times £800$
> $= \frac{6 \times £800}{100}$
> $= \frac{£4800}{100}$
>
> Increase in wage $= £48$
> Karen's new wage $= £800 + £48$
> $= £848$
>
> **b** Price reduction $= 17\%$ of £3400 $= \frac{17}{100} \times £3400$
> $= 0.17 \times £3400$
> Price reduction $= £578$
> New price of car $= £3400 - £578$
> $= £2822$

- Calculate 6% of Karen's monthly wage.
- Add this to her monthly wage.

1 Calculate these amounts without using a calculator.

a 10% of £400   **b** 10% of 2600 cm   **c** 5% of 64 kg
d 25% of 80 m   **e** 50% of 380p   **f** 5% of £700
g 25% of 12 kg   **h** 20% of £31   **i** 15% of 360
j 1% of 720 m   **k** 30% of £25   **l** 25% of 444

2 Calculate these percentages, giving your answer to two decimal places where appropriate.

a 45% of 723 kg   **b** 25% of $480   **c** 23% of 45 kg
d 21% of 28 kg   **e** 17.5% of £124   **f** 34% of 230 m

3 Calculate these percentages, giving your answer to two decimal places where appropriate.

a 4.5% of £320   **b** 2.5% of $4300   **c** 3.6% of 54 kg
d 13.2% of 220 m²   **e** 4.8% of 245 litres   **f** 5.1% of 2050 hectares

A02 Functional Maths

4 a There are 62 million people living in the UK. 23% of the population are under 18. How many people are under 18?
  b The price of a pair of trainers is normally £85. In a sale the price is reduced by 30%. How much cheaper are the trainers in the sale?
  c The recommended daily allowance (RDA) of iron is 14 mg. A bowl of cereal provides 45% of the RDA of iron. How much iron is there in a bowl of cereal?
  d Joanne earns £78 450 a year. She pays 36% of her earnings in tax. How much money does she pay in tax?

5 Calculate these percentage changes.

a Increase £450 by 10%   **b** Decrease 840 kg by 20%
c Increase £720 by 5%   **d** Decrease 560 km by 30%
e Increase £560 by 17.5%   **f** Decrease 320 m by 20%

A02 Functional Maths

6 a A drink can contains 330 ml. The size is increased by 15%. How much drink does it now contain?
  b The price of a coat was £95. The price is reduced by 20% in a sale. What is the sale price of the coat?
  c A holiday package is advertised in the brochure at a price of £2400. The travel agent reduces the price by 8%. What is the new price of the holiday package?
  d A house is bought for £190 000. During the next two years the house increases in price by 23%. What is the new value of the house?

Calculating with fractions and percentages

This spread will show you how to:

- Calculate a fraction or a percentage of an amount using a variety of methods

Keywords

Fraction
Percentage

You can calculate a **fraction** or a **percentage** of something using different methods.

Mental methods

Example

Calculate   **a** $\frac{2}{3}$ of £240   **b** 20% of €104

a Find $\frac{1}{3}$ of £240 = 240 ÷ 3 = £80

   Calculate $\frac{2}{3}$ of £240 = 2 × 80 = £160

b 20% of €104

   Find 10% of €104 = $\frac{1}{10}$ of €104

                  = $\frac{1}{10}$ × €104

                  = €104 ÷ 10 = €10.4

   Calculate 20% of €104 = 2 × 10.4 = €20.80

Written methods

Example

Calculate   **a** $\frac{4}{7}$ of £63   **b** 45% of 320 kg

a $\frac{4}{7}$ of £63 = $\frac{4}{7}$ × £63

           = 4 × $\frac{1}{7}$ × £63   Multiplying by $\frac{1}{7}$

           = $\frac{4 \times 63}{7}$ is the same as

           = $\frac{252}{7}$ dividing by 7.

           = £36

b 45% of 320 kg = $\frac{45}{100}$ × 320

                    = $\frac{45 \times 1 \times 320}{100}$

                    = $\frac{45 \times 320}{100}$

                    = $\frac{14\,400}{100}$

                    = 144 kg

This is the same as multiplying the amount by 45 and dividing by 100, that is, you work out 45 × 320 ÷ 100

Calculator methods

Example

Calculate

a $\frac{7}{16}$ of 130 m (to one decimal place)   **b** 43% of £75

a Decimal equivalent of $\frac{7}{16}$ = 7 ÷ 16 = 0.4375

   $\frac{7}{16}$ of 130 m = $\frac{7}{16}$ × 130 m

               = 0.4375 × 130 m

               = 56.875 m = 56.9 m (1 dp)

b Decimal equivalent of 43% = 43 ÷ 100 = 0.43

   43% of £75 = 0.43 × £75 = £32.25

Another method of finding a percentage of an amount is to find 1%, and then multiply by the percentage. To find 12% of 3500 m

1% of 3500 = 3500 ÷ 100 = 35

12% of 3500 = 12 × 35 = 420 m

1 Use a mental method to calculate each of these amounts.

   a $\frac{1}{4}$ of 60 carrots   **b** $\frac{1}{3}$ of 24 rulers   **c** $\frac{1}{8}$ of 32 windows

2 Use a mental method to calculate each of these amounts.

   a 50% of £90   **b** 1% of 600 m^2 **c** 10% of 48 kg

   d 25% of 60 kg   **e** 20% of 70p   **f** 1% of £65

> Try to use the equivalent fractions.

3 Calculate these fractions of amounts without using a calculator.

   a $\frac{3}{4}$ of €40   **b** $\frac{2}{3}$ of 60p   **c** $\frac{5}{8}$ of 48 g

   d $\frac{3}{10}$ of 80p   **e** $\frac{1}{7}$ of £84   **f** $\frac{5}{9}$ of $45

4 Calculate these percentages without using a calculator.

   a 25% of £60   **b** 5% of 40   **c** 10% of 272p

   d 75% of 40   **e** 70% of £40   **f** 30% of £50

   g 15% of 35 m   **h** 2.5% of £26   **i** 45% of 400 mm

A02 Functional Maths

5 Calculate these fractions of amounts without using a calculator.

   a A jacket normally costs £130. In a sale the jacket is priced at $\frac{4}{5}$ of its normal selling price. What is the new price of the jacket?

   b Hector rents out a holiday flat. His flat is available for 45 weeks of the year. He rents the flat out to tourists for $\frac{7}{9}$ of the time it is available. For how many weeks is Hector's flat occupied by tourists?

6 Calculate these percentages without using a calculator.

   a Kelvin collects models. He owns 170 models. He has painted 20% of the models. How many of the models has he painted?

   b A barrel can hold 70 litres. Water is poured into the barrel until it is 80% full. How much water is there in the barrel?

7 Use a suitable method to calculate each of these quantities. Where appropriate round your answer to two decimal places.

   a $\frac{7}{12}$ of 450   **b** $\frac{9}{10}$ of 360 m   **c** $\frac{2}{7}$ of 400 kg   **d** $\frac{7}{9}$ of 250 mm

   e $\frac{3}{4}$ of 9 tonnes **f** $\frac{4}{11}$ of 2365 m   **g** $\frac{7}{25}$ of 43 000   **h** $\frac{3}{7}$ of £345

8 Calculate these using an appropriate method.

   a Increase £450 by 10%.   **b** Decrease 76 kg by 5%.

   c Increase $990 by $\frac{1}{3}$.   **d** Decrease 620 km by $\frac{1}{100}$.

This spread will show you how to:
- Convert between fractions, decimals and percentages
- Express a quantity as a proportion of another

p.104

Keywords
Decimal
Equivalent
Fraction
Percentage
Proportion

- A **proportion** is a part of the whole. It is usually written using a **fraction** or a **percentage**.

You can use fractions to express one number as a proportion of another number.

Steven has £40 in his wallet. He spends £30 on a new shirt.
What proportion of the money in his wallet did Steven spend?
Give your answer as a fraction in its simplest form.

Steven had £40 (the whole).

Steven spent £30.

Fraction spent $= \frac{£30}{£40} = \frac{30}{40} = \frac{3}{4}$.

So Steven spent $\frac{3}{4}$ of the money in his wallet.

Cancel by the
common factor 10.

You can express a proportion as a percentage of a whole in three steps:
1. Write the proportion as a fraction.
2. Convert the fraction to a decimal by division.
3. Convert the decimal to a percentage by multiplying by 100.

You can compare proportions by converting them to percentages.

Skye took two tests.
In German she scored 35 out of 50, and in French she scored
60 out of 80.
In which test did she do the best?

German

35 out of 50 $= \frac{35}{50}$
$= 35 \div 50$
$= 0.7$
$= 70\%$

French

60 out of 80 $= \frac{60}{80}$
$= 60 \div 80$
$= 0.75$
$= 75\%$

Skye did better in French.

1 Write the proportion of each of these shapes that is shaded.
Write each of your answers as a fraction in its simplest form.

a

b

c

d

e

f

2 Give your answers to each of these questions as fractions in their simplest form.

  a There are 20 students in a class. 16 are boys and 4 are girls. What proportion of the class are **i** boys **ii** girls?

  b Tina has 12 T-shirts and 8 blouses. What proportion of her clothes are **i** T-shirts **ii** blouses?

  c Joachim earns £600 a week. He pays £180 of his money each week in tax. He saves £100 each week. What proportion of his weekly wage does Joachim **i** pay in tax **ii** save?

3 Write each of your answers as a percentage.

  a In a class there are 40 students. 25 of the students have brown hair. What proportion of the class have brown hair?

  b In a survey of 80 people, 35 said they enjoyed school meals. What proportion of the people said they enjoyed school meals?

  c At a rugby club there are 38 members. 15 players have been picked for the first team. What proportion of the members have been picked for the first team?

Give your answer to one decimal place.

4 Put these in order of size starting with the smallest first.

Convert them all to percentages.

  a 72% $\frac{3}{4}$ 0.74

  b 0.29   31% $\frac{3}{10}$

  c 0.8   83% $\frac{7}{8}$ 0.78

  d $\frac{2}{5}$ 0.39   41% $\frac{3}{7}$

  e $\frac{8}{10}$ $\frac{3}{4}$ 83%   0.84

  f 28% $\frac{3}{11}$ 0.3 $\frac{7}{24}$

5 Sunita took three tests. In Maths she scored 48 out of 60, in English she scored 39 out of 50 and in Science she scored 55 out of 70. In which subject did she do

  a the best

  b the worst?

  c Suggest a way in which you could give Sunita a single overall score for her three tests.

This spread will show you how to:
- Simplify a ratio
- Solve problems involving proportion

Keywords
Proportion
Ratio
Unitary method

You can compare the size of two objects using a **ratio**.

Example

Henry the snake is only 30 cm long.
George the snake is 90 cm long.
Express this as a ratio.

The ratio of Henry's length
compared to George's length

= Henry's length : George's length
= 30 cm : 90 cm
= 30 : 90

You can simplify a ratio by dividing both parts of the ratio by the same number. When a ratio cannot be simplified any further it is said to be in its **simplest form**.

The ratio 1 : 3 means that 90 is three times bigger than 30.

Example

Express the ratio 30 : 90 in its simplest form.

$$\div 10 \left(\begin{array}{c} 30 : 90 \\ = 3 : 9 \end{array} \right) \div 10$$
$$\div 3 \left(\begin{array}{c} \\ = 1 : 3 \end{array} \right) \div 3$$

You can use **proportion** to solve simple problems. In the next example, the cost is **proportional** to the number of items.

Example

a Four pizzas cost £2.60.
Each pizza costs the same.
What is the cost of 12 pizzas?

a $\times 3 \left(\begin{array}{l} \text{4 pizzas cost} \quad £2.60 \\ \text{12 pizzas cost } 3 \times £2.60 \\ \qquad\qquad\qquad = £7.80 \end{array} \right) \times 3$

Alternatively you could find the cost of one item, then multiply up. This is the **unitary method**.

4 pizzas → £2.60
1 pizza →
2.60 ÷ 4 = 0.65
12 pizzas →
   0.65 × 12 = £7.80
Try the same method for the chocolates in part **b**.

Example

b 15 boxes of chocolates cost £22.50.
Each box of chocolates costs the same.
What is the cost of three boxes of chocolates?

b $\div 5 \left(\begin{array}{l} \text{15 boxes cost} \quad £22.50 \\ \text{3 boxes cost } £22.50 \div 5 \\ \qquad\qquad\qquad = £4.50 \end{array} \right) \div 5$

1 Write each of these ratios in its simplest form.

a 2 : 6   **b** 15 : 5   **c** 6 : 18
d 4 : 28   **e** 5 : 50   **f** 30 : 6
g 24 : 8   **h** 2 : 30   **i** 7 : 56

2 Write the number of blue squares to the number of red squares as a ratio in its simplest form for each of these shapes.

a   **b**   **c**

3 How many times bigger than

a 15 is 60   **b** 3 is 21   **c** 12 is 72
d 20 is 180   **e** 18 is 36   **f** 9 is 45
g 16 is 80   **h** 6 is 72   **i** 20 is 240
j 25 is 625   **k** 10 is 15   **l** 36 is 90?

4 Copy and complete this table for working out the cost of buying carpet.

Area of carpet (m²)	Cost (£)
6 m²	£39.00
12 m²	
18 m²	
30 m²	
60 m²	
3 m²	

5 Copy and complete this table for converting inches and centimetres.

Inches (in)	Centimetres (cm)
6	15
3	
	30
	45
60	
1	

6 a 5 pizzas cost £12.50. What is the cost of 10 pizzas?
  b 12 boxes of eggs cost £12. What is the cost of 4 boxes of eggs?
  c 3 packets of seeds cost £4.50. What is the cost of 9 packets of seeds?
  d 2 boxes of cornflakes cost £4.40. What is the cost of 8 boxes of cornflakes?
  e 4 tennis balls cost £1.80. What is the cost of 8 tennis balls?
  f 5 chocolate bars cost £3.00. What is the cost of 15 chocolate bars?
  g 7 bags of wood cost £27.93. What is the cost of 14 bags of wood?

Summary

Check out

You should now be able to:

- Understand and interpret percentages
- Recognize the equivalence of fractions, decimals and percentages
- Convert between fractions, decimals and percentages
- Order fractions, decimals and percentages
- Express a number as a fraction of another number
- Calculate a fraction and a percentage of an amount
- Use ratio notation, including simplifying a ratio.

Worked exam question

1 **a** Four out of every five members of a running club are men. The club has 240 members.

   How many are men? (2)

   b Membership fees are £3 each month.

   Show that the total paid in one year by all 240 members is £8640. (2)

   c The following year the club needs £10 000 from membership fees.
   The number of members is expected to increase by 10%.

   Work out the new monthly fee required, assuming membership increases as expected. (5)

   (AQA, 2009)

a

$$\frac{4}{5} \times 240 = 0.8 \times 240$$
$$= 192 \text{ men}$$

$\frac{4}{5}$ is the same as 0.8

b

$240 \times 3 = 720$
$720 \times 12 = £8640$ per year

c

10% of 240 = 0.1 × 240 = 24
240 + 24 = 264 members
10 000 ÷ 264 = 37.8787....
37.8787 ÷ 12 = 3.1565...
New monthly fee should be £3.16

Divide by 12 because there are 12 months. Round the first answer to give pounds and pence.

Exam questions

1 **a** Copy and shade $\frac{3}{5}$ of this shape.

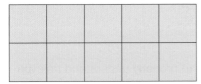

(1)

b Copy and shade 0.2 of this shape.

(1)

2 Copy and complete the table.

Decimal	Fraction	Percentage
0.3	$\frac{3}{10}$	30%
	$\frac{1}{4}$	25%
0.7		70%
0.02	$\frac{1}{50}$	

(3)
(AQA, 2009)

3 Adam scored 24 marks out of 40 in a test.
Ben scored 65% in the same test.

Who obtained the better result?
You **must** show your working.

(2)
(AQA, 2008)

4 Calculate 36% of €2500.

(2)

Introduction

Car insurance companies keep data on past road accidents and are able to use this to work out the probability (risk) of a person having a car accident. They then work out the cost of your insurance premium based on your age, type of vehicle, driving experience and other factors.

What's the point?

All forms of insurance rely on risk assessment, and to properly understand risk you need to have a good grasp of probability.

1   Choose a number from the rectangle that is
    a prime   **b** square
    c triangular   **d** a multiple of 4
    e a factor of 10.

```
    5              6      2
            4
       10        8
  1
     7    9        3
```

2   Cancel these fractions to their simplest form.
    a $\frac{12}{15}$ **b** $\frac{8}{10}$ **c** $\frac{5}{20}$
    d $\frac{15}{25}$ **e** $\frac{10}{10}$

3   Work out each of these subtractions.
    a $1 - \frac{1}{4}$ **b** $1 - \frac{7}{10}$ **c** $1 - \frac{3}{5}$

4   Work out each of these multiplications.
    a $\frac{1}{5} \times 50$ **b** $\frac{2}{5} \times 100$ **c** $\frac{2}{3} \times 300$

Rich task

Inside a bag are three cards with the names Anna, Neve and Davma written on them.

You are allowed to pick one card from the bag and then replace the card in the bag.

What is the probability you pick the same name twice?

This spread will show you how to:

- Understand and use the probability scale
- Calculate probabilities of outcomes, including equally likely outcomes, giving answers in their simplest form
- List all outcomes for single events

Keywords
Event
Outcome
Probability
Probability scale

An **event** is an activity, for example, spinning a spinner.

The possible **outcomes** are Blue, Yellow, Green, Red.

The **probability** is a number that measures how likely it is that an outcome will happen.

All probabilities have a value between 0 and 1.

0 means impossible.
1 means certain.

- You can show a probability on a **probability scale**.

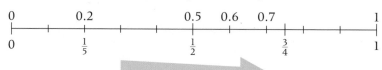

more and more likely to happen

You can use decimals, fractions or percentages.

p.24

- You can calculate the probability using these formulae:

$$\text{Probability of an outcome happening} = \frac{\text{number of ways the outcome can happen}}{\text{total number of all possible outcomes}}$$

Probability of an outcome not happening = 1 − probability of the outcome happening

Probability of an outcome can be written as P(outcome).

Example

20 counters are put into a bag. There are 1 red, 3 blue, 4 yellow and 12 green counters. Edward takes out a counter without looking. Calculate, giving your answers in simplest form, the probability that Edward takes out
a a red counter
b any colour that is not red
c a green or yellow counter
d a purple counter.

'Simplest form' means cancel the fraction.

. . . .

a There is one red counter. There are 20 possible outcomes.
$P(\text{red}) = \frac{1}{20}$

b $1 - \frac{1}{20} = \frac{19}{20}$ $P(\text{not red}) = \frac{19}{20}$

c There are 16 green or yellow counters. $P(\text{green or yellow}) = \frac{16}{20} = \frac{4}{5}$

d There are 0 purple counters. $P(\text{purple}) = \frac{0}{20} = 0$

For all these questions, the outcomes are equally likely.

1 A bag contains four red and six blue balls. One
   ball is taken out of the bag.
   a Calculate the probability that the ball is red.
   b Calculate the probability that the ball is blue.
   c Draw a probability scale as shown.

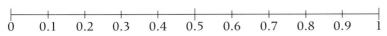

   On your scale mark the positions of P(red) and P(blue).
   d Which colour ball is most likely to be taken out?
   e Which colour ball is least likely to be taken out?

2 This spinner is spun. Calculate the probability that
   the spinner lands on
   a a 3
   b an even number
   c a number greater than 6
   d a number less than 6
   e a square number
   f a multiple of 3
   g a multiple of 4
   h a prime number.

3 A raffle has only one prize. 200 raffle tickets
   are sold. Calculate the probability of winning
   the prize if you buy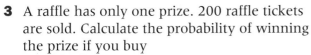
   a one ticket
   b two tickets.

4 There are 25 students in a class. Each student is
   given a different number from 1 to 25. The 25
   numbers are put into a bag, and one is taken out.
   Calculate the probability that the number is
   a odd   **b** not odd
   c a multiple of 5   **d** a multiple of 10
   e a square number   **f** a prime number
   g greater than 18   **h** less than 10
   i not less than 10.

Expected frequency

This spread will show you how to:

- Calculate the expected frequency of an event

Keywords

Expect
Expected
  frequency
Trial

The probability is a number that measures how likely it is that an event will happen.

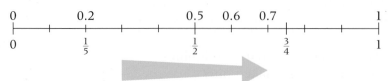

more and more likely to happen

0 means impossible.
1 means certain.

If you know the probability of an event, you can calculate how many times you **expect** the outcomes to happen.

Example

The probability of getting a Tail when you spin a coin is $\frac{1}{2}$. How many Tails would you expect if the coin was spun 100 times?

$\frac{1}{2}$ of 100 = 50 Tails

- The **expected frequency** is the number of times you expect the outcomes to happen.

- Expected frequency = probability × number of trials

Each spin of the coin is called a **trial**.

Example

Red and yellow counters are put in a bag.
The probability of taking out a red counter is $\frac{3}{5}$.

a Calculate the probability of taking out a yellow counter.
b If a counter is taken out and replaced 20 times, how many yellow counters would you expect to be taken out?

a $1 - \frac{3}{5} = \frac{2}{5}$

P(yellow counter) = $\frac{2}{5}$

b Expected frequency = probability × number of trials

$= \frac{2}{5} \times 20$

$= 8$ yellow counters

The expected frequency does not guarantee the outcomes.
For example, if you spin a coin 100 times you may not always get the outcomes of 50 Tails.

1 A coin is spun.
  a State the probability of spinning a Head.
  b If the coin is spun 50 times, how many Heads would you expect?

2 An ordinary dice is rolled.
  a Find the probability of rolling a 3.
  b If the dice is rolled 60 times, how many 3s would you expect?

3 The spinner is made from a regular pentagon.
  a Calculate the probability of spinning an even number.
  b If the spinner is spun 100 times, how many even numbers would you expect?

4 A bag contains 3 red balls and 7 green balls. One ball is taken out and then replaced back in the bag.
  a Calculate the probability that the ball is red.
  b Calculate the probability that the ball is green.
  If a ball is taken out and replaced 100 times, how many of the balls would you expect to be
  c red
  d green?

5 The probability of sun on a day in June on the Costa del Sunny is $\frac{2}{3}$. Calculate the number of days in June on which you would expect sun on the Costa del Sunny.

> 30 days has September, April, June and November.

6 The probability that a fuchsia plant will survive after a severe ground frost is $\frac{4}{5}$.
  a Calculate the probability that the fuchsia will not survive after a severe ground frost.
  A gardener has 50 of these fuchsia plants.
  b How many of the plants should he expect to die after a severe ground frost?

7 The probability of seeing a red car is $\frac{7}{20}$.
  a Calculate the probability of not seeing a red car.
  b If 100 cars go past you, how many of these would you expect not to be red?

8 The probability that a seed germinates is $\frac{9}{10}$.
If 60 seeds are planted, how many seeds would you expect to germinate?

This spread will show you how to:

• Understand and use relative frequency

Keywords
Biased
Estimate
Fair
Relative frequency
Trial

You can calculate a **theoretical** probability for objects such as coins and dice.

It is not always possible to calculate the theoretical probability, for example the probability of a car accident on a stretch of road.

You can, however, **estimate** the probability from experiments.

• The estimated probability is called the **relative frequency**.

This topic is extended on page 440.

Example

James spins a square spinner 50 times.
The results are shown in the data collection sheet.

Colour	Tally	Frequency
Red	ЖЖ	10
Blue	ЖЖ IIII	14
Yellow	Ж IIII	9
Green	ЖЖЖ II	17

a Estimate the probability of getting green on the spinner.
b Do you think the spinner is biased?
Explain your answer.

....

a The spinner was green on 17 out of 50 occasions.
Estimated probability of getting green $= \frac{17}{50}$

b You would expect each frequency to be about the same for a fair spinner.

The spinner could be biased as there are many more green than yellow.

However, James needs to spin the spinner many more times before he can make the decision.

The spinner is **biased** if the colours are NOT all equally likely.

The spinner is **fair** if the colours are all equally likely.

• The estimated probability becomes more and more reliable the greater the number of trials.

Each spin of the spinner is called a **trial**.

1 A tetrahedron dice is rolled 50 times. The scores are shown.

```
4  3  2  2  1  4  2  3  1  4
3  2  1  4  4  3  2  1  1  2
4  2  2  3  1  1  2  4  4  3
3  3  2  1  4  3  4  2  2  1
2  1  4  2  4  3  4  2  1  1
```

a Copy and complete the frequency chart to show the 50 scores.

Score	Tally	Frequency
1		
2		
3		
4		

b State the modal score.

c Estimate the probability of rolling a
  i 1   **ii** 2   **iii** 3   **iv** 4

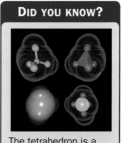

DID YOU KNOW?

The tetrahedron is a shape that is commonly seen in molecular structures, for example methane.

2 A spinner is made from a regular octagon.
The spinner is spun 40 times and the colour is recorded.

Orange	Red	Orange	Green	Orange	Orange
Orange	Green	Red	Green	Orange	Orange
Orange	Green	Orange	Orange	Orange	Orange
Orange	Green	Orange	Orange	Red	Green
Green	Green	Orange	Green	Green	Green
Orange	Orange	Orange	Red	Green	Green
Green	Orange	Green	Red		

a Copy and complete the frequency chart to show the 40 colours.

Colour	Tally	Frequency
Orange		
Green		
Red		

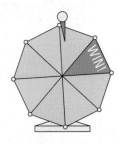

b State the modal colour.

c Estimate the probability of spinning
  i orange   **ii** green   **iii** red.

A02

3 A coin is spun 100 times. The outcomes are shown in the frequency table.
  a Calculate the estimated probability of spinning a Head.
  b Calculate the estimate probability of spinning a Tail.
  c Do you think the coin is biased? Explain your answer.
  d How could you improve the estimated probability of a Head or a Tail?

	Frequency
Head	45
Tail	55

This spread will show you how to:

- List all outcomes for two successive events in a systematic way

Keywords
Event
Outcome
Successive
Systematic

Successive means following on, for example, 6, 7, 8.

- You can list the possible **outcomes** for two successive events.

Example

A restaurant decides to offer a two-course meal for £5.99.

The meal must be one starter and one main course.

List the different choices that are possible.

PARK AVENUE BISTRO

MENU
2 Courses - £5.99
Onion Soup
Caesar Salad

Beef Steak
Grilled Salmon
Veggie Pasta

Onion Soup – Beef Steak
Onion Soup – Grilled Salmon
Onion Soup – Veggie Pasta
Caesar Salad – Beef Steak
Caesar Salad – Grilled Salmon
Caesar Salad – Veggie Pasta

This list is **systematic**. It is in order.

Example

A spinner has colours red, yellow, blue and green.
A coin has two faces, Heads or Tails.

Matthew spins the spinner and the coin.

a List all the possible outcomes.
b What is the probability that he gets green and a Head?

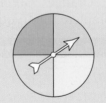

a

Colour on spinner	Red	Red	Yellow	Yellow	Blue	Blue	Green	Green
Head/Tail on coin	Head	Tail	Head	Tail	Head	Tail	Head	Tail

b Green and Head occurs once.
There are 8 possible outcomes.

$$P(\text{Green and a Head}) = \frac{1}{8}$$

1 At a sports club, there are three activities, but only two sessions. You have to choose one different activity for each session. Copy and complete the table to show the possible choices.

Session 1	Session 2
Tennis	Badminton
Tennis	

Choose 2 from
Tennis
Badminton
Squash

2 Four people, Arthur, Ben, Chris and Darryl, enter a competition.
  a List the four possible winners of the competition.
    It is decided to give another award, for 'Most improved player'.
  b Copy and complete the table to show the 12 possible prize winners.

Winner	Most improved player
A	B
A	

3 A spinner is labelled 1, 2, 3. Another spinner is labelled A, B, C. Both spinners are spun.
  a List the nine possible outcomes.
  b Calculate the probability of getting a 3 and a C.

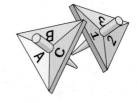

4 A dice is numbered from 1 to 6. A coin has Head or Tail. The dice is rolled and the coin is spun.
  a List the 12 possible outcomes.
  b Calculate the probability of getting a 3 and a Head.
  c Calculate the probability of getting an even number and a Tail.

5 Three tracksuit tops are in a drawer. Another drawer has three tracksuit bottoms. One top and one bottom are randomly taken out of the drawers.
  a List the nine possible outcomes.
  b Calculate the probability of getting blue and yellow.
  c Calculate the probability of not getting blue and yellow.
  d Calculate the probability of getting blue and orange.
  e Calculate the probability of not getting blue and orange.

Red (R) Green (G) Blue (B)

Yellow (Y) Pink (P) Orange (O)

135

Summary

Check out
You should now be able to:

- Understand and use the vocabulary of probability scale
- Calculate probabilities of events, including equally likely outcomes, giving answers in their simplest form
- Calculate the expected frequency of an event
- Understand and use relative frequency
- List all outcomes for single events and for two successive events in a systematic way

Worked exam question
Rosie and Josh want to estimate the number of blue beads in a bag of 400 beads.
A trial consists of taking a bead at random, recording the colour and replacing the bead in the bag.
The results of their trials are shown in the table.

	Number of trials	Number of blue beads chosen
Rosie	25	7
Josh	100	19

a **i** Write down the relative frequency of Rosie taking a blue bead from the bag. (1)

   ii Write down the relative frequency of Josh taking a blue bead from the bag. (1)

b Whose experiment gives the more reliable estimate of the proportion of blue beads in the bag?
Give a reason for your answer. (1)

(AQA, 2007)

....

a

  i $\dfrac{7}{25}$

  ii $\dfrac{19}{100}$ ← Use the formula for relative frequency

b Josh's experiment, because there are more trials

Exam questions

1 An eight-sided spinner is labelled with colours.

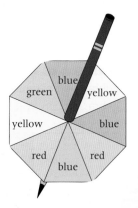

The arrows on the scale show the probability of certain events occurring for this spinner.

a Which letter shows the probability of the spinner landing on blue? (1)

b Which letter shows the probability of the spinner landing on purple? (1)

c Which letter shows the probability of the spinner landing on blue or yellow? (1)

d P and Q are shown on this probability scale.

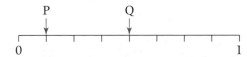

Describe an event, for this spinner, which is shown by

i P (1)

ii Q (1)

(AQA, 2009)

2 There are 500 plastic shapes in a box.
The shapes are circles, triangles, squares and rectangles.

A shape is chosen at random from the box.
The table shows some of the probabilities of shapes being chosen. (4)

Shape	Probability
Circle	0.2
Triangle	
Square	
Rectangle	0.1

The probability of choosing a triangle is equal to the probability of choosing a square.

Calculate the number of triangles in the box. (AQA, 2009)

Introduction

Engineers and scientists use algebraic expressions to model and explain the behaviour of real events and activities. Without algebra there would be no aircraft, mobile phones or plasma TVs.

What's the point?

Algebra is an extension of arithmetic, but using letters instead of numbers. By using algebra, we can invent and use rules to explain real-life phenomena.

Check in

1   Work out
    a 3^2 **b** 2^2 **c** 4^2

2   There are 5 CDs in a packet.
    How many CDs are there in 3 packets?

3   Work out
    a $4 - -3$ **b** $2 + -3$
    c $-3 + 5$ **d** $-4 - -1$

4   Work out
    a -3×2 **b** 4×-2
    c $6 \div -3$ **d** $-8 \div -2$

Orientation

What I need to know	What I will learn	What this leads to
Key stage 3 →	■ Use letters to represent numbers ■ Simplify expressions by collecting like terms ■ Substitute positive and negative numbers into an expression	→ A2 + 5

Rich task

Think of a number between 1 and 10.
- Double it.
- Add 4.
- Halve your answer.
- Take away the number you first thought of.

The answer is always 2.

Investigate.

This spread will show you how to:

- Use letters to represent numbers in algebraic expressions

Keywords
Expression

- You can use letters to represent numbers.

There are 6 eggs in a box.

In 2 boxes there are $6 \times 2 = 12$ eggs.
In 3 boxes there are $6 \times 3 = 18$ eggs.
In n boxes there are $6 \times n = 6n$ eggs.

In algebra
$6n = 6 \times n$.
You do not write
the $\times$ sign.

Example

There are 12 sweets in one packet.

a How many sweets are there in 4 packets?
b How many sweets are there in x packets?

....

a $12 \times 4 = 48$ sweets
b $12 \times x = 12x$ sweets

- An **expression** is a collection of letters and numbers with no $=$ sign.

Example

One apple costs 20 pence.

a Work out the cost of 3 apples.
b Write an expression for the cost of y apples.

....

a 3 apples cost $3 \times 20 = 60$ pence
b y apples cost $y \times 20 = 20y$ pence

$y \times 20 = 20 \times y$
Write numbers
before letters.

You can write expressions to represent real situations.

Example

There are m pens in one box.

a How many pens are there in 3 boxes?
b Write an expression for the number of
pens in 3 boxes plus 5 extra pens.
c 6 pens are taken out of a box.
Write an expression for the number of
pens left in the box.

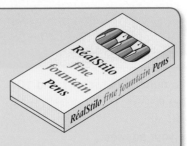

....

a $3 \times m = 3m$ pens
b $3m + 5$
c $m - 6$

$3m$ in 3 boxes,
plus 5 more.

Unit 2

1 Stamps cost 30 pence each.
  a How much do 8 stamps cost?
  b How much do *n* stamps cost?

2 Chews cost 20 pence each.
  a How much do 10 chews cost?
  b How much do *x* chews cost?

3 Pencils cost 8 pence each.
  a How much do 8 pencils cost?
  b How much do *m* pencils cost?

4 There are 12 biscuits in a packet.
How many biscuits are there in
  a 5 packets
  b 3 packets
  c *x* packets
  d *n* packets?

5 Work out the cost of
  a 2 kg of potatoes   **b** 3 kg of carrots
  c 10 kg of potatoes   **d** 4 kg of carrots.
Write an expression for the cost of
  e *n* kg of potatoes   **f** *x* kg of carrots
  g *y* kg of potatoes   **h** *p* kg of carrots.

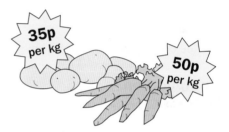

6 Daniel has *x* DVDs.
  a Lisa has twice as many DVDs as Daniel.
Write an expression in terms of *x* for the number of DVDs
Lisa has.
  b Charlie has 4 more DVDs than Daniel.
Write an expression in terms of *x* for the number of DVDs
Charlie has.
  c Sareeta has 3 fewer DVDs than Lisa.
Write an expression in terms of *x* for the number of DVDs
Sareeta has.

A03 Problem

7 Match each expression in box **A** with an expression in box **B**.

A	B
$n + n$ $6n$	$5n$ $7m$
$3 \times n$ $4m$	$m \times 4$ $3m$
n oranges at 5p each	6 stamps at *n* pence each
m toys at £3 each $7 \times m$	3 chews at *n* pence each $2n$

Simplifying expressions

This spread will show you how to:
- Use the four rules of arithmetic
- Simplify expressions by collecting like terms

Keywords
Simplify
Squared
Term

- You can add and subtract in algebra, just like you do with numbers.

$m + m + m + m = 4$ lots of $m = 4 \times m = 4m$

Addition

$4m$　　　　　$+ 2m$　　$= 6m$

$m + m + m + m$　$+ m + m$　$= m + m + m + m + m + m$

$2 + 2 + 2 + 2$
$= 4$ lots of 2
$= 4 \times 2 = 8$

Subtraction

$4m$　　　　　$- m$　　$= 3m$

$m + m + m + m$　$- m$　$= m + m + m$

- You can **simplify** multiplications and divisions in **algebra**.

Multiplication
$3 \times a = 3a$
$x \times y = xy$
$y \times y = y^2$

You say 'y **squared**'
$3 \times 3 = 3^2 \ (=9)$

Division
$x \div 2 = \dfrac{x}{2}$　　$4a \div 7 = \dfrac{4a}{7}$

This topic is extended to expanding and factorising on page 418.

Example

Simplify these expressions.

a $n + n + n$　　　**b** $c + c + c + c + c$　　　**c** $7x + 4x$
d $9y - y$　　　　**e** $4p + 8p - 3p$

. . . .

a $n + n + n = 3n$　　**b** $c + c + c + c + c = 5c$　　**c** $7x + 4x = 11x$
d $9y - y = 9y - 1y$　　**e** $4p + 8p - 3p = 12p - 3p$
　　　　$= 8y$　　　　　　　　　　　　　　$= 9p$

- A **term** is an individual part of an expression.

$4x - 2x$ is an expression. $4x$ and $2x$ are terms.

To make calculations easier you can write terms in a different order. Keep each term with its sign.

Example

Simplify these expressions.

a $3q - 5q + 2q$　　　　　　　**b** $t - 4t + 8t$

. . . .

a $3q - 5q + 2q = 3q + 2q - 5q$　　**b** $t - 4t + 8t = t + 8t - 4t$
　　　　　　　$= 5q - 5q$　　　　　　　　　　　$= 9t - 4t$
　　　　　　　$= 0$　　　　　　　　　　　　　　$= 5t$

1 Write each statement as a single amount. Use a letter to represent each item.
  For example, 6 apples + 2 apples can be written as $6a + 2a = 8a$.
  a 8 apples + 7 apples   **b** 6 boys + 5 boys
  c 3 CDs + 5 CDs   **d** 8 chairs and 13 chairs
  e 9 toys and 23 toys   **f** 18 books + 8 books
  g 13 chocolates − 8 chocolates **h** 6 cakes − 6 cakes
  i 15 sweets − 7 sweets   **j** 13 bananas − 6 bananas

2 Simplify these expressions.
  a $m + m + m$ **b** $n + n + n + n + n + n + n$
  c $y + y + y + y + y + y$ **d** $z + z + z - z + z$

3 Collect the terms and simplify each expression.
  a $6a + 7a$ **b** $5n + 12n$ **c** $6t + 9t$ **d** $3x + 16x$
  e $9r - 5r$ **f** $6f - 2f$ **g** $12g - 5g$ **h** $15r - 7r$
  i $16n + 4n + 3n$ **j** $6c + 8c + 3c$

4 Write each of these as a single term.
  a $4 \times m$ **b** $p \times 3$ **c** $r \times s$ **d** $12 \times q$
  e $5 \times g$ **f** $c \times 4$ **g** $d \times 8$ **h** $j \times k$
  i $n \times n$ **j** $e \times 15$ **k** $t \times t$ **l** $6 \times m \times n$

5 Simplify each expression.
  a $8n + 3n + 4n$ **b** $3m + 2m + 7m$
  c $8p + 6p + 3p$ **d** $5q + 7q + 6q$
  e $12x - 7x - 4x$ **f** $8w - w - 3w$
  g $4a + 6a - 3a$ **h** $12b - 3b - 4b$
  i $3j - 4j + 2j$ **j** $k - 5k + 6k$

6 Simplify these divisions. The first one has been done for you.
  a $d \div 4 = \dfrac{d}{4}$ **b** $x \div 3$ **c** $y \div 7$ **d** $t \div 9$
  e $2a \div 3$ **f** $3n \div 4$ **g** $5p \div 7$ **h** $2v \div 4$

A03 Problem

7 Use these four terms and three signs to make the different totals.

$3x$	$2x$
$5x$	$7x$

$+$	$-$
$+$	

  a $13x$ **b** $3x$ **c** $7x$ **d** $11x$

Collecting terms

This spread will show you how to:

- Simplify expressions by collecting like terms
- Rearrange algebraic expressions involving different letters

Keywords
Like terms

- An expression can include terms with different letters.

Example

Bags of sweets come in two sizes.

Small

Large

n **sweets**

p **sweets**

There are n sweets in a small bag

There are p sweets in a large bag

a Rupal buys 1 large bag and 1 small bag.
How many sweets does he buy altogether?

b Maisie buys 2 small bags and 3 large bags.
How many sweets does she buy altogether?

a 1 small bag + 1 large bag
n sweets + p sweets
$n + p$ sweets

b 2 small bags + 3 large bags
$2 \times n$ sweets + $3 \times p$ sweets
$2n + 3p$ sweets

- Terms with the same letter are called like terms.
  You can simplify expressions by collecting like terms.

Example

Simplify

a $4m + 2p + 3m$

b $2x + 5y + 3x + y$

a $4m + 2p + 3m = 4m + 3m + 2p$
$= 7m + 2p$

b $2x + 5y + 3x + y = 2x + 3x + y + 5y$
$= 5x + 6y$

Rearrange the terms to collect like terms together.

$y = 1y$

Example

Simplify these expressions.

a $2e + 5f + 6e - 2f$ **b** $6u - v - 3u + 4v$ **c** $3m + 2n - m - 4n$

a $2e + 5f + 6e - 2f$ **b** $6u - v - 3u + 4v$ **c** $3m + 2n - m - 4n$
$= 2e + 6e + 5f - 2f$ $= 6u - 3u + 4v - v$ $= 3m - m + 2n - 4n$
$= 8e + 3f$ $= 3u + 3v$ $= 2m + {-2n}$
$= 2m - 2n$

Keep each term with its sign.

1 Bags of peanuts come in two sizes. There are x peanuts in a small bag. There are y peanuts in a large bag.

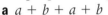

  a Sebastian buys 1 small bag and 1 large bag.
    How many peanuts does he buy?
  b Adam buys 3 large bags.
    How many peanuts does he buy?
  c Gabi buys 2 small bags and 1 large bag.
    Write an expression for the number of peanuts she buys.
  d Sushma buys 4 small bags.
    Write an expression for the number of peanuts she buys.
  e Kofi buys 3 small and 2 large bags.
    Write an expression for the number of peanuts he buys.

2 Simplify each expression by collecting like terms together.
  a $a + b + a + b$ **b** $c + d + c + c + c$
  c $3e + 2f + 4e + 3f$ **d** $5g + 7h + 2g + h$
  e $3i + j + 4i + 5j$ **f** $3u + 5v + 2v + u$

3 Simplify these expressions.
  a $4a + 2b - 3a + b$ **b** $6x + 4y - 2x + 2y$
  c $5m + 3n + 2m - n$ **d** $8s + 3t + s - 2t$
  e $3p + 2q - p + 3q$ **f** $2c + 3d + 3c - 2d$

4 Simplify these by collecting like terms.
  a $4a - 6b - 3a + 8b$ **b** $3c - 4d - 2c + 5d$
  c $7u - 4v - 2u + 5v$ **d** $6x - 5y - 5x + 11y$
  e $12m - 5n - 3m + 10n$ **f** $9p - 4q - 3p + 6q$

5 Simplify these expressions.
  a $5e - 3f - 2e + 2f$ **b** $4g - 6h - 3g + 4h$
  c $j - 3k + 4j + 2k$ **d** $2r - 4s - r + s$
  e $7t + 3u - 4t - 5u$ **f** $9v - 5w + 3v - 2w$

6 Make sets of three matching expressions, using one expression from each box in each set.

A	B	C
$3x + 5y - x + 2y$	$2x + 5y$	$7y - 3x + 5x - 2y$
$2x - 4y + 3x + 2y$	$3y + 7x + 4y - 5x$	$4x + 4y - 3x$
$2x + 4y - x$	$5x - 2y$	$7y + 2x$
$2y + 3x - x + 3y$	$3x + 6y - 2x - 2y$	$2x - 4y + 2y + 3x$

This spread will show you how to:

- Substitute numbers into an expression and work out its value
- Substitute numbers into a formula

p.234

Keywords
Substitute
Formula

You can replace letters with number values.
This is called **substituting**.

Example

If $c = 4$, work out

a $5c$ **b** $2c + 1$ **c** $3c - 2$

. . . .

a $5c = 5 \times c$ Write the multiplication sign.
$\quad = 5 \times 4$ Write 4 instead of c.
$\quad = 20$ Follow the order of operations.

b $2c + 1 = 2 \times c + 1$ **c** $3c - 2 = 3 \times c - 2$
$\quad\quad\quad = 2 \times 4 + 1$ $\quad\quad\quad = 3 \times 4 - 2$
$\quad\quad\quad = 8 + 1 = 9$ $\quad\quad\quad = 12 - 2 = 10$

- You can substitute values into expressions with more than one letter.

Example

Work out the value of each expression when $x = 2$ and $y = 1$.

a $x + 3$ **b** $y + 4$ **c** $x + y$
d $2x - y$ **e** $3y - 2x$ **f** x^2

. . . .

a $x + 3 = 2 + 3$ **b** $y + 4 = 1 + 4$ **c** $x + y = 2 + 1$
$\quad\quad\quad = 5$ $\quad\quad\quad = 5$ $\quad\quad\quad = 3$

d $2x - y = 2 \times x - y$ **e** $3y - 2x = 3 \times y - 2 \times x$ **f** $x^2 = x \times x$
$\quad\quad\quad = 2 \times 2 - 1$ $\quad\quad\quad = 3 \times 1 - 2 \times 2$ $\quad\quad = 2 \times 2 = 4$
$\quad\quad\quad = 4 - 1 = 3$ $\quad\quad\quad = 3 - 4 = -1$

Remember:
x^2 means 'x squared.'

- A **formula** shows a relationship between quantities.
  This formula works out pay: Pay = hours worked $\times$ hourly rate
  Using algebra, $P = h \times r = hr$
  Jim works 5 hours. His hourly rate is £5.60. Substitute $h = 5$
  and $r = £5.60$, into the formula.
  $\quad P = hr = 5 \times £5.60 = £28$ Jim's pay is £28.

1 If $a = 3$, work out the value of these expressions.
a $2a$ **b** $a + 1$ **c** $4a$ **d** $a - 2$
e $2a + 3$ **f** $3a - 4$ **g** $4a + 2$ **h** $4a - 5$

2 If $c = 4$ and $d = 2$, calculate the value of these expressions.
a $3c$ **b** $2d$ **c** $d + c$ **d** cd
e $2c + 4d$ **f** $3c - 2d$ **g** $3d - c + 2$ **h** $4c + d - 5$

3 Find the value of each expression when $m = 2$ and $n = 5$.
a $m + n$ **b** $n - m$ **c** $2m + n$ **d** $m - n$
e m^2 **f** $n - 4m$ **g** $3m + n - 5$ **h** $2m - 3n + 1$

4 Work out the value of each expression when $x = 3$, $y = 5$ and $z = 2$.
a $4x + 3$ **b** $2z + y$ **c** $3y - z$ **d** $x + y + z$
e $2x - y + 3z$ **f** $3z - 2x + y$ **g** $4x^2$

5 Work out the value of these when $a = 3$, $b = 5$, $c = 4$ and $d = 6$.
a a^2 **b** $2a^2$ **c** b^2 **d** $2b^2$
e c^2 **f** $2c^2$ **g** d^2 **h** $2d^2$

---

6 A taxi company calculates its fares using a formula
$$F = 2 + n$$
where F is the fare in pounds and n is the number of miles.
a What is the fare for a journey of 2 miles?
b What is the fare for a journey of 6 miles?

7 A rent-a-car company charges for its cars using the formula
$$C = 30 + 20n$$
where C is the cost in £s and n is the
number of days hired.

a What is the charge for 3 days' hire?
b What is the charge for 14 days' hire?
c If the charge is £210, for how many days was the car hired?

---

8 Work out the value of each capital letter, then read the coded word.

$m = 3$	$n = 8$	$p = 5$	$q = -2$

H = $4n + 2q$	L = $6m + 3p$	O = $m^2 + 7$	A = $2q + 10$
T = pq	C = $2n - 3p$	E = $np + 2m$	

1	28	16	1	16	33	6	−10	46

Unit 2

A02 Functional Maths

A03 Problem

More substituting

This spread will show you how to:

- Substitute numbers into an expression and work out its value
- Substitute negative numbers into a formula

Keywords
Negative
Formula
Expression
Substitute

- You can substitute **negative** values into expressions.
- You use the rules for calculating with negative numbers.

Example

When $x = 2$ and $y = -3$, work out the value of

a $x - 3$ **b** $y + 5$ **c** $x - y$

....

a $x - 3 = 2 - 3$
       $= -1$

b $y + 5 = -3 + 5$
        $= +2$

c $x - y = 2 - -3$
        $= 2 + 3$
        $= 5$

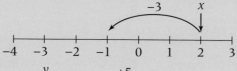

'Subtract -3'
is the same as
'add $+3$'.

Example

Find the value of these expressions when $p = -2$ and $q = 4$.

a $3p - q$ **b** p^2

....

a $3p - q = 3 \times -2 - 4$
          $= -6 - 4$
          $= -10$

b $p^2 = p \times p$
      $= -2 \times -2$
      $= 4$

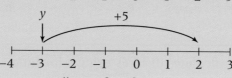

Negative $\times$ negative
$=$ positive

- You can substitute values into expressions involving division.

Example

Work out the value of each expression when $a = 3$ and $b = -2$.

a $\dfrac{4a}{6}$ **b** $\dfrac{a - b}{5}$

....

a $\dfrac{4a}{6} = \dfrac{4 \times a}{6}$

     $= \dfrac{4 \times 3}{6} = \dfrac{12}{6} = 2$

b $\dfrac{a - b}{5} = \dfrac{3 - -2}{5}$

     $= \dfrac{3 + 2}{5} = \dfrac{5}{5} = 1$

1 Use this number line to work out the answers.

$$-20 \qquad -10 \qquad 0 \qquad 10 \qquad 20$$

a $-7 + 3$ **b** $4 - 8$ **c** $-4 + 11$ **d** $-3 - 7$

e $-6 + 4$ **f** $6 - 18$ **g** $4 - 6 - 7$ **h** $-3 - 8 + 5$

2 If $x = -5$, work out the value of these expressions.

a $3x$ **b** $x + 2$ **c** $2x - 1$ **d** $1 - x$

e x^2 **f** $3 - 2x$ **g** $2x^2$ **h** $4x + 15$

3 Work out the value of these expressions when $c = 3$ and $d = -2$.

a $3c + 1$ **b** $3d$ **c** d^2 **d** $2d + 5$

e c^2 **f** $2d + 4c$ **g** $2c - d$ **h** $d - c$

4 If $x = -3$, $y = 2$ and $z = 4$, work out the value of these expressions.

a $x + y$ **b** $y^2 - 5$ **c** $x^2 + 2$ **d** $2y + z$

e $3y + 2x$ **f** $z^2 - 2y$ **g** $3z + 2x$ **h** $3x + 2y - z$

5 Work out the value of each of these expressions when
$e = 4$, $f = 2$, $g = 5$ and $h = -3$.

a $\dfrac{3e}{g}$ **b** $\dfrac{8g}{10}$ **c** $\dfrac{6f}{3}$ **d** $\dfrac{2g + 3}{7}$

e $\dfrac{6g}{f}$ **f** $\dfrac{3h + 4g}{8}$ **g** $\dfrac{5e}{fg}$ **h** $\dfrac{(2g + 6)}{(e - f)}$

6 Calculate the value of each expression when $r = 2$, $s = 4$ and $t = -3$.

a $\dfrac{s}{2}$ **b** $\dfrac{6r}{3}$ **c** $\dfrac{t}{3}$ **d** $\dfrac{s + r}{3}$

e $\dfrac{t - 5}{2}$ **f** $\dfrac{s \times r}{3}$ **g** $\dfrac{3r}{t}$ **h** $\dfrac{st}{r}$

7 You can use this **formula** to convert temperatures in °C to °F

$$F = \frac{9C}{5} + 32$$

where F represents the temperature in °F and C represents the temperature in °C.

a Substitute the temperature 15 °C into the formula to convert it to °F.

b Convert -5 °C to °F.

c When people talk about 'sub-zero' temperatures in the UK, do you think they are referring to °C or °F? Give a reason for your answer.

DID YOU KNOW?

The coldest temperature on Earth was recorded in 1983 at Vostock Station in Antarctica. The Russian research station recorded -89.2 °C (that's a chilly -128.6 °F).

Summary

Check out
You should now be able to:

- Use letters to represent numbers in algebraic expressions
- Simplify algebraic expressions by collecting like terms
- Substitute positive and negative numbers into an expression
- Write expressions to solve problems

Worked exam question
The fast train from Apeworth to Bettenham takes y minutes.

a The slow train takes 12 minutes longer.

Write down an expression, in terms of y, for the time the slow train takes. (1)

b The bus takes twice as long as the fast train.
Write down an expression, in terms of y, for the time the bus takes. (1)

(AQA, 2009)

a

Time is $y + 12$ minutes

b

2y minutes

Write 2y instead of $2 \times y$ (which is acceptable), or y^2 (which is incorrect).

Exam questions

1 a Simplify $5c + 3c - c$ (1)

  b Simplify $7x + 2y - 3x - 5y$ (2)

  c Marek can make x free calls a month on his mobile phone.
Sue can make 20 more free calls a month than Marek.

Write down an expression for the number of free calls Sue can make. (1)

(AQA, 2009)

2 State whether each of the following
statements is True or False.

  a c multiplied by 3 is written as $3c$ (1)

  b d divided by 2 is written as $\dfrac{d}{2}$ (1)

  c a subtracted from b is written as $a - b$ (1)

(AQA, 2008)

3 A pencil costs 30p.
A pen costs 50p.
Write down an expression for the total cost, in pence, of x pencils
and y pens. (2)

A03

4 The perimeter of a rectangle is $(4x + 12)$ cm.
Give two possible alternatives for the length and
width of the rectangle.
Your answers should include x. (4)

---

5 Here is an expression:
$$y^2 - 2x$$
Find the value of the expression when

  a $x = 2$ and $y = 3$

  b $x = -1$ and $y = -1$ (3)

Functional Maths 3: Recycling

The focus on protecting the environment from further damage is now stronger than ever. Recycling and reusing waste materials have become an important part of everyday life both for manufacturers and consumers.

This time-series chart shows the total waste per person produced by households in the UK and the proportion of this waste that was recycled between 1983/4 and 2007/8.

What can you say in general about the amount of waste produced and recycled by households in the UK during this time? Justify your response by referring to the data.

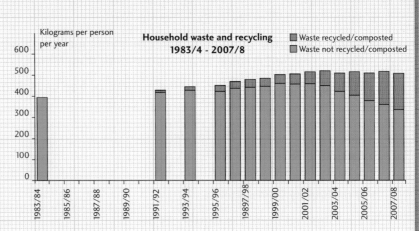

Household waste and recycling 1983/4 - 2007/8
■ Waste recycled/composted
■ Waste not recycled/composted

Copy and complete this table giving the values shown in the time-series chart.

Year	1983/84	1991/92	1993/94	1995/96	1996/97	1997/98	1998/99	1999/00	2000/01	2001/02	2002/03	2003/04	2004/05	2005/06	2006/07	2007/08
Waste not recycled/composted	394	417		423	438	441	443	457	455	456	449	425		376	359	
Waste recycled/composted	3	11	15	27	32	36			52	60	71	87	113	135	157	173
Total waste	397	427	445		469	477	483	505	507		521	512	517	511		507

The data shows that less than 0.8% of UK household waste was recycled in the year 1983/4. Work out what percentage of UK household waste (to the nearest 0.01%) was recycled each year until 2007/8. Add this information to your table.

Can you think of any reason for the trend shown by this data?

By what percentage has the amount of
a) household waste
b) waste recycled by households
changed during this time in the UK?

What realistic predictions do you think the government could have made about household waste for the year 2008/09?

Manufacturers are responsible for designing packaging that is as environmentally friendly as possible while also protecting the product.

A drinks company sells its brand of Cola in 500ml plastic (PET) bottles. The company has reduced the weight of these bottles by a third since the 1970s. The bottles weighed 39g in the 1970s. What is the weight of a new bottle?

The company plans to start using bottles that weigh 24g. What further reduction in weight (%) would this be?

Glass milk bottles are 50% lighter than they were 50 years ago.

As well as reducing the consumption of raw materials, lighter packaging also saves money in other ways such as transport costs.

A supermarket sells tomatoes in packs of six. The packaging consists of a plastic tray with a lid as shown. How much lighter (as a %) would each package be if it were made with no lid?

Do you think that not having lids would risk the quality of the tomatoes?

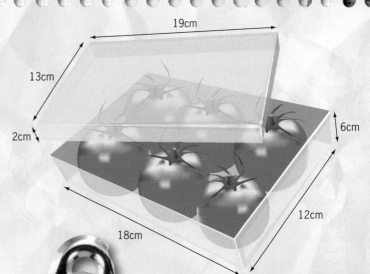

The product/pack ratio compares the weight of the packaging with the weight of the product it contains. Companies use this ratio to assess the suitability of the packaging used for each of their products. They often express it as a percentage to show how much of the overall weight is contributed by the packaging.

Look at some of the packaging you have at home. Could it be adapted to use less material without increasing the risk of damage to the product? If so, how?

Research some well-known manufacturing companies on the Internet to find out about their packaging guidelines. Do they have different rules for different products (e.g. perishable/non-perishable goods)?

How does the packaging used for perishable goods (e.g. food) differ from that used for non-perishable goods (e.g. electrical items)?

153

Introduction

The very first fractions can be traced back to the ancient Egyptians.

They wrote all their fractions as unit fractions (such as $\frac{1}{2} + \frac{1}{3}$ to mean the fraction $\frac{5}{6}$).

Since then, fractions have evolved through different cultures over the centuries.

It was not until the 17th century that fractions as we know them today existed in Europe.

What's the point?

Understanding how fractions work enables us to make a lot of connections in mathematics, for instance in solving real life problems involving ratio and proportion.

Check in

1 What fraction of this shape is shaded?

2 Write down two fractions equivalent to $\frac{1}{2}$.

Orientation

What I need to know	What I will learn	What this leads to
Key stage 3 →	■ Recognise the equivalence of fractions and decimals	→ N7
N3 →	■ Use written methods for addition, subtraction, multiplication and division of decimals	

Rich task

The number 16 can be split into pairs of numbers such as (16, 0); (15, 1), (14.5 and 1.5).

The two numbers are multiplied together:

$16 \times 0 = 0$ $15 \times 1 = 15$ and $14.5 \times 1.5 = 21.75$

The products are different.

a Find the maximum product of a pair of numbers that add together to make 16.

b Choose a starting number of your own and investigate splitting the number into pairs and then finding the maximum product for that number.

This spread will show you how to:
- Convert terminating decimals into fractions
- Convert fractions into decimals
- Order decimals on a number line

Keywords
Decimal
Equivalent
Fraction
Terminating
  decimal

A **decimal** is another way of writing a **fraction**.

You should learn some common fractions and their decimal **equivalents**.

A decimal is
often called a
decimal fraction.

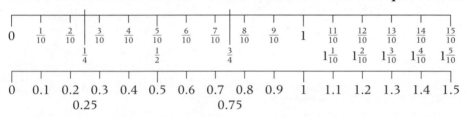

- A terminating decimal has a finite number of decimal digits. For example, 0.75 or 0.8329.

- You can write a **terminating decimal** as a fraction by using place value.

Decimal					Fraction
Units 1	•	tenths $\frac{1}{10}$	hundredths $\frac{1}{100}$	thousandths $\frac{1}{1000}$	
0	•	3			$\frac{3}{10}$
0	•	4	8		$\frac{48}{100}$
3	•	1	5	8	$3\frac{158}{1000}$

$$0.48 = \frac{48}{100}$$
$$\div 4$$
$$\frac{48}{100} = \frac{12}{25}$$
$$\div 4$$

- You can convert a fraction into a decimal

Using equivalent fractions

$$\overset{\times 5}{\underset{\times 5}{\frac{3}{20} = \frac{15}{100}}}$$

Convert the fraction to
an equivalent fraction
with a denominator of
10, 100, 1000 etc.

$$\frac{3}{20} = \frac{15}{100} = 0.15$$

Change the equivalent
fraction to a decimal.

Using division

$$\frac{3}{20} = 3 \div 20 = 0.15$$

Divide the numerator by the
denominator.

You can add and subtract fractions...

... if they have the same
denominator

$$\frac{1}{5} + \frac{3}{5} = \frac{4}{5}$$

Just add the numerators.

... if they have the different
denominators

$$\frac{1}{5} + \frac{3}{10} = \frac{2}{10} + \frac{3}{10}$$
$$= \frac{5}{10} + \frac{1}{2}$$

Convert to an equivalent fraction
with the same denominator.

Don't forget to
simplify your answer
if you can.

p.106

1 Write these decimals as fractions.

   a 0.3   **b** 0.9   **c** 0.23   **d** 0.39

   e 0.88   **f** 0.274   **g** 0.814   **h** 0.037

2 Write these decimals as fractions in their simplest form.

   a 0.4   **b** 0.8   **c** 0.75   **d** 0.36

   e 0.85   **f** 0.08   **g** 0.005   **h** 2.65

3 Change these fractions to decimals without using a calculator.

   a $\frac{7}{10}$ **b** $\frac{1}{2}$ **c** $\frac{47}{50}$ **d** $\frac{13}{25}$ **e** $\frac{22}{25}$

   f $\frac{11}{10}$ **g** $\frac{31}{25}$ **h** $\frac{145}{500}$ **i** $\frac{2}{8}$ **j** $\frac{32}{40}$

4 Change these fractions into decimals using an appropriate method. Give your answers to two decimal places where necessary.

   a $\frac{19}{50}$ **b** $\frac{1}{3}$ **c** $\frac{7}{20}$ **d** $\frac{3}{50}$

   e $\frac{11}{16}$ **f** $\frac{5}{2}$ **g** $\frac{51}{60}$ **h** $\frac{8}{13}$

5 Write the number each of the arrows is pointing to.

   a

   b

   c

6 a Copy this decimal number line.

   b Mark on these fractions.

   i $\frac{8}{10}$ **ii** $\frac{28}{20}$ **iii** $\frac{7}{8}$

7 Put these lists of numbers in order, starting with the smallest.

   a 2.13   2.09   2.2   2.12   2.07

   b 0.345   0.35   0.325   0.3   0.309

   c 1.32   1.4   1.35   1.387   1.058

   d 5.306   5.288   5.308   5.29   5.3

8 Copy and complete these fraction sums.

   a $\frac{1}{2} + \frac{1}{3} = \frac{3}{6} + \frac{\square}{6} =$ **b** $\frac{1}{4} + \frac{1}{5} = \frac{5}{20} + \frac{\square}{20} =$

   c $\frac{1}{4} + \frac{1}{6} =$ **d** $\frac{1}{3} - \frac{1}{8} =$

This spread will show you how to:

- Round numbers to any given power of 10
- Round to the nearest integer and to one significant figure
- Estimate answers to problems involving decimals

Keywords
Decimal places
  (dp)
Estimate
Rounding
Significant figure

You can **round** a number to the nearest 10, 100, 1000, and so on.

p.12

You can also round a number to the nearest whole number or to a given number of **decimal places**.

Example

Round 16.473
a to the nearest whole number   b to 1 decimal place
c to 2 decimal places   d to the nearest 10.

....

a 16.473 ≈ 16. Look at the tenths digit.
b 16.473 ≈ 16.5. Look at the hundredths digit.
c 16.473 ≈ 16.47. Look at the thousandths digit.
d 16.473 ≈ 20. Look at the units digit.

Look at the next digit. If it is 5 or more then the number is rounded up, otherwise it is rounded down.

- The first digit that is not zero in a number is called the **first significant figure**. It has the highest value in the number.

This topic is extended to more significant figures on page 408.

You can round a number to one significant figure.

Example

Round the numbers to one significant figure.
a 7560   b 52.3   c 1.5

....

Thousands	Hundreds	Tens	Units	•	tenths
a	7	5	6	0	•	
b			5	2	•	3
c				1	•	5

a First significant figure is 7, so round up to 8000.
b First significant figure is 5, so round down to 50.
c First significant figure is 1, so round up to 2.

You can **estimate** the answer to a calculation by first rounding the numbers in the calculation.

p.332

Example

Estimate the answer to this calculation. $\dfrac{4.23 \times 5.89}{9.7}$

....

You can round each of these numbers to the nearest whole number.
$$\dfrac{4.23 \times 5.89}{9.7} \approx \dfrac{4 \times 6}{10} = \dfrac{24}{10} = 2.4$$

You have to decide how much to round the numbers to make a good estimate for the calculation.

1 Write the value of the red digit in each of these numbers.
  a 1324   **b** 21894   **c** 234897   **d** 54327

2 Round each of these numbers to the nearest
  i 10   **ii** 100   **iii** 1000.
  a 2568   **b** 4297   **c** 7853   **d** 1432
  e 12473   **f** 18258

3 Here is a table showing the populations of five cities.

Town	Population
London	7 172 091
Paris	2 142 800
New York	8 085 742
Mumbai	16 368 084
Beijing	7 441 000

Round the population of each city to the nearest
10 000 and then place the cities in order of size
from smallest to largest.

4 Round each of these numbers to the nearest
  i 10   **ii** 100.
  a 458.2   **b** 1329.5   **c** 342.52   **d** 354.82

5 Round each of these numbers to the nearest whole number.
  a 3.7   **b** 8.7   **c** 18.63   **d** 69.49
  e 109.9   **f** 6.899

6 Round each of these numbers to 1 decimal place.
  a 0.27   **b** 2.89   **c** 3.82   **d** 12.48

7 Round each of these numbers to
  i 2 decimal places   **ii** one significant figure.
  a 0.327   **b** 2.869   **c** 3.802   **d** 14.458

8 **a** Irwin estimates the value of to
  $\dfrac{47.3 \times 18.9}{8.72}$ to be 100.
  Write three numbers Irwin could use to get his estimate.
  b Sarah estimates the value of
  $\dfrac{21.4 \times 4.87}{49.8}$ to be 2.
  Write three numbers Sarah could use to get her estimate.

For more
questions on
rounding, see
page 408.

This spread will show you how to:

- Use a range of mental methods for calculations with whole numbers and decimals

Keywords
Compensation
Mental method
Multiple
Partitioning
Place value

There are lots of **mental methods** you can use to help you work out calculations in your head.

p.50

You can use **place value**.

> **Example**
>
> Use the fact that $35 \times 147 = 5145$ to write the value of
>
> **a** 3.5×1.47 **b** $0.35 \times 147\,000$ **c** $51.45 \div 3.5$
>
> ---
>
> **a** $3.5 \times 1.47 = (35 \div 10) \times (147 \div 100)$ **b** $0.35 \times 147\,000 = (35 \div 100) \times (147 \times 1000)$
> $\qquad\qquad\quad = 35 \times 147 \div 1000$ $\qquad\qquad\qquad\qquad\qquad\quad = 35 \times 147 \times 10$
> $\qquad\qquad\quad = 5145 \div 1000$ $\qquad\qquad\qquad\qquad\qquad\quad = 5145 \times 10$
> $\qquad\qquad\quad = 5.145$ $\qquad\qquad\qquad\qquad\qquad\quad = 51\,450$
>
> **c** $51.45 \div 3.5 = \dfrac{51.45}{3.5} = \dfrac{514.5}{35}$
> $\qquad\qquad\quad = \dfrac{(5145 \div 10)}{35}$
> $\qquad\qquad\quad = 147 \div 10$
> $\qquad\qquad\quad = 14.7$

You can use **partitioning**.

> **Example**
>
> **a** Calculate $18.5 - 7.7$.   **b** Calculate 6.3×12.
>
> ---
>
> **a** $18.5 - 7.7 = 18.5 - 7 - 0.7$ **b** $\qquad\quad 12 = 10 + 2$
> $\qquad\qquad\quad = 11.5 - 0.7$ $\qquad 6.3 \times 12 = (6.3 \times 10) + (6.3 \times 2)$
> $\qquad\qquad\quad = 10.8$ $\qquad\qquad\qquad\quad = 63 + 12.6$
> $\qquad\qquad\qquad\qquad\qquad\qquad\qquad\quad = 75.6$
>
> Split **12** into **10 + 2**.
> Then work out **10** × 6.3 and **2** × 6.3.
> Add your two answers together.

You can use **compensation**.

> **Example**
>
> Calculate   **a** $12.4 - 4.9$ **b** 23.2×1.9
>
> ---
>
> **a** $12.4 - 4.9 = 12.4 - 5 + 0.1$ **b** $\qquad\quad 1.9 = 2 - 0.1$
> $\qquad\qquad\quad = 7.4 + 0.1$
> $\qquad\qquad\quad = 7.5$ $\qquad 23.2 \times 1.9 = (23.2 \times 2) - (23.2 \times 0.1)$
> $\qquad\qquad\qquad\qquad\qquad\quad = 46.4 - 2.32$
> $\qquad\qquad\qquad\qquad\qquad\quad = 44.08$
>
> Rewrite **1.9** as **2 − 0.1**.
> Work out 2 × 23.2 and **0.1** × 23.2.
> Subtract your two answers.

1 Calculate these.
   a 9×7 **b** $121 \div 10$ **c** 2×2.7 **d** $48.4 \div 2$
   e 3.6×100 **f** $430 \div 100$ **g** 23.6×10 **h** $0.78 \div 100$

2 Use an appropriate mental method to calculate these. Show the
   method you have used.
   a 1.4×11 **b** 21×9 **c** 5.3×11 **d** 41×2.8
   e 19×7 **f** 12×5.3 **g** $147 \div 3$ **h** $276 \div 4$
   i 3.2×11 **j** 31×5.6 **k** 14.9×9 **l** 25.3×31
   m 14×8 **n** $51 \div 1.5$ **o** $81 \div 4.5$ **p** 4.4×4.5

3 Use the mental method of partitioning to work out each of these.
   a $19.5 - 7.6$ **b** $45.3 + 12.6 + 7.2$ **c** $132.6 - 21.4$
   d 7.2×13 **e** 8.4×12 **f** 11×19.2
   g $129 \div 3$ **h** $292 \div 4$

4 Use the mental method of compensation to work out each of these.
   a $19.5 - 7.9$ **b** $48.4 - 12.8$ **c** $164.5 - 15.9$
   d 8.1×19 **e** 36×3.9 **f** 17×5.9

5 Use an appropriate mental method to calculate each of these.
   a $27.6 + 21.7$ **b** $1623 - 897$ **c** 32×2.1 **d** 2.9×23

   e 19×1.4 **f** 9×7.5 **g** $2.4 \div 0.2$ **h** $\dfrac{30 \times 0.2}{0.15}$

6 **a** Using the information that $69 \times 147 = 10\ 143$, write the value of
      each of these.
      i 69×1470 **ii** 690×1470 **iii** 6.9×147
      iv 0.69×14.7 **v** 6.9×0.147 **vi** 690×1.47
      vii 0.069×14.7 **viii** 0.69×0.147
   b Using the information that $37 \times 177 = 6549$, write the value of
      each of these.
      i 3.7×17.7 **ii** 0.37×1770
      iii $654.9 \div 177$ **iv** $65.49 \div 3.7$

7 **a** Using the information that $43 \times 217 = 9331$, write the value of
      each of these.
      i 4.3×2170 **ii** 0.43×2.17
      iii $933.1 \div 4.3$ **iv** $93.31 \div 0.217$
   b Using the information that $48 \times 164 = 7872$, write the value of
      each of these.
      i 4.8×16.4 **ii** $0.48 \times 16\ 400$
      iii $787.2 \div 1640$ **iv** $78.72 \div 4.8$

Written methods with decimals

This spread will show you how to:

Keywords
Divide
Estimate
Multiply

- Use a range of written methods for calculations with whole numbers and decimals
- Use checking procedures, including approximation to estimate the answer to multiplication and division problems

p.56

You can multiply decimals by replacing them with an equivalent **whole-number** calculation that is easier to work out.

p.2

Example

Carol is working out the area of carpet she needs for her floor. The floor is in a rectangle with a length of 4.8 m and a width of 3.12 m. What is the area of Carol's floor?

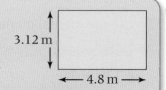

3.12 m

← 4.8 m →

$4.8 \times 3.12 = (48 \div 10) \times (312 \div 100)$
$= 48 \times 312 \div 1000$

×	300	10	2
40	$40 \times 300 = 12\,000$	$40 \times 10 = 400$	$40 \times 2 = 80$
8	$8 \times 300 = 2400$	$8 \times 10 = 80$	$8 \times 2 = 16$

Estimate the answer first.
$4.8 \times 3.12 \approx 5 \times 3$
$= 15\,m^2$

$48 \times 312 = 12\,000 + 400 + 80 + 2400 + 80 + 16 = 14\,976$
The area of Carol's floor is $4.8 \times 3.12 = 48 \times 312 \div 1000$
$= 14\,976 \div 1000$
$= 14.98\,m^2$ (2 decimal places)

You can divide a number by a decimal by rewriting the calculation as an equivalent whole-number division.

Example

Mandy has a floor with an area of $91\,m^2$.
She fills the floor with carpet tiles which have an area of $2.8\,m^2$.
How many tiles does she need to cover the floor?

$91 \div 2.8 = 910 \div 28$

$$
\begin{array}{r}
28\overline{)910} \\
-840 \\
\hline
70 \\
-56 \\
\hline
14.0 \\
-14.0 \\
\hline
0
\end{array}
$$

28×30

28×2

$28 \times 0.5 \qquad 30 + 2 + 0.5 = 32.5$

Estimate the answer first.
$91 \div 2.8 \approx 90 \div 3$
$= 30$

$910 \div 28 = 91 \div 2.8 = 32.5$
Mandy needs $91 \div 2.8 = 32.5$ tiles.

1 Use a written method for each of these calculations.
  a $16.4 + 9.68$ **b** $27.3 + 5.41$ **c** $9.51 - 6.7$
  d $24.3 + 7.69$ **e** $34.76 - 8.29$ **f** $38.29 - 24.8$
  g $16.5 - 12.67 + 5.34$ **h** $78.7 - 14.92 + 16.66 - 12.9$

2 Use an appropriate method of calculation to work out each of these.
  a 15×3.4 **b** 5.6×18 **c** 8.4×13
  d 23×7.6 **e** 28×4.2 **f** 9.7×49

3 Use an appropriate method of calculation to work out each of these.
  a $27.3 \div 7$ **b** $36.6 \div 6$ **c** $70.4 \div 8$
  d $73.8 \div 6$ **e** $119.7 \div 9$ **f** $119.2 \div 8$

A02 Functional Maths

4 Use a mental or written method to solve each of these problems.
  a Oliver sells tomatoes at the market. On Thursday he sells 78.6 kg; on Saturday he sells 83.38 kg. What mass of tomatoes has he sold during the two days?
  b A mobile phone without a battery weighs 188.16 g. When the battery is inserted the combined mass of the mobile phone and battery is 207.38 g. What is the mass of the battery?
  c A recycling box is full of things to be recycled.
  The empty box weighs 1.073 kg.

Bottles	12.45 kg
Cans	1.675 kg
Paper	8.7 kg
Plastic objects	? kg

  The total weight of the box and all the objects to be recycled is exactly 25 kg. What is the weight of the plastic objects?

DID YOU KNOW?

At least half the household waste produced in the UK each year could be recycled. Unfortunately in 2005 only 12% was recycled!

5 Use an appropriate method of calculation to work out each of these.
  a 2.3×1.74 **b** 1.6×2.75 **c** 1.7×44.3
  d 2.5×5.88 **e** 8.7×4.79 **f** 38×4.78
  g 3.4×4.45 **h** 0.54×8.28 **i** 0.93×3.87

A02 Functional Maths

6 a Scooby buys 1.8 m of carpet. Each metre costs £1.85. How much does this cost in total?
  b Shaggy buys 7.8 kg of apples. Each kilogram of apples costs £1.45. How much money does Shaggy pay for the apples?
  c Brian is a gardener. He plants trees at a rate of 11.8 trees per hour. How many trees does he plant in 6.4 hours?
  d Clarke works as a car mechanic. He charges £31.70 per hour for his work. How much does he charge for working 2.5 hours?

N4.5 Adding and subtracting decimals

This spread will show you how to:

- Use written methods for addition and subtraction of whole numbers and decimals
- Add and subtract mentally numbers with up to two decimal places

Keywords
Addition
Decimals
Estimate
Subtraction
Written method

p.52

There is a standard written method for **addition** of **decimals**.

Example

Liam measures the lengths of three vehicles.
Car 2.4m   Lorry 5m   Motorbike 1.68m
What is the total length of the three vehicles?

Estimate the answer first.

$2.4 + 5 + 1.68 \approx 2 + 5 + 2$
$= 9\text{m}$

Set out the calculation in columns, lining up the decimal points.

	Units	•	tenths	hundredths
	2	•	4	
	5	•		
+	1_1	•	6	8
=	9	•	0	8

So the combined length = 9.08m.

Start by adding hundredths to hundredths, then tenths to tenths, units to units and so on.

There is a standard written method for **subtraction** of decimals.

Example

Calculate 27.8 litres− 14.45 litres.

Estimate the answer first.

$27.8 - 14.45 \approx 28 - 14$
$= 14 \text{ litres}$

Set out the calculation in columns, lining up the decimal points.
You could write the numbers in a place value table.

$$\begin{array}{r} 27.\overset{7}{\cancel{8}}\overset{1}{0} \\ -14.45 \\ \hline 13.35 \end{array}$$

Start with the smallest place value (in this case hundredths), and subtract hundredths from hundredths, tenths from tenths, and so on.
27.8 litres− 14.45 litres =13.35 litres

You could also use 'shopkeeper's subtraction'.

Add a zero here so that both numbers have the same number of decimal places.

1 Use an appropriate method for each of these calculations.
  a 83 + 57   **b** 93 + 32   **c** 275 + 958
  d 843 + 872   **e** 838 + 697   **f** 834 + 787

Get into the habit of estimating your answer first.

2 Use an appropriate method for each of these calculations.
  a 62 − 47   **b** 83 − 68   **c** 487 − 356
  d 852 − 728   **e** 548 − 387   **f** 589 − 387

3 Use an appropriate method for each of these calculations.
  a 25 + 38 + 68   **b** 123 + 76 − 58
  c 173 − 27 + 56   **d** 327 + 176 − 255

4 Use a mental or written method to work out these calculations.
  a 33.4 + 15.2   **b** 34.6 + 13.7   **c** 19.8 + 8.8   **d** 18.7 + 26.5

5 Use a mental or written method to work out these calculations.
  a 8.7 − 2.5   **b** 15.8 − 8.4   **c** 26.3 − 7.9   **d** 53.6 − 27.8

A02 Functional Maths

3 Jodie buys

    3 pens at 14p each
    2 writing pads at £1.89 each
    1 calculator at £2.79

She pays with a £10 note.
Work out how much change Jodie should get from £10.

---

7 Use a written method to work out these additions.
  a 3.52 + 4.6   **b** 13.62 + 2.9   **c** 8.5 + 14.81   **d** 75.8 + 28.39

8 Use a written method to work out these subtractions.
  a 17.3 − 4.22   **b** 16.6 − 3.47   **c** 37.7 − 18.86   **d** 57.28 − 38.4

9 Use a written method for each of these calculations.
  a 16.4 + 9.87   **b** 49.2 + 7.72   **c** 9.42 − 5.9
  d 26.9 + 9.82   **e** 36.57 − 8.59   **f** 36.28 − 17.4

A02 Functional Maths

10 Use a mental or written method to solve each of these problems.
  a Sean sells olives at the weekend. On Saturday he sells 8.9 kg; on Sunday he sells 3.38 kg. What weight of olives has Sean sold altogether during the weekend?
  b Naomi is building a wooden cold frame for growing vegetables. She needs three lengths of wood to finish the frame. The lengths are 1.82 m, 1.3 m and 1.79 m. What is the total length of wood she will need to buy?

Unit 2

Multiplying and dividing decimals

This spread will show you how to:

- Use written methods for multiplication and division of whole numbers and decimals
- Use approximation to estimate the answers to problems

p.56

Keywords

Divisor
Estimate
Grid method
Standard
 method
Whole number

You can multiply decimals by replacing them with an equivalent **whole number** calculation that is easier to work out.

p.342

Example

Bruce buys 28 lengths of wood. Each length is 4.8m long.
What is the total length of wood he buys?

Estimate the answer first.
$$28 \times 4.8 \approx 30 \times 5$$
$$= 150 \text{ m}$$
Rewrite as a whole number calculation $\quad 28 \times 4.8 = 28 \times 48$
Work out 28×48 using the standard method.

$$
\begin{array}{r}
48 \\
\times 28 \\
\hline
\end{array}
$$

$20 \times 48 \quad 960$
$8 \times 48 \quad +384$
$28 \times 48 = \overline{1344}$

Bruce buys
$28 \times 4.8 = 28 \times 48 \div 10$
$= 1344 \div 10$
$= 134.4\text{m of wood}$

You could also use
the grid method:

×	40	8
20	800	160
8	320	64

$28 \times 48 =$
$800 + 320 +$
$160 + 64 = 1344$

Adjust your answer
for the decimals.

You can divide any number including decimals by a whole number using the 'chunking method'.

Example

Andrew packs tins into boxes. Each box will hold 12 tins.
Andrew has 159 tins. How many boxes will he fill?

Estimate the answer first.
$$159 \div 12 \approx 150 \div 10$$
$$= 15 \text{ boxes}$$

$$
\begin{array}{r}
12)159 \\
-120 \\
\hline
39 \\
-36 \\
\hline
3
\end{array}
$$

$12 \times \mathbf{10}$

$12 \times \mathbf{3}$
$159 \div 12 = \mathbf{13}$ remainder 3

Andrew will fill 13 boxes with 3 tins left over.

1 Calculate these using an appropriate written method.
Remember to do a mental approximation first.
- **a** 13×16
- **b** 18×13
- **c** 13×13
- **d** 16×19
- **e** 17×19

2 Use an appropriate method of calculation to work out:
- **a** 23×8
- **b** 9×64
- **c** 8×147
- **d** 17×21
- **e** 16×28
- **f** 24×23
- **g** 12×114
- **h** 25×135
- **i** 28×154

3 Use an appropriate method of calculation to work out each of these.
Where appropriate leave your answer in remainder form.
- **a** $56 \div 6$
- **b** $84 \div 8$
- **c** $95 \div 5$
- **d** $116 \div 7$
- **e** $123 \div 9$
- **f** $144 \div 8$
- **g** $155 \div 12$
- **h** $185 \div 14$
- **i** $284 \div 12$

4 a Beatrice plants 8 seeds in a pot. She has 114 seeds.
How many pots will she fill with seeds? How many seeds will
there be left?

b Melinda packs 7 boxes into every crate. She has 103 boxes.
How many crates will she be able to fill?

5 Use an appropriate method of calculation to work out:
- **a** 13×2.1
- **b** 3.7×13
- **c** 5.4×13
- **d** 23×3.3
- **e** 28×3.2
- **f** 6.3×29

6 Use an appropriate method of calculation to work out:
- **a** $25.9 \div 7$
- **b** $34.8 \div 6$
- **c** $66.4 \div 8$
- **d** $73.8 \div 6$
- **e** $117.9 \div 9$
- **f** $122.4 \div 8$

7 Use an appropriate method of calculation to work out:
- **a** 12×1.64
- **b** 13×1.42
- **c** 13×1.35
- **d** 15×1.32
- **e** 18×1.43
- **f** 28×1.52

8 a Wally buys 13 bags of potatoes. Each bag costs £1.23.
How much does this cost in total?

b Ashley buys six CDs. Each CD costs £8.79. How much is this
in total?

c Christina buys 12 ready meals. Each meal costs £1.79.
What is the cost of the 12 ready meals?

9 Use an appropriate method of calculation to work out:
- **a** $54.16 \div 4$
- **b** $85.32 \div 6$
- **c** $130.72 \div 8$
- **d** $62.23 \div 7$
- **e** $188.7 \div 6$
- **f** $219.51 \div 9$

Check out
You should now be able to:

- Recognise the equivalence of fractions and decimals
- Order decimals and fractions on a number line
- Round numbers to any given power of 10, the nearest whole number and one significant figure
- Use rounding to estimate answers to calculations
- Use method and written methods for addition, subtraction, multiplication and division of whole numbers and decimals

Worked exam question

3 **a** Write $\frac{4}{5}$ as a decimal. (1)

   b Work out $\frac{4}{5}$ of 85. (2)

   c What percentage of this grid is shaded?

   (1)

   d Joanna wants to shade whole squares in the grid to the right so that exactly $\frac{4}{5}$ of the grid is shaded.

   Explain why this is **not** possible. (4)

   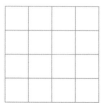

   (AQA, 2007)

a
$$\frac{4}{5} = 4 \times \frac{1}{5} = 4 \times 0.2$$
$$= 0.8$$

b
$\frac{1}{5}$ of 85 $= 85 \div 5$

$5\overline{)8^3 5}\,^{17}$ $85 \div 5 = 17$

So $\frac{4}{5}$ of 85 $= 4 \times 17$
$$=68$$

c
$$\frac{8}{10} = 80\%$$

d
$\frac{4}{5}$ of 16 is not a whole number

so there will be part squares.

Exam questions

1   **a** A candle costs £1.35
       Ronnie buys four candles.
       i Work out the cost of four candles.   (2)
       ii He pays with a £10 note.

       How much change does he get?   (1)

    b Ronnie now has six coins in his pocket.
       The total value of these coins is £6.80

       List the six coins.   (2)

    c A box of matches costs 45 p.

       What is 45 p as a fraction of £1.35?
       Give your answer in its simplest form.   (2)
(AQA, 2007)

2   **a** Work out   78 ÷ 6   (1)

    b Work out   364 × 79   (3)

3   Use approximation to estimate the answer to

$$\frac{297.1 \times 4.08}{5.903}$$ (3)
(AQA, 2009)

Introduction

When you hire a car, the price often increases in equal amounts for each extra day of hiring. This is an example of a linear function, and the graph will be a straight line.

What's the point?

Linear functions occur commonly in man-made situations, such as in currency conversion and in working out tariffs and charges. If you understand how to create and use linear graphs, you can often solve real-life problems much quicker than calculating from scratch.

1   Work out the value of the letter.
    a $2 + p = 5$ **b** $3 + q = 11$
    c $5 - r = 3$ **d** $2 - s = -3$

2   Work out the value of each expression when $x = 2$.
    a $x + 6$ **b** $3x - 1$
    c $2x + 4$ **d** $\frac{x}{4} + 3$

3   Substitute $x = 0$ into these expressions and evaluate them.
    a $2x + 5$ **b** $3x - 4$
    c $10x + 1$ **d** $4x + 11$

4   Substitute $x = -1$ into these expressions and evaluate them.
    a $2x + 1$ **b** $3x - 2$
    c $4x + 5$ **d** $2x - 5$

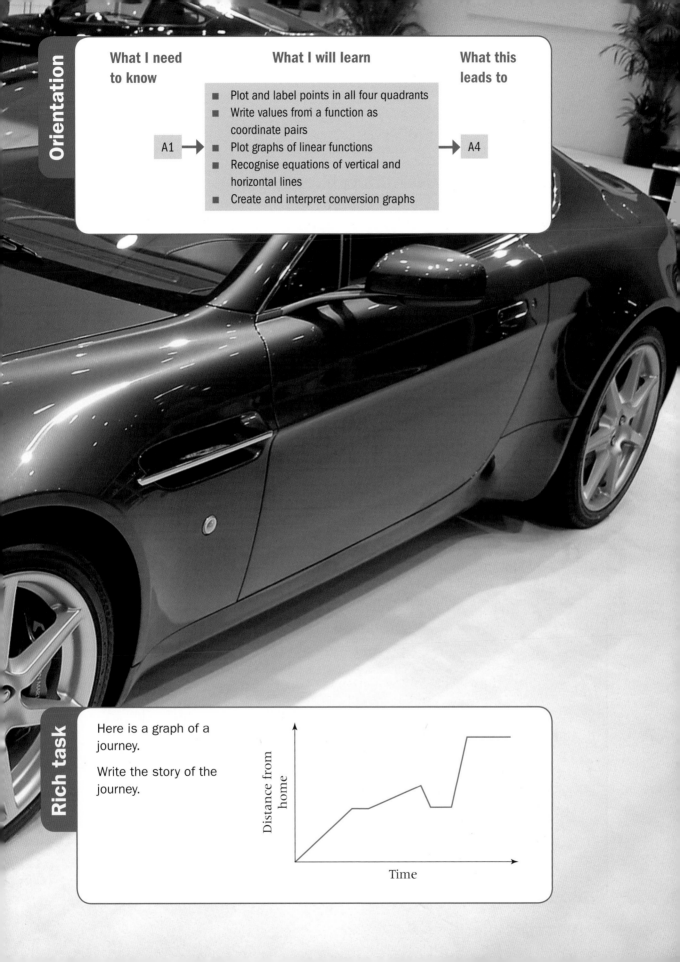

What I need to know

What I will learn

What this leads to

A1 →

- Plot and label points in all four quadrants
- Write values from a function as coordinate pairs
- Plot graphs of linear functions
- Recognise equations of vertical and horizontal lines
- Create and interpret conversion graphs

→ A4

Rich task

Here is a graph of a journey.

Write the story of the journey.

Distance from home

Time

Coordinates

This spread will show you how to:

- Plot coordinates
- Locate points with given coordinates

Keywords
Coordinates
Negative
Origin
Positive
Quadrant
x-axis
y-axis

- **Coordinates** are a pair of numbers (x, y) that fix a point on a grid.

You can plot coordinates on a grid.

- A grid has two perpendicular axes: the x-axis and the y-axis.

You write the coordinates as a pair
(x-coordinate, y-coordinate)
The x-value comes first.

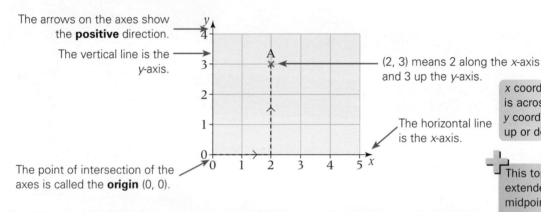

The arrows on the axes show the **positive** direction.

The vertical line is the y-axis.

(2, 3) means 2 along the x-axis and 3 up the y-axis.

The horizontal line is the x-axis.

x coordinate is across, y coordinate is up or down.

The point of intersection of the axes is called the **origin** (0, 0).

This topic is extended to the midpoint of a line on page 434.

Example

a Plot and join the points
A(1, 3), B(3, 3) and C(3, 1).
Name the shape you have drawn.

a

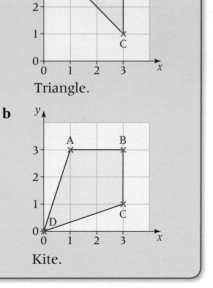

Triangle.

b Add and join the point D(0, 0).
Name the new shape.

b

Kite.

1 Give the coordinates of the points A to Z.
The first one is done for you.
A(2, 8)
B(__, __)

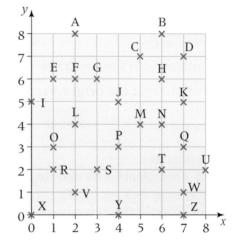

2 a Copy this coordinate grid onto square
grid paper.
b Plot and label these points.
A(2, 3)   B(8, 3)   C(8, 9)   D(2, 9)
c Join the points in order.
d Write the name of the shape ABCD.

3 a Copy the coordinate grid in question **2**
onto square grid paper.
b Plot, label and join each of these sets
of points, then write the name of the
shape you have made.
  i A(7, 6), B(7, 9), C(3, 9), D(3, 6)
  ii E(5, 1), F(3, 4), G(1, 1)
  iii H(8, 3), I(10, 5), J(7, 5), K(5, 3)
  iv L(8, 6), M(9, 8), N(8, 9), P(7, 8)

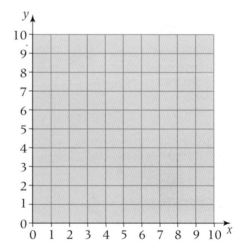

4 Write the coordinates of all the corner points
of this shape.
Start at the origin, then point A, ...

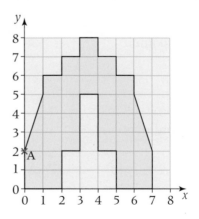

Coordinates in all four quadrants

This spread will show you how to:

- Plot points in all four quadrants

Keywords

Axes
Coordinates
Origin
Quadrant
x-coordinate
y-coordinate

A coordinate grid has two **axes**.

The axes meet at the **origin**, O.

- You can describe the position of a point on the grid by giving its **coordinates**.
  The **x-coordinate** is the distance you move along the x-axis from O.
  The **y-coordinate** is the distance you move parallel to the y-axis from O.

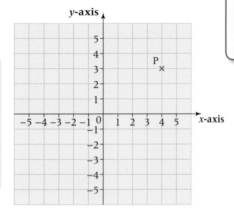

The coordinates of *P* are (4, 3). *x* comes before *y* in the alphabet.

You can extend the *x*- and *y*-axes into negative numbers.
The axes divide the grid into four sections, called **quadrants**.

The coordinates of Q are (−3, 2). From 0 you move −3 along the x-axis and then +2 parallel to the y-axis.

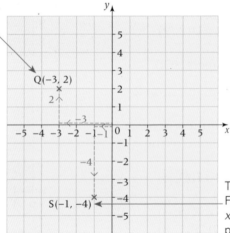

The coordinates of S are (−1, −4). From 0 you move −1 along the x-axis and then −4 (downwards) parallel to the y-axis.

- You can plot and label points in all four quadrants.

Example

Plot the points
A(1, 4),
B(−2, 3),
C(4, −2)
D(−2, −3)
on a coordinate grid.

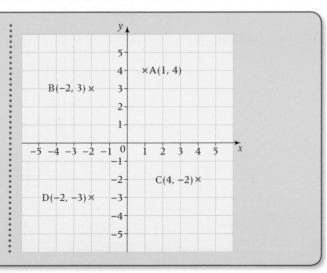

1 Write the coordinates of the points O, P, Q, R, S and T.

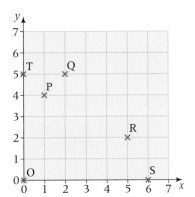

2 Write the coordinates of the points in each diagram.

a

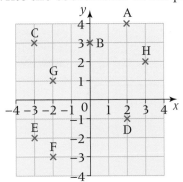

b

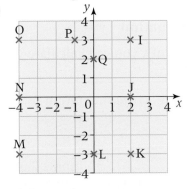

DID YOU KNOW?

The system of coordinates that are commonly use today was devised by René Descartes, the 17th century French mathematician and philosopher.

3 a Plot these sets of points on a copy of this grid.
   i (3, 2)   (−1, 2)   (−1, −1)
   ii (1, 2)   (−1, 0)   (3, 0)

   b Join each set of points in order.
   c What is the name of each shape?

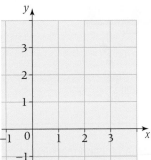

4 a Copy a coordinate grid from question 2 onto square grid paper.
   b Plot and label these points on your grid.
      A (3, 3)   B (−2, 3)   C (−4, −1)
   c A, B and C are three corners of a parallelogram.
      Write the coordinate of the fourth corner, D.

5 a Copy a coordinate grid from question 2 onto square grid paper.
   b On your grid, draw a triangle with each corner in a different quadrant. Label the corners A, B and C.
   c Write the coordinates of A, B and C.
   d Repeat for
      i   a square
      ii a kite, with each corner in a different quadrant.

Do **not** copy the points.

This spread will show you how to:

- Use function machines to represent equations
- Write the input and output values for functions as pairs in a table

Keywords
Equation
Function
Input
Output

Here is a **function machine:**

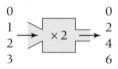

input   output

0	0
1	2
2	4
3	6

 p.260

When you know the **input**, you can calculate the **output**.

In this machine   input ⟶ output
             x $2x$

You can write this as an **equation** $y = 2x$.

When you know the value of x you can calculate y.   When $x = 1$, $y = 2 \times 1 = 2$.
                                                      When $x = 2$, $y = 2 \times 2 = 4$.

y is the output.

You will learn about **solving** equations on page 262.

Example

For each function machine, write the output for the inputs given.

a $x \longrightarrow \boxed{\times 3} \longrightarrow y$

inputs 0, 2, 5, 10

b $x \longrightarrow \boxed{\div 2} \longrightarrow y$

inputs 2, 4, 10, 18

a

Input	Output
0	0
2	6
5	15
10	30

b

Input	Output
2	1
4	2
10	5
18	9

- You can draw a function machine to represent an equation.

Example

Draw function machines to represent the equations.
a $y = x + 2$ **b** $y = \frac{x}{4}$

a $x \longrightarrow \boxed{+2} \longrightarrow y$

b $x \longrightarrow \boxed{\div 4} \longrightarrow y$

$\frac{x}{4}$ means $x \div 4$.

Functions can have more than one step.

Example

a Draw a function machine for the equation $y = 3x - 2$.
b Work out the outputs for these inputs: 0, 2, 4.

a $x \longrightarrow \boxed{\times 3} \longrightarrow \boxed{-2} \longrightarrow y$

b $0 \rightarrow 0 \times 3 - 2 = 0 - 2 = -2$
$2 \rightarrow 2 \times 3 - 2 = 6 - 2 = 4$
$4 \rightarrow 4 \times 3 - 2 = 12 - 2 = 10$

$3x = 3 \times x$

First multiply x by 3 then subtract 2.

1 Copy and complete the tables for these function machines.

a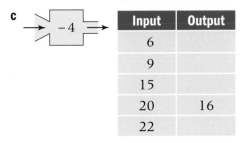

Input	Output
0	3
1	4
4	
7	
9	12

b

Input	Output
0	
3	9
6	
7	
9	27

c

Input	Output
6	
9	
15	
20	16
22	

d

Input	Output
6	
12	
15	
	8
30	

2 Draw function machines for these equations.

  a $y = x + 5$ **b** $y = x - 3$ **c** $y = 3x$ **d** $y = x + 1$

  e $y = \frac{x}{3}$ **f** $y = x - 2$ **g** $y = 6x$ **h** $y = \frac{x}{2}$

3 Draw a function machine for each equation.
Use your machines to calculate the outputs when

  i $x = 1$ **ii** $x = 2$ **iii** $x = 3$

  a $y = 2x$ **b** $y = x + 4$ **c** $y = x - 1$ **d** $y = \frac{x}{4}$

4 Copy and complete the tables for these two-step function machines.

a

Input	Output
0	1
1	3
2	
3	
4	
10	21

b

Input	Output
2	
4	11
5	
6	
7	20
10	

5 Draw function machines for these equations.
Use your machines to calculate the outputs when

  i $x = -2$ **ii** $x = 2$ **iii** $x = 4$

  a $y = 2x - 1$ **b** $y = 3x + 2$ **c** $y = \frac{x}{2} - 1$ **d** $y = 4x - 5$

Unit 2

Drawing tables of values

This spread will show you how to:

- Write the input and output values for functions as pairs in a table
- Identify explicit and implicit functions

Keywords
Equation
Function
Implicit equation
Table of values

This function machine represents the equation $y = x - 3$.

Input → x → -3 → Output → y

You can work out the value of y for different values of x.

Input		Output
$x = 3$		$y = 0$
$x = 5$		$y = 2$
$x = 7$ → -3 →		$y = 4$
$x = 12$		$y = 9$
$x = 15$		$y = 12$

You can write the pairs of x and y values in a table of values.

x	3	5	7	12	15
y	0	2	4	9	12

Input this x-value and you get this y-value.

Example

Complete the table of values for this function machine.

x → $+4$ → y

x	0	2	3	6	9
y					

∙∙

Input each x value in turn.

$x = 0$ → $+4$ → $y = 4$

$x = 2$ → $+4$ → $y = 6$

x	0	2	3	6	9
y	4	6	7	10	13

Example

Complete the table of values for the equation $x + y = 5$.

x	0	2	4	5
y				

$x + y = 5$ is an **implicit** equation. x and y appear on the same side of the equals sign.

∙∙

When $x = 0$ the equation is $0 + y = 5$, so $y = 5$
When $x = 2$ $\qquad\qquad\qquad$ $2 + y = 5$, so $y = 3$
When $x = 4$ $\qquad\qquad\qquad$ $4 + y = 5$, so $y = 1$
When $x = 5$ $\qquad\qquad\qquad$ $5 + y + 5$, so $y = 0$

x	0	2	4	5
y	5	3	1	0

1 Copy and complete the table of values for each function machine.

a Input → x → $+5$ → y → Output

x	0	2	3	6	9
y					

b Input → x → $\times 3$ → y → Output

x	0	2	3	6	9
y					

c Input → x → -6 → y → Output

x	6	7	8	9	10
y					

d Input → x → $\div 4$ → y → Output

x	4	8	12	16	20
y					

2 Copy and complete the table of values for each function machine.

a Input → x → $+3$ → y → Output

x	−5	−2	3	6	9
y					

b Input → x → $\times 6$ → y → Output

x	−2	0	3	5	7
y					

c Input → x → -4 → y → Output

x	−2	0	3	5	7
y					

d Input → x → $\div 3$ → y → Output

x	−6	−3	3	6	9
y					

3 Match each equation to a table of values.

a $y = 3x$

i

x	−2	0	2	4	6
y	−2	4	10	16	22

b $y = x + 4$

ii

x	−1	2	3	5	7
y	−1	11	15	23	31

c $y = 3x + 4$

iii

x	−2	0	2	4	6
y	−6	0	6	12	18

d $y = 4x + 3$

iv

x	−4	−2	1	2	4
y	0	2	5	6	8

Plotting graphs from tables of values

This spread will show you how to:

- Plot graphs of functions in which y is or is not the subject
- Read values from a graph

Here is a table of values for the equation

$$y = 3x$$

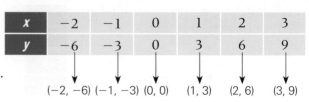

x	−2	−1	0	1	2	3
y	−6	−3	0	3	6	9

In the table, each y-value links to an x-value.

(−2, −6) (−1, −3) (0, 0)　(1, 3)　(2, 6)　(3, 9)

- You can write the linked x- and y-values as coordinate pairs.

- You can plot the coordinate pairs on a grid.

Plot each point.

Join the points with a straight line.

All the points on the line **satisfy** the equation $y = 3x$. This means that for every point on the line,

$$y\text{-value} = x\text{-value} \times 3$$

- You can read values from a graph.

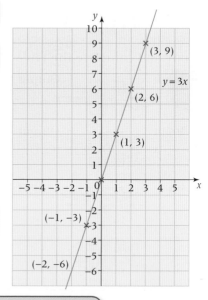

Here is the graph of $y = 2x + 3$.
Use the graph to find

a the value of x when $y = 7$
b the value of y when $x = 3\frac{1}{2}$.

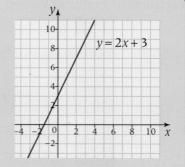

This topic is extended to the intersection of two lines on page 420.

a Find $y = 7$ on the y-axis.
Draw a horizontal line to the graph line.
Draw a vertical line to the x-axis.
Read off the value of x.
$x = 2$

b Find $x = 3\frac{1}{2}$ on the x-axis.
Draw a vertical line to the graph line.
Draw a horizontal line to the y-axis.
Read off the value of y.
$y = 10$

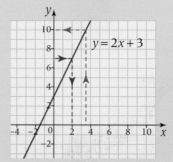

1 Here is the graph of $y = 2x - 1$.
Find the value of x when

a $y = 7$

b $y = 0$

c $y = -9$

d $y = -6$

Find the value of y when

e $x = 4$

f $x = -4$

g $x = 2\frac{1}{2}$

h $x = -1\frac{1}{2}$

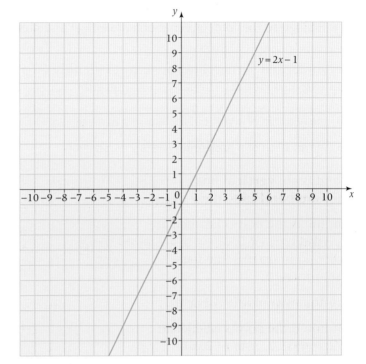

2 a Copy and complete this table of values for the equation $y = 3x + 1$.

x	−3	−2	0	1	2
y				4	

b Copy and complete this list of coordinate pairs from your table.
(−3, __) (−2, __) (0, __) (1, 4) (2, __)

c Copy the grid in question **1** onto square grid paper.

d Plot the points from part **b** on your grid.
Join them with a straight line.

e From your graph, find the value of x when $y = -2$.

> Do not copy the graph line.

3 a Copy and complete this table of values for the equation $y = \frac{x}{2}$.

x	−4	−2	0	2	6
y	−2				

b Write a list of coordinate pairs from your table.

c Copy the grid in question **1** onto square grid paper.

d Plot the points from part **b** on your grid.
Join them with a straight line.

e From your graph, find the value of y when $x = 9$.

> Do not copy the graph line.

4 Repeat question **3** for the equation $x + y = 7$.

Unit 2

Horizontal and vertical lines

This spread will show you how to:

● Recognise the form of equations of vertical and horizontal lines

Keywords
Horizontal
Parallel
Vertical

Horizontal and vertical lines are easy to identify on a graph.
You can also identify them by their equation.

● The equation of a **vertical** line is $x =$ a number.

● The equation of a **horizontal** line is $y =$ a number.

A and B are **vertical** lines.
They are **parallel** to the y-axis.

For line A the points labelled are
$(1, -4)$ $(1, 2)$ $(1, 7)$.
Every point on this line has
x-coordinate 1.

The equation of line A is $x = 1$.

For line B the points labelled are
$(-2, -6)$ $(-2, -1)$ $(-2, 6)$.
Every point on this line has
x-coordinate -2.

The equation of line B is $x = -2$.

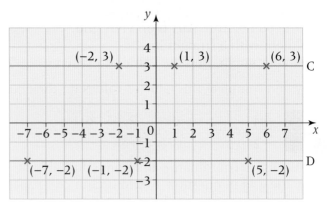

C and D are **horizontal** lines.
They are parallel to the x-axis.

For line C the points labelled are
$(-2, 3)$ $(1, 3)$ $(6, 3)$.
Every point on this line has
y-coordinate 3.

The equation of line C is $y = 3$.

For line D the points labelled are
$(-7, -2)$ $(-1, -2)$ $(5, -2)$.

Every point on this line has
y-coordinate -2.

The equation of line D is $y = -2$.

1 Name the lines on the grid.

Copy and complete

The equation of the *x*-axis is *y* = _____

The equation of the *y*-axis is _____

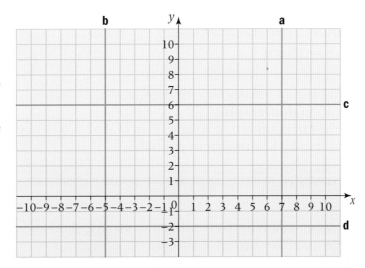

Unit 2

2 Copy the axes from question **1** onto square grid paper.
For each part, plot the points and join them to make a straight line.
Name each line.

Do not copy the graph lines in blue.

a Line 1: $(-4, -6)$ $(-4, -3)$ $(-4, 1)$ $(-4, 7)$
b Line 2: $(-7, 1)$ $(-2, 1)$ $(4, 1)$ $(6, 1)$
c Line 3: $(-3, -3)$ $(-1, -3)$ $(4, -3)$ $(8, -3)$

3 Name these lines without plotting the points.
a Line 1: $(-5, 5)$ $(-2, 5)$ $(5, 5)$ $(9, 5)$
b Line 2: $(-8, -3)$ $(-8, 3)$ $(-8, 6)$ $(-8, 10)$

4 Copy the axes from question **1** onto square grid paper.
a Draw these lines on your grid.
$x = -2$ $y = -4$ $x = 7$ $y = 1$
b What shape do your lines enclose?

5 Copy the axes from question **1** onto square grid paper.
a Draw four lines to enclose a square.
b Write the equations of your four lines.
c Write the coordinates of the vertices of your square.

A03 **Problem**

6 Match the points in set B with lines they lie on in set A.

Some points may lie on more than one line.

Set A

$x = 3$ $x = -5$ $x = 6$ $x = -2$
$y = 4$ $y = -2$ $y = 5$ $y = -3$

Set B

$(-2, 6)$ $(3, 3)$ $(-5, -5)$ $(6, 5)$ $(2, 4)$
$(6, -3)$ $(-2, -3)$ $(-5, 4)$ $(-5, 7)$ $(3, 6)$
$(6, 1)$ $(8, -3)$ $(3, 4)$ $(1, -3)$ $(5, -2)$
$(6, 3)$ $(-3, 4)$ $(3, -3)$ $(-2, -2)$ $(-5, 5)$

Conversion graphs

This spread will show you how to:
- Use and interpret conversion graphs
- Read values from graphs

Keywords
Conversion graph
Convert
Scale
Unit

Weights can be measured in kilograms or pounds.
You can use a **conversion graph** to
- **convert** a weight in pounds to a weight in kg
- convert a weight in kg to a weight in pounds.

kg is the metric **unit**, pound is the imperial unit.

- You can use a conversion graph to convert between units of measurement.

Example

Here is a conversion graph for converting pounds to kg and kg to pounds. Use the graph to convert
a 12 pounds to kilograms **b** 7 kilograms to pounds.

p.236 ▶

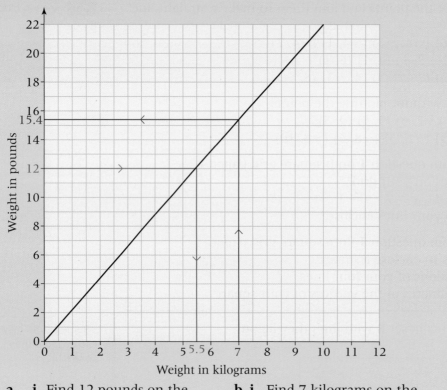

The vertical scale goes up in 2s.

a i Find 12 pounds on the pounds (vertical) axis.
ii Draw a line across to the graph.
iii Draw a line down from the graph to the kilograms (horizontal) axis.
iv Read the value off the axis.
12 pounds = 5.5 kilograms

b i Find 7 kilograms on the kilograms (horizontal) axis.
ii Draw a line up to the graph.
iii Draw a line across from the graph to the pounds (vertical) axis.
iv Read the value off the axis. Use the scale to estimate the value.
7 kilograms = 15.4 pounds

The horizontal scale goes up in 1s.

A02 Functional Maths

Unit 2

1 Use the conversion graph on page 184 to convert
  a 22 pounds to kilograms   **b** 11 pounds to kilograms
  c 3 kilograms to pounds   **d** 9 kilograms to pounds
  e 8.5 pounds to kilograms   **f** 3.5 pounds to kilograms
  g 7.5 kilograms to pounds   **h** 2.5 kilograms to pounds.

2 Here is a conversion graph for
  • euros to pounds
  • pounds to euros.

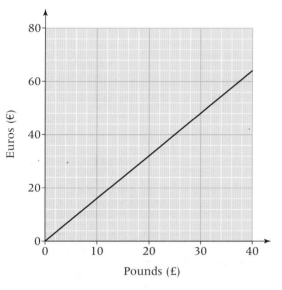

For your **Unit 3** assessment you should know these imperial to metric conversions :
5 miles $\simeq$ 8 kilometres
4.5 litres $\simeq$ 1 gallon
2.2 pounds $\simeq$ 1 kilogram
1 inch $\simeq$ 2.5 centimetres.

  a Use the graph to convert
    i €32 to pounds
    ii €48 to pounds
    iii £40 to euros
    iv £25 to euros
    v €50 to pounds
    vi €35 to pounds
  b Which is worth more: £1 or €1?
  Explain how you know.

3 Here is a conversion graph for
  • miles to kilometres
  • kilometres to miles.
  a Use the graph to convert
    i 4 km to miles
    ii 5 miles to km
    iii 1 mile to km
    iv 1 km to miles.
  b Which is longer, 1 mile or 1 km?
  Explain how you know.

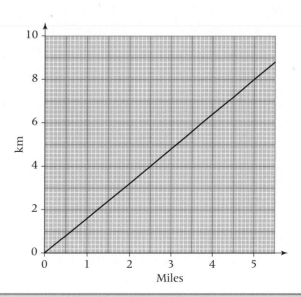

More conversion graphs

This spread will show you how to:
- Use and interpret conversion graphs
- Read values from graphs

You can use this conversion graph to convert
- temperatures in °C to °F
- temperatures in °F to °C.

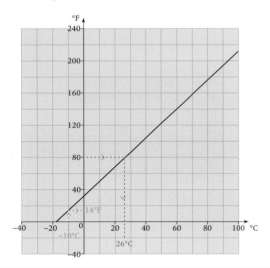

A weather forecast often gives temperatures in degrees Fahrenheit (°F) and degrees Celsius (°C).

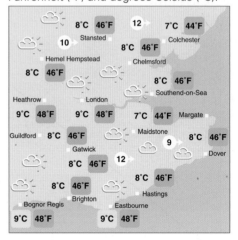

Example

Use the conversion graph to convert
a 80 °F to °C
b −10 °C to °F.

....

a To convert 80 °F to °C
  i Find 80 °F on the °F (vertical) axis. (This scale goes up in 40s.)
  ii Draw a line across to the graph.
  iii Draw a line down from the graph to the °C (horizontal) axis.
  iv Read the value off the axis.
    80 °F = 26 °C

b To convert −10 °C to °F
  i Find −10 °C on the °C (horizontal) axis.
  ii Draw a line up to the graph.
  iii Draw a line across from the graph to the °F (vertical) axis.
  iv Read the value off the axis.
    −10 °C = 14 °F

Example

Use the conversion graph to help you write these temperatures in order, from coldest to hottest.
    10 °F   60 °F   10 °C   80 °C   160 °F

....

To compare temperatures, they need to be measured in the same units.

From the graph, 10 °C = 50 °F
             80 °C = 176 °F

So in order the temperatures are   10°F   50°F   60°F   160°F   176°F
                                        ↓   ↓   ↓   ↓   ↓
                                       10°F   10°C   60°F   160°F   80°C

Use the original values in the answer.

Use the conversion graph for °F to °C on page 186 to answer questions **1** to **3**.

1 Convert these temperatures.
  a 120 °F to °C   **b** 60 °F to °C   **c** 40 °C to °F   **d** 65 °C to °F
  e 75 °F to °C   **f** 8 °F to °C   **g** −5 °C to °F   **h** −20 °C to °F

2 Which is hotter?
  a 20 °C or 20 °F   **b** 150 °F or 40 °C   **c** 18 °C or 60 °F
  d 90 °F or 30 °C   **e** −8 °C or 8 °F   **f** −30 °F or −30 °C

3 **a** The melting point of ice is 32 °F. What is this in °C?
    b The boiling point of water is 100 °C. What is this in °F?
    c Average body temperature for humans is 37 °C.
      What is this in °F?

A02 Functional Maths

4 Here is a conversion graph for inches to centimetres.
  a Use the conversion graph to convert
    i 6 inches to cm   **ii** 10 cm to inches
    iii 4 cm to inches   **iv** 10 inches to cm.
  b Use the graph to help you write these sets of lengths in order.
    i 2 inches   12 cm   13 inches   9 cm   4 inches
    ii 23 cm   1 inch   16 cm   5 inches   3 cm
  c For a handling data project, a group of students measured the lengths of their feet. Some measured in inches instead of centimetres.
    i Convert all the measurements in inches to centimetres.
    ii Write the students' feet in order of size.

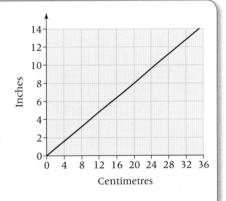

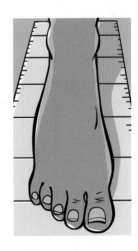

Name	Length of foot
Nadia	19 cm
Mel	10 inches
Jonathan	13 inches
Omar	23 cm
Shelley	10.5 inches
Dustin	12 inches
Jake	29 cm

A2

Summary

Check out

You should now be able to:

- Use axes and coordinates to describe the position of a point in all four quadrants
- Plot straight line graphs of functions
- Read values from a graph
- Use and interpret conversion graphs

Worked exam question

The points *A* and *B* are shown on the grid.

a Write down the coordinates of A and B. (2)

b Plot the points *C* (−2, 4) and *D* (−2, 2). (2)

c Join the points *ABCD*. (1)
What is the name of the shape *ABCD*?

(AQA, 2008)

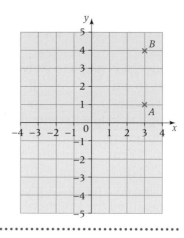

a

A(3, 1)   B(3, 4)

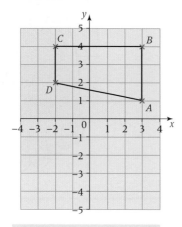

Trapezium

A trapezium is a quadrilateral (4-sided shape) with one pair of parallel sides.

Exam questions

1

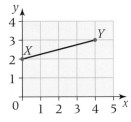

  a Write down the coordinates of the point
    i *X*
    ii *Y*   (2)
  b On a copy of the grid, mark with a cross (×) the midpoint of the line *XY*.   (1)

2   **a** Complete the table of values for $y = 2x + 6$ (1)

x	0	1	2	3	4	5
y	6		10		14	16

  b On a copy of the grid draw the graph of $y = 2x + 6$ for values of
    x from 0 to 5.   (2)

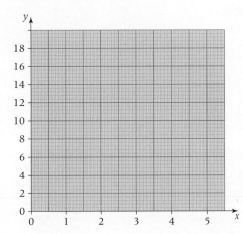

(AQA, 2008)

Introduction

When you use the Internet to pay for goods you need to know that your financial details are safe. To make these details secure they are turned into a secret code (encrypted). The message can be encrypted using the product of two very large prime numbers – the person receiving the message has to know both of these prime numbers so that they can decrypt the message.

What's the point?

The problems involved in identifying very large prime numbers make it very difficult for someone intercepting an encrypted message to crack the code.

1 Calculate

   a 7×7 **b** $2 \times 2 \times 2$

   c $10 \times 10 \times 10$ **d** $32 \div 100$

2 Find the missing number in this expression.

   $\_\_ \times \_\_ = 25$

3 Does 244 divide by 4?

   Explain how you know.

- Recognise and use squares and cubes, and corresponding roots
- Multiply and divide by powers of 10
- Recognise prime numbers and use divisibility tests
- Understand and use the terms factor and multiple
- Find the highest common factor and least common multiple

N1 → → +3

Rich task

This diagram shows a 5 by 3 rectangular grid of squares.

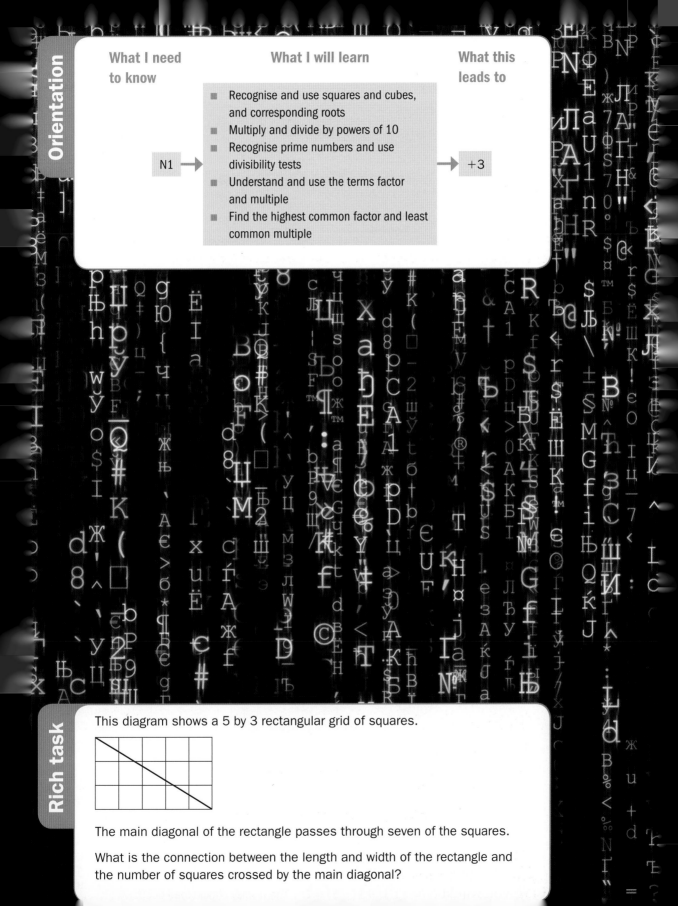

The main diagonal of the rectangle passes through seven of the squares.

What is the connection between the length and width of the rectangle and the number of squares crossed by the main diagonal?

This spread will show you how to:
- Use square and cube numbers
- Use the square and cube functions of a calculator

Keywords
Cube
Index
Power
Square

- A **square** number is the result of multiplying a **whole** number by itself.

1st square number	2nd square number	3rd square number	4th square number
1	4	9	16

$1 \times 1 = 1^2$ $2 \times 2 = 2^2$ $3 \times 3 = 3^2$ $4 \times 4 = 4^2$

Square numbers can be written using **index** notation.

$$5^2 = 5 \times 5 \qquad 12^2 = 12 \times 12$$
$$= 25 \qquad\qquad = 144$$

Use the x^2 function key on a calculator to find the square of a number.

To find 34^2, type $\boxed{3}$ $\boxed{4}$ $\boxed{x^2}$ $\boxed{=}$ The display should read 1156.

You can say 5^2 in lots of different ways

5^2 = '5 to the **power** of 2'
= '5 squared'
= 'the square of 5'

- A **cube** number is the result of multiplying a whole number by itself and then multiplying by that number again.

Cube numbers can be represented using 3D drawings of cubes.

1st cube number	2nd cube number	3rd cube number	4th cube number
1	8	27	64

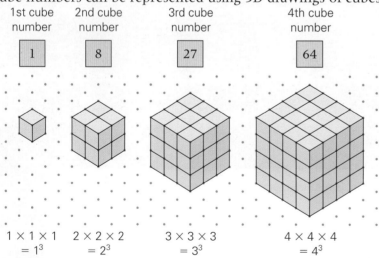

$1 \times 1 \times 1$ $2 \times 2 \times 2$ $3 \times 3 \times 3$ $4 \times 4 \times 4$
$= 1^3$ $= 2^3$ $= 3^3$ $= 4^3$

Cube numbers can be written using index notation.

$$4^3 = 4 \times 4 \times 4 \qquad 14^3 = 14 \times 14 \times 14$$
$$= 64 \qquad\qquad\quad = 2744$$

Use the x^3 function key on a calculator to find the cube of a number.

To find 19^3, you would type $\boxed{1}$ $\boxed{9}$ $\boxed{x^3}$ $\boxed{=}$ The display should read 6859.

You can say 4^3 in lots of different ways:

4^3 = '4 to the power of 3'
= '4 cubed'
= 'the cube of 4'

Unit 2

1 Find these numbers.
   a the 4th square number　　　　**b** the 8th square number
   c the 20th square number　　　　**d** the 5th cube number
   e the 7th cube number　　　　　**f** the 10th cube number

2 Use your calculator to work out each of these squares and cubes.
   a 6^2　　　**b** 11^2　　　**c** 14^2　　　**d** 23^2
   e 31^2　　**f** 47^2　　　**g** 4^3　　　**h** 6^3
   i 8^3　　　**j** 13^3　　　**k** 18^3　　　**l** 21^3

> **Remember:**
> You will not be allowed to use a calculator in your unit 2 assessment. You should know the squares up to 15^2, and cubes up to 5^3.

> **A03 Problem**
>
> 3 Some numbers can be represented as the sum of two square numbers.
>   For example $1^2 + 2^2 = 1 + 4 = 5$.
>   Try to find all the numbers less than 50 that can be represented as the sum of two square numbers.

4 Use your calculator to work out each of these.
   a $3^2 + 2^2$　　**b** $5^2 - 3^2$　　**c** $6^2 - 2^3$
   d $4^3 + 4^2$　　**e** $10^2 - 8^2$　　**f** $13^2 + 4^3$
   g $14^2 - 5^3$　　**h** $6^3 - 13^2$　　**i** $12^2 + 13^2 + 14^2$
   j $6^3 + 7^3 + 8^3$

5 Use the x^2 and x^3 function keys on your calculator to work out each of these. Give your answer to two decimal places as appropriate.
   a 2.5^2　　**b** 49^2　　　**c** 3.2^3　　**d** 4.8^2
   e 7.3^2　　**f** 4.9^3　　　**g** 1.2^2　　**h** 0.5^2
   i 9.9^2　　**j** 9.9^3　　　**k** $(5\ \text{cm})^2$　　**l** $(4\ \text{m})^3$

> **A03 Problem**
>
> 6 **a** Work out these.
> $3^2 - 2^2 = \underline{\ \ }$　　　$4^2 - 3^2 = \underline{\ \ }$　　　$5^2 - 4^2 = \underline{\ \ }$
>   **b** Write anything you have noticed about your answers.
>   **c** Copy and complete this table and investigate for the next seven pairs of consecutive integers.
>
> | Square number | Square number | | Answer |
> |---|---|---|---|
> | 3^2 | 2^2 | $3^2 - 2^2 = 9 - \underline{\ \ }$ | |
> | 4^2 | 3^2 | $4^2 - 3^2 = 16 - \underline{\ \ }$ | |
> | 5^2 | | | |
> | 6^2 | | | |

Consecutive means 'next to', for example 4 and 5

This spread will show you how to:
- Estimate and use square roots and cube roots
- Use the square root and cube root functions of a calculator

Keywords
Cube root
Square root

- A **square root** is a number that when multiplied by itself is equal to a given number.

$7 \times 7 = 49$ so you can say that the square root of $49 = 7$.
- Square roots are written using $\sqrt{}$ notation. $\sqrt{49} = 7$

You should try to learn the first 10 square numbers, then you will also know their square roots.

1st square number	$= 1 \times 1 = 1$	$\sqrt{1} = 1$
2nd square number	$= 2 \times 2 = 4$	$\sqrt{4} = 2$
3rd square number	$= 3 \times 3 = 9$	$\sqrt{9} = 3$

You can estimate the square root of a square number.

Example

289 is a square number. Work out $\sqrt{289}$ without using a calculator.

$15 \times 15 = 225$ This is too low, so $\sqrt{289}$ is greater than 15
$20 \times 20 = 400$ This is too high, so $\sqrt{289}$ is less than 20
$17 \times 17 = 289$ Correct
So $\sqrt{289} = 17$

You can use the grid method if you are stuck!

×	10	7	
10	$10 \times 10 = 100$	$10 \times 7 = 70$	100
7	$7 \times 10 = 70$	$7 \times 7 = 49$	70
			70
			$+49$
			289

Use the $\sqrt{x}$ function key on a calculator to find the square root of a number.

To find $\sqrt{289}$, you would type  The display should read 17.

You will not be allowed to use a calculator in your Unit 2 assessment.

- A **cube root** is a number that when multiplied by itself and then multiplied by itself again is equal to a given number.

$2 \times 2 \times 2 = 8$ so the cube root of $8 = 2$ or $\sqrt[3]{8} = 2$

Use the $\sqrt[3]{x}$ function key on a calculator to find the cube root of a number.

To find $\sqrt[3]{1728}$, you would type  The display should read 12.

Square roots and cube roots are often not whole numbers so you usually round your answer to two decimal places.
$\sqrt{300} = 17.320\ 508\ 08...$
      $= 17.32$ (2 dp)

1 Find these numbers.

 a $\sqrt{25}$ **b** $\sqrt{9}$ **c** $\sqrt{16}$ **d** $\sqrt{1}$ **e** $\sqrt{4}$

2 Calculate these using a calculator, giving your answer to 2 dp as appropriate.

 a $\sqrt{40}$ **b** $\sqrt{61}$ **c** $\sqrt{180}$ **d** $\sqrt{249}$ **e** $\sqrt{676}$

3 Calculate these using the $\sqrt[3]{}$ key on your calculator. Give your answers to 2 dp where appropriate.

 a $\sqrt[3]{27}$ **b** $\sqrt[3]{512}$ **c** $\sqrt[3]{3375}$ **d** $\sqrt[3]{100}$ **e** $\sqrt[3]{24\,389}$

A03 | Problem

4 Harry has mixed up his answers to these questions.

 a Without using a calculator, match each of these questions to the correct answer.

Questions		Estimates	
1	$\sqrt{169}$	A	9
2	$\sqrt[3]{343}$	B	8
3	$\sqrt{121}$	C	7
4	$\sqrt{81}$	D	4
5	$\sqrt{64}$	E	11
6	$\sqrt[3]{1000}$	F	13
7	$\sqrt{196}$	G	10
8	$\sqrt[3]{64}$	H	14

 b Check your answers using your calculator.
 See how many of the questions and answers you matched correctly.

A02 | Functional Maths

5 a A square has an area of 144 m². What is the side length of the square?

 b John thinks of a number. He multiplies the number by itself. The answer is 529. What number did John think of?

 c Mr Mow designs a paddock. The paddock has to be in the shape of a square. The area of the paddock has to be 4000 m². What length should each of the sides of the paddock be? (Give your answer to the nearest metre.)

 d Nelly digs a hole in the shape of a cube. The volume of the earth she digs out to make the hole is 64 000 cm³. How deep is the hole?

6 Do not use a calculator for these questions.

 a Between which two numbers does $\sqrt{95}$ lie?

 b Between which two numbers does $\sqrt{150}$ lie?

 c Between which two numbers does $\sqrt{300}$ lie?

 d Between which two numbers does $\sqrt[3]{80}$ lie?

This spread will show you how to:

- Understand and use index notation
- Multiply and divide by powers of 10

- **Index notation** is used to represent powers of any number.

  The **index** (or **power**) tells you how many times the number must be multiplied by itself.

  $$7^4 = 7 \times 7 \times 7 \times 7 = 2401$$
  $$6^3 = 6 \times 6 \times 6 \quad = 216$$

OUR POWERS COMBINED WE ARE 2401.

The small number is the index (or power).

Use your calculator to work out powers of a number.

To work out 13^5, you might type [1] [3] [y^x] [5] [=]

The display should read 371 293.

Your calculator may work differently. If you are unsure, ask your teacher or check your manual.

- The decimal system is based upon **powers of 10**.

1 ten	= 10	= 10	= 10^1
1 hundred	= 100	= 10 × 10	= 10^2
1 thousand	= 1000	= 10 × 10 × 10	= 10^3
10 thousand	= 10 000	= 10 × 10 × 10 × 10	= 10^4
100 thousand	= 100 000	= 10 × 10 × 10 × 10 × 10	= 10^5
1 million	= 1 000 000	= 10 × 10 × 10 × 10 × 10 × 10	= 10^6

- It is easy to multiply and divide by **powers of 10**.
  $\times 10^1 \Rightarrow$ digits move 1 place left
  $\times 10^2 \Rightarrow$ digits move 2 places left

p.4

	Thousands	Hundreds	Tens	Units		tenths	hundredths
				3	•	2	
3.2×10^1			3	2	•		
3.2×10^2		3	2	0	•		

The '0' holds the digits in place so that the '3' digit is in the Hundreds column and the '2' digit is in the Tens column.

$\div 10^1 \Rightarrow$ digits move 1 place right
$\div 10^2 \Rightarrow$ digits move 2 places right

	Thousands	Hundreds	Tens	Units		tenths	hundredths
			4	5	•		
$4.5 \div 10^1$				4	•	5	
$4.5 \div 10^2$				0	•	4	5

1 Find the value of
   a 5^2 **b** 2^3 **c** 3^3 **d** 8^2 **e** 12^2

2 Find the value of
   a 3^4 **b** 1^5 **c** 2^7 **d** 3^6 **e** 10^6

3 Use the y^x function key on your calculator to work out these.
   a 12^3 **b** 6^6 **c** 21^3 **d** 16^5 **e** 13^3

4 Use your calculator to work out these powers. In each case copy the question and fill in the missing numbers.
   a $3^? = 9$ **b** $5^? = 25$ **c** $4^? = 64$ **d** $2^? = 8$
   e $24^? = 576$

> Use a place value diagram.

5 Calculate each of these.
   a 1.2×10 **b** $655 \div 10$ **c** 3.4×10^3
   d $48 \div 100$ **e** 74×100 **f** $43.3 \div 10^2$

6 Here are some conversion rates for metric measurements.

1 km	=	1000 m	1 tonne	=	1000 kg	1 litre	= 1000 ml
1 m	=	100 cm	1 kg	=	1000 g	1 m^3	= 1000 litres
1 cm	=	10 mm					

Change these lengths to the units indicated in brackets.
You will need to multiply and divide by powers of 10.

> You will need to revise how to change between units to answer these questions.

   a 30 mm   (centimetres)   **b** 7 cm   (millimetres)
   c 3 km   (metres)   **d** 2500 m   (kilometres)
   e 240 cm   (metres)   **f** 7.2 m   (centimetres)
   g 2.4 tonnes (kg)   **h** 3750 kg   (tonnes)
   i 450 g   (kg)   **j** 2.04 kg   (grams)
   k 330 ml   (litres)   **l** 4.54 litres (ml)
   m 15 m^3 (litres)   **n** 2300 litres (m^3)

7 Copy these and fill in the missing numbers.
   a $34 \div 10 =$ ___   **b** $2800 \div$ ___ $= 28$
   c $6.1 \times$ __ $= 610$ **d** $5.7 \times 10^3 =$ ___

This spread will show you how to:
- Understand the terms 'factor' and 'multiple'
- Find the common factors and common multiples of two numbers

Keywords
Common factor
Common
  multiple
Factor
Multiple
Product

Any number can be written as the product of two **factors**.

$20 = 2 \times 10$ so 2 and 10 are factors of 20.

- The factors of a number are those numbers that divide into it exactly, leaving no remainder.

Product means multiply together.

You can often write a number as the **product** of two factors.

24 can be written as 4×6 or 3×8 or 2×12 or 1×24.

The factor pairs are 1×24, 2×12, 3×8 and 4×6.

You can write the factors in a list: 1, 2, 3, 4, 6, 8, 12, 24.

- A **common factor** is a factor that is common to two different numbers.

p.202

Example

Write the common factors of 30 and 42.

The factors of 30 are   1   2   3   5   6   10   15   30

The factors of 42 are   1   2   3   6   7   14   21   42

The common factors of 30 and 42 are 1, 2, 3 and 6.

You can use factor pairs:
1×30
2×15
3×10
5×6

The first five **multiples** of 20 are 20, 40, 60, 80 and 100.

$1 \times 20 = 20$ $2 \times 20 = 40$ $3 \times 20 = 60$
$4 \times 20 = 80$ $5 \times 20 = 100$

- A **common multiple** is a multiple that is common to two different numbers.

Example

Write the first three common multiples of 8 and 12.

The multiples of 8 are   8   16   24   32   40   48   56   64   72   80   ...

The multiples of 12 are   12   24   36   48   60   72   84   ...

The first three common multiples of 8 and 12 are 24, 48 and 72.

1 This factor diagram shows all the factor pairs of 12.

$1 \times 12 = 12 \qquad 2 \times 6 = 12 \qquad 3 \times 4 = 12$

The factors of 12 are 1, 2, 3, 4, 6 and 12.

Copy and complete these factor diagrams.

a 18

b 20

c 30

d 14
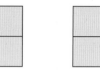

2 Draw factor diagrams for
   a 15   **b** 22   **c** 28   **d** 36   **e** 40

3 Write all the factor pairs for each number.
   a 8   **b** 16   **c** 23   **d** 34   **e** 10
   f 26   **g** 42   **h** 48   **i** 39   **j** 44

4 Write the first three multiples of each number.
   a 7   **b** 9   **c** 12   **d** 15   **e** 17
   f 25   **g** 30   **h** 32   **i** 45   **j** 50

5 Find the common factors of
   a 10 and 20   **b** 12 and 15   **c** 20 and 25
   d 8 and 20   **e** 21 and 28   **f** 30 and 40
   g 12 and 28   **h** 9 and 36   **i** 24 and 30

6 Find the first two common multiples of
   a 6 and 10   **b** 9 and 12   **c** 4 and 6
   d 10 and 15   **e** 14 and 21   **f** 20 and 30

7 a Write a multiple of 20 that is bigger than 200.
   b Write a multiple of 15 that is between 100 and 140.
   c Write a multiple of 6 that is bigger than 70 but less than 100.

Problem

A03

Prime numbers

This spread will show you how to:

- Recognise prime numbers
- Use simple divisibility tests to check if a number is prime

Keywords
Factor
Prime number
Prime factor

Any whole number can be written as the product of two **factors**.

To list all the factors of 12, draw rectangles.

○○○○○○○○○○○○
$1 \times 12 = 12$

○○○○○○
○○○○○○
$2 \times 6 = 12$

○○○○
○○○○
○○○○
$3 \times 4 = 12$

The factors of 12 are {1, 2, 3, 4, 6 and 12}.

1, 2, 3, 4, 6 and 12 are factors of 12 because all these numbers divide exactly into 12 with no remainder.

- A **prime number** is a number with only two factors, these are 1 and the number itself.

29 is a prime number because it has only two factors, the numbers 1 and 29.

The first ten prime numbers are: 2, 3, 5, 7, 11, 13, 17, 19, 23, 29.

- A **prime factor** is a prime number that is also a factor of another number.

Factors of 20 = {1, 2, 4, 5, 10, 20}
Prime factors of 20 = {2, 5}

You can use simple divisibility tests to help you check if a number is a prime number.
Here are the divisibility tests for the first five prime numbers.

This topic is extended to prime factor decomposition on page 412.

÷2	the number ends in 0, 2, 4, 6 or 8
÷3	the sum of the digits is divisible by 3
÷5	the number ends in 0 or 5
÷7	there is no check for divisibility by 7
÷11	the alternate digits add up to the same sum

Example

Which of the numbers in this list are prime numbers: 42, 27, 43, 55?
....

42 ⇒ 2 is a factor (because it ends in a 2)
　　　　　42 is not a prime number.
27 ⇒ 2 is not a factor
　　　3 is a factor (because 2 + 7 = 9, a multiple of 3)
　　　　　27 is not a prime number.
43 ⇒ 2 is not a factor
　　　3 is not a factor
　　　5 is not a factor
　　　7 is not a factor (because 6 × 7 is 42)
　　　　　43 is a prime number.
55 ⇒ 2 is not a factor
　　　3 is not a factor
　　　5 is a factor (because it ends in a 5)
　　　　　55 is not a prime number.

Unit 2

1 Write all the factors of these numbers.
  a 8   **b** 12   **c** 11   **d** 14
  e 28   **f** 30   **g** 40   **h** 50

A03 Problem

2 Your task is to find all the prime numbers from 1 to 100.
  a Copy this 1–100 number square.
  b Follow these instructions.
    • 1 is not a prime number so you can cross it out.
    • 2 is the lowest prime number. Cross out all the multiples of 2 except for the number 2.
    • 3 is the next number not crossed out. It is the next prime number. Cross out all the multiples of 3 except for the number 3.
    • 5 is the next number not crossed out. It is the next prime number. Cross out all the multiples of 5 except for the number 5.
  c Carry on until you have only prime numbers left.
  d Make a list of all the prime numbers from 1 to 100.

1	2	3	4	5	6	7	8	9	10
11	12	13	14	15	16	17	18	19	20
21	22	23	24	25	26	27	28	29	30
31	32	33	34	35	36	37	38	39	40
41	42	43	44	45	46	47	48	49	50
51	52	53	54	55	56	57	58	59	60
61	62	63	64	65	66	67	68	69	70
71	72	73	74	75	76	77	78	79	80
81	82	83	84	85	86	87	88	89	90
91	92	93	94	95	96	97	98	99	100

3 Use the divisibility tests to answer each of these questions. In each case explain your answer.
  a Is 5 a factor of 135?   **b** Is 5 a factor of 210?
  c Is 2 a factor of 321?   **d** Is 11 a factor of 231?
  e Is 7 a factor of 91?

DID YOU KNOW?

The largest prime number to date was discovered in 2008, and it is almost 13 million digits long. To find a prime number this big, you need a very large computer!

4 Look at these numbers.

1	2	3	5	6	8	9
10	11	12	13	16	18	20

  a Write all the numbers that are factors of 10.
  b Write all the numbers that are square numbers.
  c Write all the numbers that are prime factors of 44.
  d Write all the numbers that are prime numbers.

5 Use the mental method of halving and doubling to calculate each of these. Show the method you have used.
  a 4×21 **b** 3×16 **c** 23×4 **d** 16×15

Hint for question 6: List all the factors. Find the ones that are prime.

6 Write all the prime factors of each of these numbers.
  a 20   **b** 27   **c** 55   **d** 35
  e 22   **f** 70   **g** 120   **h** 110

This spread will show you how to:

- Understand and use the terms factor and multiple
- Understand and use simple divisibility tests
- Understand the terms highest common factor and least common multiple

Keywords
Common factor
Common multiple
Factor
HCF
LCM
Multiple

You can use a range of strategies to find all the **factors** of larger numbers.

Example

Find all the factors of 252.

You can list the factors by factor pairs.
Factors of 252 are

1 × 252	4 × 63	9 × 28
2 × 126	6 × 42	12 × 21
3 × 84	7 × 36	14 × 18

Factors of 252 are
{1, 2, 3, 4, 6, 7, 9, 12, 14, 18, 21, 28, 36, 42, 53, 84, 126, 252}.

You can use doubling and halving to help find factors:

7 × 36 = 252
14 × 18 = 252

p.198 You can find the **highest common factor (HCF)** of two numbers by listing all the factors of both numbers.

This topic is extended to prime factors on page 412.

Example

Find the HCF of 24 and 60.

The factors of 24 are: 1 2 3 4 6 8 12 24
The factors of 60 are: 1 2 3 4 5 6 10 12 15 20 30 60

1, 2, 3, 4, 6 and 12 are **common factors** of 24 and 60.
12 is the **highest common factor** of 24 and 60.

- The **multiples** of a number are those numbers that divide by it exactly, leaving no remainder.

The multiples of 18 are 18, 36, 54, 72, ...
     1 × 18 = 18   3 × 18 = 54
     2 × 18 = 36   4 × 18 = 72

You can find the **least common multiple (LCM)** of two numbers by listing the first few multiples of each number.

You can think of multiples as being the numbers in the 'times tables'.

Example

Find the least common multiple of 24 and 60.

The first six multiples of 24 are: 24   48   72   96 120 144
The first six multiples of 60 are: 60 120 180 240 300 360

120, 240, 360 are **common multiples** of 24 and 60.
120 is the **least common multiple** of 24 and 60.

1 Write all the factor pairs of each of these numbers.
   a 18   **b** 14   **c** 30   **d** 48

2 Look at these numbers.

2	3	4	5	6	8	10
12	15	16	17	18	19	20

   a Write all the numbers that are factors of 40.
   b Write all the numbers that are factors of 90.
   c Write all the numbers that are multiples of 2.
   d Write all the numbers that are prime numbers.

3 Write the first three multiples of each of these numbers.
   a 6   **b** 11   **c** 19   **d** 25
   e 65   **f** 105   **g** 187   **h** 308

4 Use divisibility tests to answer each of these questions.
   In each case explain your answer.
   a Is 5 a factor of 95?   **b** Is 10 a factor of 710?
   c Is 9 a factor of 321?   **d** Is 11 a factor of 451?
   e Is 6 a factor of 98?

5 Find the highest common factor of
   a 6 and 4   **b** 12 and 18   **c** 14 and 16
   d 28 and 35   **e** 30 and 54   **f** 56 and 64

6 Find the least common multiple of
   a 6 and 4   **b** 6 and 8   **c** 12 and 18
   d 15 and 25   **e** 21 and 28   **f** 26 and 39

7 a Copy and complete this table.

Numbers	Product	HCF	LCM
6 and 4	6 × 4 = 24	2	12
8 and 10	8 × 10 = ——		
12 and 18			
6 and 9			
15 and 20			
15 and 25			

   b Write anything you notice about the numbers in your table.
   c Write a quick way to find the LCM if you know the HCF.

Summary

Check out
You should now be able to:

- Use the terms square, square root, cube and cube root
- Understand and use index notation for squares, cubes and powers of 10
- Multiply and divide by powers of 10
- Identify factors, multiples and prime numbers from a list of numbers
- Find the highest common factor and the least common multiple of two numbers

Worked exam question
Here is a list of numbers.

                12 8 16 3 19 36

a Write down **three** numbers from the list that add up to 30.   (1)
b Write down **one** number from the list that is a square number.   (1)
c Write down the number from the list that is a factor of 40.   (1)
d Write down the number from the list that is 50% of 24.   (1)

(AQA, 2008)

a
8, 3, 19

b
16   ←   You could have chosen 36 instead.

c
8

d
12

Exam questions

1 Here is a list of numbers.

> 5   6   7   8   9   10

From the list of numbers write down
a an even number (1)
b a square number (1)
c a multiple of 4 (1)
d a factor of 14. (1)

2 Here is a list of numbers.

> 4   5   6   7   8   9   10   11   12

From the list write down
a two odd numbers, (1)
b a prime number (1)
c the highest common factor (HCF) of 32 and 40. (2)

3 **a** Write down a multiple of 7 between 40 and 50. (1)
b Two numbers multiply to make 80.
The same two numbers add to make 21.

What are the two numbers? (2)
(AQA, 2009)

4 **a** Explain why the cube of 5 is equal to 125. (1)

b Calculate 6^3 (1)

c Is 196 a cube number?
Explain your answer. (1)

d Find **one** number which is both a square number and a cube number. (1)
(AQA, 2009)

5 Find the Highest Common Factor (HCF) of 60 and 84. (2)

AO2 + 3

6 Two airport towers flash at regular intervals.
One flashes every 12 seconds and the other flashes every 9 seconds.
An aircraft pilot sees both towers flashing at the same time.
How many seconds will pass before they both flash together again? (3)

Mathematics can help you to plan and budget for a holiday, as well as to understand currency, temperature and other units of measure at your destination.

holiday

Paris

LOUISE'S family are planning to go on holiday. Her parents will pay for the trip, but she must raise her own spending money.

VALID FOR DATE OF PERFORMANCE ONLY
MANAGEMENT RESERVES THE RIGHT TO REFUSE ADMISSION

Screen 13   **Cinemaland**
29/11/09   CINEMAS
17:50
A GOOD NIGHT   £4.50

YOU WERE SERVED BY DS AT TERMINAL 4. PAID BY: Cash

Hire charge
£1.99 per film!   SIGN UP
4 easy steps to online   NOW!!

1 How much money could Louise save in the three months from March to May if she hired a DVD once a week instead of going to the cinema?

2 A neighbour offers to pay Louise £10 per week if she takes her dog for a 30-minute walk every weekday before school.

What hourly rate of pay does this represent?

How much would Louise earn if she walked the dog every weekday throughout March, April and May?

3 Louise's brother sold 18 of his CDs for £45. How much did he sell each CD for?

He then sold another two CDs and 11 DVDs for £43.50. How much did he charge for each DVD?'

How could you raise money towards a holiday fund or to buy a new item? How long would it take you to reach your target amount?

If you are going on holiday outside of the UK, then you will need to convert your money from £ Sterling to the local currency of your destination. Many European countries now use the Euro, €.

In 2005, the average £ Sterling : Euro exchange rate was 1 : 1.46 .

In that year, how many

a) Euros would you receive in exchange for £150

b) £ Sterling would you receive in exchange for 120EUR?

Suppose that you are charged £70 (with no commission) to buy 91.7EUR.

What is the exchange rate? Give your answer as a ratio £ Sterling : Euro.

Some companies charge a commission fee to exchange currency. With an added charge of 1%, how many Euros would you now receive (at the same exchange rate) for £70?

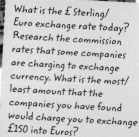

What is the £ Sterling/ Euro exchange rate today? Research the commission rates that some companies are charging to exchange currency. What is the most/ least amount that the companies you have found would charge you to exchange £150 into Euros?

Deciding on your method of transport is an important part of planning a holiday.

Some travel options between Oxford and Paris are shown.

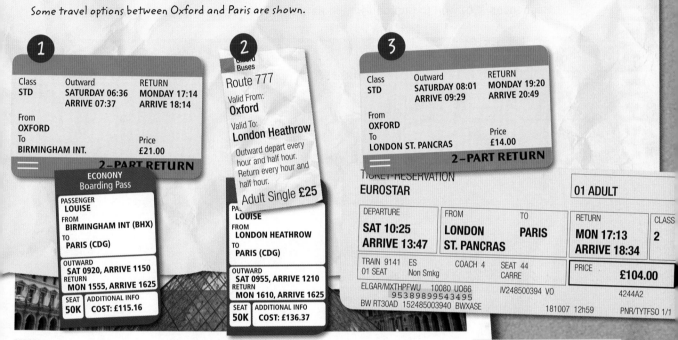

1

Class STD	Outward SATURDAY 06:36 ARRIVE 07:37	RETURN MONDAY 17:14 ARRIVE 18:14

From
OXFORD
To
BIRMINGHAM INT.
Price
£21.00

2 – PART RETURN

ECONOMY
Boarding Pass

PASSENGER
LOUISE
FROM
BIRMINGHAM INT (BHX)
TO
PARIS (CDG)
OUTWARD
SAT 0920, ARRIVE 1150
RETURN
MON 1555, ARRIVE 1625

SEAT	ADDITIONAL INFO
50K	**COST: £115.16**

2

Oxford
Buses

Route 777

Valid From:
Oxford

Valid To:
London Heathrow

Outward depart every
hour and half hour.
Return every hour and
half hour.

Adult Single **£25**

PASSENGER
LOUISE
FROM
LONDON HEATHROW
TO
PARIS (CDG)
OUTWARD
SAT 0955, ARRIVE 1210
RETURN
MON 1610, ARRIVE 1625

SEAT	ADDITIONAL INFO
50K	**COST: £136.37**

3

Class STD	Outward SATURDAY 08:01 ARRIVE 09:29	RETURN MONDAY 19:20 ARRIVE 20:49

From
OXFORD
To
LONDON ST. PANCRAS
Price
£14.00

2 – PART RETURN

TICKET RESERVATION
EUROSTAR

01 ADULT

DEPARTURE **SAT 10:25** **ARRIVE 13:47**	FROM **LONDON** **ST. PANCRAS**	TO **PARIS**	RETURN **MON 17:13** **ARRIVE 18:34**	CLASS **2**
TRAIN 9141 ES 01 SEAT Non Smkg	COACH 4	SEAT 44 CARRE	PRICE **£104.00**	

ELGAR/MXTHPFWU   10080 U066   IV248500394 VO   4244A2
95389899543495
BW RT30AD 152485003940 BWXASE   181007 12h59   PNR/TYTFSO 1/1

WHICH travel option would you choose? Explain your response with reference to the travel times and costs. All times given are local. Paris is in the time zone GMT + 1 hour.

The foreign travel legs of the same journey options can be paid for in Euros for the following prices:

Return flight BHX to Paris CDG 151.49€; return Eurostar journey 130€, return flight London Heathrow to Paris CDG 162.82€.

How does each of the prices in Euros compare with the corresponding price in GBP?

Explore travel options from your hometown to different destinations. Be careful, there are some times hidden costs such as additional taxes and fees.

■ Different countries often use different units of measure for quantities such as temperature.

An Internet site states that the maximum and minimum temperatures in Rome on a particular day are 99°F and 63°F respectively.

A formula that can be used to convert between °C and °F is temp(°C) = 5(temp(°F) − 32)/9

What are the corresponding maximum and minimum temperatures in Rome?

The maximum and minimum temperatures in London on the same day were 25°C and 16°C. What are these temperatures in °F?

What are the maximum and minimum temperatures in your home town today? Use the formula in the example to convert the temperatures you have found from °C to °F.

STREET MAP
Paris
1:13,000 and 1:8,600

Introduction

There are lots of different types of sequences in mathematics: from the most basic arithmetic sequences such as the set of even numbers, to the curious Fibonacci sequence used to describe plant growth, through to the elegant and complex world of iterative sequences used in chaos theory.

What's the point?
Sequences allow you to find patterns in nature, so that you can understand it better.

1 Find the missing numbers in these multiplication calculations.
   a $4 \times \square = 12$ **b** $3 \times \square = 27$
   c $8 \times \square = 32$ **d** $6 \times \square = 18$

2 Work out the square numbers from 1^2 to 10^2.

3 Copy and complete.
   a $2 + \square = 7$ **b** $16 - \square = 12$
   c $11 + \square = 18$ **d** $25 - \square = 19$

4 Copy and complete.
   a $3 \times \square = 6$ **b** $12 \div \square = 6$
   c $7 \times \square = 21$ **d** $18 \div \square = 6$

5 Substitute $n = 3$ into these expressions.
   a $n + 5$ **b** $2n$ **c** $3n + 3$ **d** $4n - 2$

Rich task

You have 15 circles. Here is a sequence of patterns that you can make.

Devise the first three terms of a different sequence using all 15 circles
Find the nth term of your sequence.

Can you find another sequence that uses all 15 circles?
Investigate finding the first three terms of sequences for different numbers of circles.

This spread will show you how to:

- Understand and use the vocabulary associated with sequences
- Generate terms of a sequence using a term-to-term rule

Keywords
Ascending
Consecutive
Descending
Difference
Sequence
Term

- The numbers in a **sequence** follow a pattern.
  Each number in a sequence is called a **term**.

- You can see how a sequence grows by looking at the **differences** between **consecutive** terms.

Consecutive terms are next to each other.

The first five terms of a sequence are

$$1, \quad 4, \quad 7, \quad 10, \quad 13, \ldots$$

Difference: $\quad +3 \quad +3 \quad +3 \quad +3$

You can follow the pattern to work out more terms.
$13 + 3 = 16$, $16 + 3 = 19$, etc.

The numbers are getting higher. The sequence is **ascending**.

- A linear sequence goes up (or down) in equal sized steps.

Example

The first five terms of a sequence are
    14, 12, 10, 8, 6, ...
Work out the next two terms in the sequence.

$$14, \quad 12, \quad 10, \quad 8, \quad 6, \ldots$$

Difference: $\quad -2 \quad -2 \quad -2 \quad -2$

The next two terms are $6 - 2 = 4$ and $4 - 2 = 2$.

The numbers are getting lower. The sequence is **descending**.

In a sequence that is not linear, the differences between terms may follow a pattern.

Example

The first five terms of a sequence are
    1, 2, 5, 10, 17, ...
Work out the next two terms.

$$1, \quad 2, \quad 5, \quad 10, \quad 17, \ldots$$

Difference: $\quad +1 \quad +3 \quad +5 \quad +7$

The next term is $17 + 9 = 26$.

The term after is $26 + 11 = 37$.

The difference pattern is the odd numbers. The next odd number is 9. The next odd number is 11.

1 Find the next two terms for each sequence.
  a 3, 5, 7, 9, ...
  b 2, 5, 8, 11, ...
  c 1, 5, 9, 13, ...
  d 4, 6, 8, 10, ...

2 Work out the next two terms for each sequence.
  a 26, 21, 16, 11, ...
  b 32, 28, 24, 20, ...
  c 22, 19, 16, 13, ...
  d 86, 76, 66, 56, ...

3 Find the next two terms for each sequence.
  a 6, 9, 12, 15, ...
  b 15, 13, 11, 9, ...
  c 2, 9, 16, 23, ...
  d 50, 42, 34, 26, ...

4 Write the next two terms of the sequence 15, 17, 19, 21, ...
Explain why 72 is **not** a term in this sequence.

5 For each sequence,
  i Work out the differences between consecutive terms.
  ii Follow the pattern to work out the next two terms.
  a 2, 3, 5, 8, 12, ...
  b 21, 20, 18, 15, ...
  c 4, 5, 8, 13, 20, ...
  d 20, 15, 11, 8, ...

6 Follow the patterns in these sequences to work out the next two terms.

  a 1,   2,   4,   ...
         ×2   ×2   ×2

  b 128,   64,   32,   ...
          ÷2   ÷2   ÷2

  c 5, 10, 20, ...
  d 81, 27, 9, ...

7 The first three terms of a sequence are 3, 6, 12, ...
Jim says 'Double a term to get the next one.'
Sophie says 'The differences are +3 then +6. Add 9 to get the next term.'
  a Write the first four terms of
    i Jim's sequence   **ii** Sophie's sequence.
  b Write the first four terms of two different sequences that begin 1, 2, 4, ...

8 Work out the next two terms in each sequence.
  a −5, −3, −1, 1, 3, ...
  b 15, 12, 9, 6, 3, ...
  c −4, −3, −1, 2, 6
  d 21, 19, 16, 12, 7, ...

9 In each part, two sequences have been mixed up.
Write out each sequence in the correct order.
  a 2, 4, 6, 6, 8, 10, 10, 12, 14, 18   **b** 1, 4, 5, 7, 9, 10, 13, 13, 17

A03 Problem

Generating sequences

This spread will show you how to:

- Use term-to-term rules to work out missing terms in a sequence
- Generate terms of a sequence using a position-to-term rule
- Describe a sequence by giving its start number and term-to-term rule

Keywords

nth term
position-to-term
term-to-term

- A **term-to-term** rule tells you how to work out the next term in a sequence.

For the sequence   5,   8,   11,   14,   17, ...

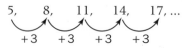

$+3$ $+3$ $+3$ $+3$

the term-to-term rule is 'add 3'.

- The term-to-term rule links one term to the next term in the sequence.

You can generate a sequence from a start number and a term-to-term rule.

Example

Generate the first five terms of the sequence with start number 7 and term-to-term rule 'add 4'.

···

7, 11, 15, 19, 23

$7 + 4 = 11$
$11 + 4 = 15$
$15 + 4 = 19$
$19 + 4 = 23$

You can use the term-to-term rule to work out missing terms in a sequence.

Example

Find the missing terms in these sequences.

a   3, 7, 11, ?, 19, ...   **b**   ?, 8, 11, 14, ...

···

a   3,   7,   11,   ?,   19, ...   **b**   ?,   8,   11,   14, ...

$+4$ $+4$ $+4$ $+4$ $+3$ $+3$

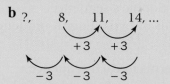

                                -3 -3 -3

The missing term is $11 + 4 = 15$.   The missing term is $8 - 3 = 5$.

Work backwards using the inverse operation.

- A **position-to-term** rule links a term to its position in the sequence.

The position-to-term rule is often called the **nth** term.
$n + 2$, $2n - 1$, $5n$, $4n + 3$ are all examples of nth terms.

1st term is in position 1,
2nd term is in position 2,
nth term is in position n.

Example

The nth term of a sequence is $2n + 1$.
Write the first three terms of the sequence.

···

Substitute the position number into $2n + 1$.
1st term $n = 1 : 2 \times 1 + 1 = 3$
2nd term $n = 2 : 2 \times 2 + 1 = 5$
3rd term $n = 3 : 2 \times 3 + 1 = 7$

This topic is extended to the general term on page 424.

1 Write the first five terms of these sequences.
   a start number 4   term-to-term rule 'add 2'
   b start number 7   term-to-term rule 'add 3'
   c start number 25   term-to-term rule 'subtract 2'
   d start number 30   term-to-term rule 'subtract 4'

2 Find the missing terms in these sequences.
   a 3, 8, 13, ?, 23   **b** 18, 15, 12, ?, 6
   c ?, 9, 13, 17, 21   **d** ?, 16, 12, ?, 4

3 Write the first five terms of the sequences with
   a start number 5   term-to-term rule 'multiply by 2'
   b start number 32   term-to-term rule 'divide by 2'
   c start number 3   term-to-term rule 'add consecutive odd
                                  numbers'
   d start number 40   term-to-term rule 'subtract consecutive even
                                  numbers'

4 Generate the first five terms of these sequences.
   a start number -5 term-to-term rule 'add 2'
   b start number 7   term-to-term rule 'subtract 3'
   c start number 3   term-to-term rule 'multiply by -1'

5 Generate the first five terms of the sequences with these nth terms.
   a $n + 1$ **b** $n + 3$ **c** $2n - 1$ **d** $2n + 3$
   e $3n - 1$ **f** $3n + 2$ **g** $4n + 3$ **h** $5n - 2$

6 Find the missing terms in these sequences.
   a -3, 0, 3, ?, 9   **b** 12, ?, 2, -3, -8
   c 2, 3, 5, ?, 12   **d** ?, 12, 8, ?, -6

7 Generate the first five terms of the sequence with nth term
   a $n - 1$ **b** $n - 3$ **c** n^2 **d** $-n + 3$

8 Match each sequence in set A to an nth term in set B.
   Set A:
          5, 9, 13, 17, …   16, 14, 12, 10, …   1, 7, 13, 19, …
          4, 7, 10, 13, …   21, 17, 13, 9, …   2, 8, 14, 20, …

   Set B:
          $6n - 4$ $4n + 1$ $25 - 4n$ $6n - 5$ $3n + 1$ $18 - 2n$

Describing sequences in words

This spread will show you how to:
- Describe a sequence by giving its start number and term-to-term rule
- Describe a sequence by comparing it to a sequence of multiples

Keywords
Multiples
Term-to-term rule

- You can describe a sequence by giving its start number and **term-to-term rule**.

WANTED
DEAD OR ALIVE
THE SEQUENCE
2, 6, 10, 14
Start number: 2
Term-to-Term Rule: +4

Example

Describe the sequence: 5, 11, 17, 23, 29, …

5   11   17   23   29
  +6   +6   +6   +6

The sequence has start number 5 and term-to-term rule 'add 6'.

Some sequences have special names.
For example:
1, 3, 5, 7, 9, … are 'the odd numbers'
2, 4, 6, 8, 10, … are 'the even numbers' or 'the **multiples** of 2'
1, 4, 9, 16, 25, … are 'the square numbers'.

- You can describe a sequence by comparing it to a sequence of multiples.

Example

a Write the first five terms of the sequence 'multiples of 3'.
b Here is a sequence
       2, 5, 8, 11, 14, …
   Describe this sequence in words by comparing it to the multiples of 3.

a 3, 6, 9, 12, 15
b Multiples of 3   3   6   9   12   15

                         −1   −1   −1   −1   −1

Term of sequence   2   5   8   11   14
The sequence is 'one less than the multiples of 3'.

Each term is one less than the corresponding term in the multiples of 3 sequence.

1 Describe each of these sequences in words, by giving the start number and the term-to-term rule.
  a 6, 7, 8, 9, 10, ...   **b** 3, 7, 11, 15, 19, ...
  c 9, 15, 21, 27, 33, ...   **d** 20, 17, 14, 11, 8, ...
  e 16, 14, 12, 10, 8, ...   **f** 33, 28, 23, 18, 13, ...

2 Each set of numbers is a jumbled sequence of multiples.
  Write each sequence in the correct order.
  Write the name of each sequence in the form 'the multiples of _____'.
  a 20, 5, 10, 15, 25, ...   **b** 21, 35, 7, 14, 28
  c 30, 6, 18, 24, 12, ...   **d** 27, 9, 36, 18, 45

3 Write the first five terms of each of these sequences.
  a The multiples of 4
  b One more than the multiples of 4
  c One less than the multiples of 4
  d The multiples of 3
  e Two less than the multiples of 3
  f Four more than the multiples of 3

4 Describe each of your sequences from question **3** by giving the start number and term-to-term rule.

5 Describe these sequences by giving the start number and the term-to-term rule.
  a 10 000, 1000, 100, 10, 1, ...   **b** 4, 8, 16, 32, 64, ...
  c 80, 40, 20, 10, 5, ...   **d** 3, 9, 27, 81, 243, ...

6 Describe these sequences by giving the start number and the term-to-term rule.
  a $-10, -4, 2, 8, 14, ...$ **b** 15, 11, 7, 3, -1
  c 100, 60, 20, -20, -60, ... **d** $-5, 0, 10, 25, 45, ...$

7 Describe these sequences in words by comparing them to the multiples of 4.
  a 6, 10, 14, 18, 22, ...   **b** 1, 5, 9, 13, 17, ...

8 The nth term of a sequence is $2n$.
  Generate the first five terms of this sequence.
  Write two names for this sequence.

Pattern sequences 1

This spread will show you how to:
- Generate and describe sequences derived from patterns

Keywords
Pattern

These **patterns** are made from dots.

○   ○ ○   ○ ○ ○
○   ○ ○   ○ ○ ○

Pattern 1   Pattern 2   Pattern 3

To get from one pattern to the next in the sequence, you add two more dots.
The term-to-term rule is 'add 2'.
The numbers of dots in the patterns make a sequence

Pattern number	1	2	3	4
Number of dots	2	4	6	8

Pattern 4 is
○ ○ ○ ○
○ ○ ○ ○

The number of dots are the multiples of 2.
The number of dots in each pattern is

pattern number × 2

This is the position-to-term rule for the sequence.
The 10th pattern has 10 × 2 = 20 dots.

- You can use the term-to-term rule and position-to-term rule to work out the number of dots in other patterns.

Example

Here is a pattern made of tiles.

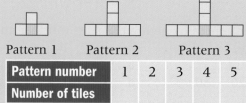

Pattern 1   Pattern 2   Pattern 3

a Copy and complete the table for the pattern sequence.

Pattern number	1	2	3	4	5
Number of tiles					

b Describe how the sequence grows.
c Work out the number of tiles in the 10th pattern.

....

a

Pattern number	1	2	3	4	5
Number of tiles	4	7	10	13	16

b Add 3 blue tiles each time, one to each arm.
c Pattern 1: 3 = 1 × 3 blue + 1 pink
Pattern 2: 6 = 2 × 3 blue + 1 pink
Pattern 3: 9 = 3 × 3 blue + 1 pink
...
Pattern 10: 10 × 3 blue + 1 pink = 31 tiles

Count the tiles in patterns 1, 2 and 3.
Each time you add 3.
So pattern 4 has 10 + 3 = 13 tiles.
Pattern 5 has 13 + 3 = 16 tiles.

Write out how the pattern grows in 3s. This links the pattern number to the number of tiles.

1 Draw the next pattern in each sequence.

a

 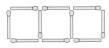 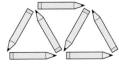

Pattern 1   Pattern 2   Pattern 3

c

 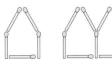 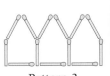

Pattern 1   Pattern 2   Pattern 3

b

Pattern 1   Pattern 2   Pattern 3

d

Pattern 1   Pattern 2   Pattern 3

2 a Copy and complete this table for pattern **a** in question **1**.

Pattern number	1	2	3	4	5
Number of matches					

b Copy and complete this table for pattern **b** in question **1**.

Pattern number	1	2	3	4	5
Number of pencils					

c Copy and complete this table for pattern **c** in question **1**.

Pattern number	1	2	3	4	5
Number of dots					

d Copy and complete this table for pattern **d** in question **1**.

Pattern number	1	2	3	4	5
Number of matches					

3 For each pattern
  i describe how the pattern grows
  ii copy and complete these statements.
    Pattern 1 has _____ + _____
    Pattern 2 has 2 × _____ + _____
    Pattern 3 has 3 × _____ + _____
    Pattern 10 has __ × _____ + _____

a

Pattern 1   Pattern 2   Pattern 3

b

Pattern 1   Pattern 2   Pattern 3

4 Here are some patterns of dots.
  a Draw pattern number 4.
  b Copy and complete the table.

Pattern 1   Pattern 2   Pattern 3

Pattern number	1	2	3	4	5	10
Number of dots						

  c Explain how you worked out the number of dots in pattern number 10.

This spread will show you how to:

- Generate and describe sequences derived from patterns

Here is a **sequence** of patterns made from dots.

The next two patterns are:

○ ○ ○   ○ ○ ○ ○   ○ ○ ○ ○ ○   ○ ○ ○ ○ ○ ○   ○ ○ ○ ○ ○ ○ ○
   ○ ○   ○ ○ ○   ○ ○ ○ ○   ○ ○ ○ ○ ○   ○ ○ ○ ○ ○ ○

Pattern 1   Pattern 2   Pattern 3   Pattern 4   Pattern 5

The numbers of dots make a sequence.

Pattern number	1	2	3	4	5
Number of dots	5	7	9	11	13

The **term-to-term** rule is 'add 2'.

- You can use the term-to-term rule to work out the number of dots in the next pattern.

Example

Here is a sequence of patterns made from stars.

a Draw the next two patterns in the sequence.
b Describe how the patterns grow.
c Complete the table for the sequence.

Pattern number	1	2	3	4	5
Number of stars					

Pattern 1   Pattern 2   Pattern 3

d Work out the number of stars in the 6th and 7th patterns.
e Work out the number of stars in the 10th pattern.

a

Pattern 4   Pattern 5

b Add one star to each side
So add three stars each time.

c

Pattern number	1	2	3	4	5
Number of stars	3	6	9	12	15

d 6th pattern: 15 + 3 = 18 stars.
7th pattern: 18 + 3 = 21 stars.

e Number of stars = 3 × pattern number.
Number of stars in pattern 10 = 3 × 10
= 30.

The relationship between the number of dots and the pattern number is the **position-to-term rule**.

The pattern number is the pattern's position in the sequence.

- You can use the position-to-term rule to work out the number of dots in any pattern.

1 For each sequence
- draw pattern number 4 and pattern number 5
- copy and complete the table.

a

Pattern 1   Pattern 2   Pattern 3

Pattern number	1	2	3	4	5
Number of dots					

b

Pattern 1   Pattern 2   Pattern 3

Pattern number	1	2	3	4	5
Number of square tiles					

2 For this sequence

  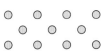

Pattern 1   Pattern 2   Pattern 3

- draw pattern number 4 and pattern number 5
- describe how the pattern grows
- copy and complete the table.
- work out the number of dots in pattern number 6 and pattern number 7.

Pattern number	1	2	3	4	5
Number of dots					

3 These patterns are made from square tiles.

Pattern 1   Pattern 2   Pattern 3

a Draw the 4th and 5th patterns in the sequence.
b Describe how the patterns grow.
c Copy and complete the table.
d Copy and complete:

Pattern number	1	2	3	4	5
Number of tiles					

    Number of tiles = ____ × pattern number + ____

e Use your formula from **d** to work out the number of tiles in pattern number 10.

Generating sequences from an *n*th term

This spread will show you how to:

- Use position-to-term rules to work out any pattern or term in a sequence

Keywords

General term
*n*th term

A position-to-term rule links a term to its position in the sequence.

- The position-to-term rule is often called the *n*th term.

Another name for the *n*th term is the **general term**.

- You can work out the terms of a sequence by substituting the position numbers 1, 2, 3, 4, ... into the *n*th term.

The 1st term is in position 1.
The 2nd term is in position 2.
The *n*th term is in position *n*.

This topic is extended to finding the general term on page 424.

Example

Generate the first five terms of the sequences with these *n*th terms.

a $3n + 2$ **b** $n^2 + 3$

....

a $3n + 2$

1st term substitute $n = 1$: $3 \times 1 + 2 = 3 + 2$ $= 5$
2nd term substitute $n = 2$: $3 \times 2 + 2 = 6 + 2$ $= 8$
3rd term substitute $n = 3$: $3 \times 3 + 2 = 9 + 2$ $= 11$
4th term substitute $n = 4$: $3 \times 4 + 2 = 12 + 2$ $= 14$
5th term substitute $n = 5$: $3 \times 5 + 2 = 15 + 2$ $= 17$
The first five terms are 5, 8, 11, 14, 17.

b $n^2 + 3$

1st term: $1^2 + 3 = 4$
2nd term: $2^2 + 3 = 4 + 3 \ = 7$
3rd term: $3^2 + 3 = 9 + 3 \ = 12$
4th term: $4^2 + 3 = 16 + 3 = 19$
5th term: $5^2 + 3 = 25 + 3 = 28$
The first five terms are 4, 7, 12, 19, 28.

Example

Here is a sequence of patterns made from counters.

The general term for the sequence is

    $C = 3n - 1$

where C is the number of counters
and n is the pattern number.
Which pattern in the sequence has 89 counters?

Pattern 1   Pattern 2   Pattern 3

....

For the pattern with 89 counters
    $89 = 3n - 1$
$89 + 1 = 3n - 1 + 1$
    $90 = 3n$
$90 \div 3 = 3n \div 3$
    $30 = n$ The 30th pattern has 89 counters.

Substitute 89 into the formula.
Solve the equation to find *n*.

Add 1 to both sides.
Divide both sides by 3.

1 Generate the first five terms of the sequences with these *n*th terms.
   a $3n - 1$ **b** $2n + 3$ **c** $2n - 5$ **d** $6n + 2$
   e $4n + 5$ **f** $3 - 2n$ **g** $4n - 2$ **h** $-3n + 8$

2 Write the first five terms of the sequences with these *n*th terms.
   a $n^2 + 1$ **b** $n^2 + 7$ **c** $n^2 - 4$ **d** $n^2 - 1$
   e $n^2 + 10$ **f** $3 - n^2$ **g** $n^2 - 2$ **h** $-n^2 + 1$

3 Here is a sequence of beach hut
   patterns made from matchsticks.
   The formula for the number of
   matchsticks in a pattern is
      $M = 4n + 1$

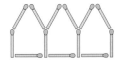

Pattern 1   Pattern 2   Pattern 3

   where *M* is the number of matchsticks and *n* is the pattern number.
   a Work out the number of matchsticks in pattern number 9.
   b Work out the number of matchsticks in pattern number 10.
   Trina has 40 matchsticks.
   c What is the pattern number of the largest pattern she can make?
   d How many matchsticks will she have left over?

4 Here is a sequence of patterns made from tiles.
   The general term for the sequence is
      $T = 3n + 1$
   where *T* is the number of tiles and *n*
   is the pattern number.
   a Work out the number of tiles in
       pattern number 15.

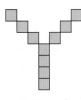

Pattern 1   Pattern 2   Pattern 3

   b Which pattern has 28 tiles?
   c Is there a pattern with 39 tiles? Explain your answer.
   d Which is the largest pattern you could make with 39 tiles?
       How many tiles would you have left over?

5 Here is a sequence of patterns made from 2p coins.
   The formula for this sequence is
      $C = 3n + 1$
      where *C* is the number of 2p coins
      and *n* is the pattern number.
   a How many 2p coins are there in
       the 5th pattern?
   b What is the value of the 5th
       pattern?
   c Which pattern has twenty-two
       2p coins?

Pattern 1   Pattern 2   Pattern 3

   d What is the value of the pattern in part **c**?
   e Which pattern has value 68p?

Summary

Check out
You should now be able to:

- Understand and use the vocabulary associated with sequences
- Generate sequences of numbers using a term-to-term rule
- Generate sequences of numbers using a position-to-term rule
- Identify which terms cannot be in a sequence
- Generate and describe sequences derived from diagrams

Worked exam question

a The rule for the next term of a sequence is
Multiply the previous term by three and subtract one.
The first two terms of the sequence are 2 and 5.
Write down the next **two** terms. (2)

b The nth term of a different sequence is $5n$.

The first term is 5.
Write down the next **three** terms. (1)

c Work out the nth term of this sequence.

$$7 \quad 10 \quad 13 \quad 16 \quad 19$$ (2)

(AQA, specimen)

> To find the nth term in part **c**, look ahead to page 424.

....

a 14, 41

b 10, 15, 20

c difference = 3, so $3\times$ table
  nth term = $3n + 4$

> First find the difference between terms (3). The nth term or **general term** will include a multiple of this. See page 424.

Exam questions

1 Here are some patterns made using sticks.

Pattern number 1   Pattern number 2   Pattern number 3

a Complete Pattern number 4. (1)

b Copy and complete the table.

Pattern number	1	2	3	4	5
Number of sticks	3	5	7		

(1)

c How many sticks are used in Pattern number 12? (1)

2 Here are the first four terms of a number sequence.

       7   11   15   19

a Write down the next two terms of the number sequence. (2)

b Work out the 10th term of this number sequence. (2)

3 Here is a list of ten numbers.

15   16   20   24   28   30   32   45   60   75

a i Use any four of these numbers to make a sequence. (1)
  ii Describe the rule for continuing your sequence. (1)

b i Use four different numbers from the list to make another sequence. (1)
  ii Describe the rule for continuing this sequence. (1)

c The first term of a sequence is x.
The term-to-term rule for the sequence is 'Add 7'.
 i Write an expression for the second term in this sequence. (1)
 ii The sum of the first three terms of this sequence is 45.

Work out the value of x. (3)

(AQA, 2009)

4 Here are the first three terms of a sequence.

1   2   4   □   □

Suggest what the next two terms could be.
Give **two** possible alternatives and give reasons. (2)

A03

Introduction

When a sky diver jumps out of an aircraft, she immediately accelerates towards the earth under the force of gravity. She will continue to accelerate until she reaches terminal velocity (speed) at about 55 m/s. When the skydiver pulls her ripcord she will decelerate before reaching a new constant speed.

What's the point?

A skydiver won't be drawing graphs or using a calculator before jumping – but she will need to make a mental calculation based on a formula in order to calculate the height at which to jump, and for how long she can freefall safely.

1 Simplify each of these expressions.
   a $x + x + x + x$ **b** $m \times m$
   c $4 \times p$ **d** $x \times 6$

2 Collect like terms for each expression.
   a $2p + q + 3p$ **b** $4x - 2y + x + 3y$
   c $m + 2n - 3p + 3n - 2m - p$

3 **a** Draw a coordinate grid with x- and y-axes from -5 to 5, using squared paper.
   b Plot these coordinates on your grid.
     i $(0, 4)$ **ii** $(2, -5)$ **iii** $(-4, 1)$ **iv** $(-2, -1)$

What I need to know

A1 + 2

What I will learn

- Use formulae from mathematics and other subjects
- Write formulae to represent real-life situations
- Simplify formulae by collecting like terms
- Substitute numbers into formulae
- Draw, use and interpret conversion graphs
- Draw, use and interpret distance–time graphs

What this leads to

Nurses and electricians both use formulae in their everyday jobs.

This L-shape is drawn on a 10 × 10 grid numbered from 1 to 100. It has 5 numbers inside it. We can call it L_{35} because the largest number inside it is 35.
The total of the numbers inside L_{35} is 138.
Find a connection between the L number and the total of the numbers inside the L shape.

1	2	3	4	5	6	7	8	9	10
11	12	13	14	15	16	17	18	19	20
21	22	23	24	25	26	27	28	29	30
31	32	33	34	35	36	37	38	39	40
41	42	43	44	45	46	47	48	49	50
51	52	53	54	55	56	57	58	59	60
61	62	63	64	65	66	67	68	69	70
71	72	73	74	75	76	77	78	79	80
81	82	83	84	85	86	87	88	89	90
91	92	93	94	95	96	97	98	99	100

This spread will show you how to:

- Use formulae from mathematics and other subjects expressed initially in words
- Substitute numbers into formulae

Keywords
Formula
Formulae
Substitute

Sarah takes a job as a shop assistant.

In her first week she works 10 hours.
In her second week she works 14 hours.

Sarah uses this **formula** to work out her pay

| Pay = number of hours worked × hourly rate |

First week: Pay = 10 × £6.20 = £62
Second week: Pay = 14 × £6.20 = £86.80

- You can **substitute** values into a formula given in words.

Replace the words with numbers.

Sarah's formula has a one-step calculation.
Formulae can have two or more steps.

The plural of formula is **formulae**.

Example

Jeremy works in telesales.

His hourly rate of pay is £5.80.
He gets a bonus for every sale he makes.

He uses this formula to work out his pay

| Pay = number of hours worked × hourly rate + bonus |

a In week 1 Jeremy works 18 hours and gets £24 bonus.
Work out his pay for the week.

b In week 2 Jeremy earns £140 and gets a £24 bonus.
How many hours does he work?

....

a Pay = 18 × £5.80 + £24
= £104.40 + £24
= £128.40

b Subtract the bonus: 140 − 24 = 116
£116 at £5.80 per hour: 116 ÷ 5.80 = 20
Jeremy works 20 hours.

BIDMAS
Multiplication
before **A**ddition.

1 Here is part of a hockey league table:

	Number of matches played	Goals for	Goals against
Woodford	15	32	13
Chorton	15	27	17
Digley	14	24	18

To find a team's goal difference you can use the formula:

Goal difference = goals for − goals against

Work out the goal difference for
a Woodford   **b** Chorton   **c** Digley

2 A music shop has a one-day sale.
In the sale, every CD costs £9.99.
The total price for a number of CDs is worked out using the formula:

Total price = number of CDs × £9.99

Work out the total price for
a 10 CDs   **b** 4 CDs   **c** 7 CDs

3 A group of volunteers are painting the village hall.
They use this formula to work out how much paint they need:

Number of cans of paint = area to be painted (square metres) ÷ 15

The area to be painted is 285 square metres.
How many cans of paint do they need?

4 Mick works in an electrical shop and is paid £5.50 per hour.
He calculates his pay using the formula:

Pay = number of hours worked × hourly rate + commission on goods sold

One week Mick works 16 hours and earns £15 commission.
Work out his pay for the week.

5 Super Snacks Catering Ltd. calculate their prices using this formula:

Price = cost per head × number of guests

For a buffet, their cost per head is £4.50.
a Work out the cost of a Super Snacks buffet for 75 guests.

Tasty Treats Catering Ltd. calculate their prices using this formula:

Price = basic charge £45 + cost per head + number of guests

For a buffet, their basic charge is £45 and their cost per head is £3.
b Work out the cost of a Tasty Treats buffet for 75 guests.
c Stephen is organising a buffet for 75 people.
  Which company should he choose?

Writing formulae in words

This spread will show you how to:
- Use formulae from mathematics and other subjects expressed in words
- Write formulae to represent real-life situations

Keywords
Formula

Katie makes and sells bead necklaces and bracelets.

For glass beads, the price is 22p per centimetre.

For a 30 cm glass bead necklace, the price is
$$30 \times 22p = 660p = £6.60.$$

For plastic beads, the price is 18p per centimetre.

For a 20 cm plastic bead bracelet, the price is
$$20 \times 18p = 360p = £3.60.$$

Katie writes a formula to work out the price of any necklace or bracelet:

Price = cost per cm × length in cm

To write a formula, you can try a few examples with numbers first, to see a pattern in the calculations.

Example

Here is a sequence of patterns made from sticks.

Pattern 1   Pattern 2   Pattern 3

a Write the number of blue sticks in
  i 1 square **ii** 2 squares **iii** 3 squares.
b Write a formula connecting the number of blue sticks with the number of squares.
c Write the number of red sticks in
  i 1 square **ii** 2 squares **iii** 3 squares.
d Use your answers to **b** and **d** to write a formula connecting the total number of sticks to the number of squares.
  Use your formula to find the number of sticks in 15 squares.

....

a **i** 1 square: 3 blue sticks
  ii 2 squares: 6 blue sticks
  iii 3 squares: 9 blue sticks
b Number of blue sticks = 3 × number of squares
c **i** 1 square: 1 red stick
  ii 2 squares: 1 red stick
  iii 3 squares: 1 red stick
d Total number of sticks = number of blue sticks + number of red sticks
  $$= 3 \times \text{number of squares} + 1$$
e In 15 squares
  Total number of sticks $= 3 \times 15 + 1$
  $$= 45 + 1 = 46$$

A02 Functional Maths

Unit 2

1 Plain ribbon costs 30p per metre.
Tartan ribbon costs 42p per metre.
a How much does 2m of plain ribbon cost?
b How much does 3m of tartan ribbon cost?
c Write a formula connecting:

cost of ribbon   length of ribbon

price per metre

2 Sareeta is making a row of coins in the High Street for charity.
She collects coins from the public and arranges them like this
on the pavement:

a What is the value of each vertical
column?
b A 10cm length includes four 10p pieces.
What is the total value of a 10cm length?
c What is the total value of a 1m length?
Give your answer in pounds (£).
d Copy and complete:
Total value of row = _____ × length of row in metres

10 cm

3 Employees in a factory are paid by the hour.
Under 18s and adults are paid different hourly rates.
Write a formula for any employee, connecting:

number of hours worked   hourly rate

pay

4 To fix a car, Tony charges £20 per hour for labour. He also charges
the cost of any parts used.
Write a formula connecting:

cost of the repair   cost of parts

number of hours worked

hourly rate for labour

Formulae using letters

This spread will show you how to:

Keywords
Symbol
Variable

- Use letter symbols to represent quantities in formulae
- Use the rules of algebra to simplify a formula written in symbols

---

- You can use letter **symbols** to represent quantities in a formula.

The formula to work out the area of a rectangle is

$$\boxed{\text{Area} = \text{length} \times \text{width}}$$

length

width

You can write this using letter symbols as

$$A = l \times w$$
$$\text{or} \quad A = lw$$

where A is the area, l is the length and w is the width.

You can use this formula to calculate the area of any rectangle.

When you write a formula, you need to use a different letter symbol for each variable.

In algebra you do not write the $\times$ sign.

*l, w and A are called **variables**. l and w can take **any** values. The value of A is determined by the values of l and w.*

Example

Write these formulae using letter symbols.
Explain what each letter symbol represents.

a goal difference = goals for − goals against
b taxi fare = basic charge + distance in miles × 0.2
c speed = distance ÷ time

....

a $D = F - A$
  D = goal difference, F = goals for, A = goals against
b $F = b + d \times 0.2$
  $F = b + 0.2d$
  F = taxi fare, b = basic charge, d = distance in miles
c $s = d \div t$
  $s = \dfrac{d}{t}$
  where s = speed, d = distance and t = time.

Write the number first and leave out the $\times$ sign.
$d \times 0.2 = 0.2d$

In algebra, write division $a \div b$ as $\dfrac{a}{b}$

Example

Recordable CDs come in packs of five.

a Write a formula in words for working out the cost of one CD.
b Write your formula using letter symbols.

....

a Cost of one CD = cost of pack of CDs ÷ 5
b $C = \dfrac{p}{5}$

where C = cost of one CD, p = cost of pack of five CDs.

1 Write these formulae using letter symbols.
Explain what each letter symbol represents.
  a Repair cost = labour cost + parts cost
  b Cost of electric cable = price per metre × length in metres
  c Monthly cost = annual cost ÷ 12
  d Cost of apples = price per kg × number of kg
  e Distance in metres = distance in km × 1000
  f Length in metres = length in centimetres ÷ 100

2 A mobile phone bill is calculated by adding the cost of calls
made and the cost of texts sent.
  a Write a formula to calculate a mobile phone bill in words.
  b Write your formula from part **a** using algebra.
  Explain what each letter symbol represents.

3 In a school hall, chairs are arranged in rows.
There are 15 chairs in each row.
  a Write a formula to work out the number of chairs in the hall.
  b Write you formula in algebra.
  Explain what each letter symbol represents.
  c Use your formula to work out the number of chairs in the hall
    when there are 13 rows of chairs.

4 Eggs are packed in boxes of six.
  a How many boxes are needed for 18 eggs?
  b Write a formula in words to work out the
    number of boxes needed for any number of eggs.
  c Write your formula using letter symbols.
  d Use your formula to work out the number of boxes needed for
    i 132 eggs   **ii** 75 eggs.

5 In a café, each table has four chairs.
Write a formula connecting the number of tables and the
number of chairs. Use *t* for the number of tables and *c* for
the number of chairs.

6 In a library, each shelf holds the same number of books.
Write a formula, using letter symbols, connecting the
number of books and the number of shelves.
Explain what each letter symbol represents.

7 Duvets cost £30 each and pillows cost £4.50 each.
Write a formula for the cost of *m* duvets and *n* pillows.

More formulae

This spread will show you how to:
- Use the rules of algebra to simplify a formula written in symbols
- Simplify formulae by collecting like terms

You can use the rules of algebra to simplify a formula written in letter symbols.

$$a + a = 2a$$
$$3 \times b = 3b$$
$$m \times m = m^2$$

Example

a Write a formula in words for the area of a square.
b Write your formula using letter symbols. Give your formula in its simplest form.

length

a Area = length × length
b $A = l \times l$
  $A = l^2$

- You can simplify a formula by collecting **like terms**.

Like terms have exactly the same letter.

Example

Write a formula for the perimeter of this rectangle.
Simplify your formula as much as possible.

l

w w

l

Perimeter $P = l + w + l + w$
            $= l + l + w + w$
$P = 2l + 2w$

A formula may connect quantities in different units.
You need to explain which units to use for each variable.

Example

A plasterer charges a basic fee, plus £2 for each square metre of plaster.
Write a formula to work out the plasterer's charge in pounds.

Charge in pounds =

basic fee in pounds + £2 × area of plaster in square metres

$C = F + 2A$ where C = charge in £
                        F = basic fee in £
                        A = area in m^2

The rate per square metre (£2) is in pounds – the charge needs to be in pounds so the basic fee needs to be in pounds.

1 Write a formula for the perimeter of this equilateral triangle.
Simplify your formula as much as possible.

2 Write a formula for the perimeter of this square.
Write your formula in its simplest form.

3 Write a formula for the perimeter of a polygon with n sides, where each side has length z.

> Look back at your answers to questions **1** and **2**.

4 A taxi charges a basic fee and an extra £1 per mile.
Write a formula for the cost of a taxi ride in pounds.
Explain what each letter represents, and the units to use for each.

5 To hire a carpet cleaner you pay a fixed amount per day and the cost of the shampoo.
Write a formula for the cost of hiring the carpet cleaner in pounds.
Explain what each letter represents, and the units to use for each.

6 To make a cover for a square cushion, you need two squares of fabric.
Write a formula for the area of fabric (in square metres) needed for a square cushion of side k metres.

7 The formula to work out average speed is
$$s = \frac{d}{t}$$
where s = speed in miles per hour, d = distance in miles, t = time in hours.
Ben uses the formula to calculate his average speed when he travels 120 km in 2 hours.

> $d = 120\,\text{km}$
> $t = 2\,\text{hours}$
> $s = \frac{120}{2} = 60$

What are the units for Ben's average speed?

8 p magazines are packed in a bundle.
  a Write an expression for the number of magazines in m bundles.

  q bundles are packed into one box.
  b Write a formula to work out the number of magazines in a lorry load of n boxes.

Unit 2

This spread will show you how to:
- Substitute numbers into formulae
- Solve simple equations

- In a formula, the letters represent quantities.

For example, in the formula for the perimeter of a rectangle
$P = 2l + 2w$
l represents the length and w represents the width of the rectangle.

If you know the values of l and w, you can **substitute** the values of l and w into the formula.
Then you work out the calculation.

This means you write the formula replacing l and w with their number values.

Example

Use the formula
$P = 2l + 2w$
to work out

a the perimeter of a rectangular field with length 20 m and width 8 m
b the perimeter of a table mat with length 25 cm and width 30 cm.

a $l = 20$ m and $w = 8$ m
$P = 2l + 2w$
$P = 2 \times 20 + 2 \times 8$
$= 40 + 16$
$P = 56$ m

b $l = 25$ cm and $w = 30$ cm
$P = 2l + 2w$
$P = 2 \times 25 + 2 \times 30$
$= 50 + 60$
$= 110$ cm

$2l$ means $2 \times l$ multiplication before addition. In part **a**, l and w are in metres, so P is also in metres.

In part **b**, l and w are in centimetres, so P is also in centimetres.

You can calculate a quantity from a formula by substituting quantities you know.
Sometimes when you substitute values into a formula you end up with an equation to solve.

Example

The formula
$v = u + at$
is used in science.
Find the value of t when $v = 16$, $u = 0$ and $a = 4$.

$v = u + at$
$16 = 0 + 4t$ Substitute the values given
$16 = 4t$
$16 \div 4 = 4t \div 4$ Solve by dividing both sides by 4
$4 = t$
The value of t is 4.

1 Here is a formula: $p = 5m$
Work out the value of p when
a $m = 4$ **b** $m = 3$ **c** $m = 10$ **d** $m = 2.5$

2 Here is a formula: $y = ax$
Work out the value of y when
a $x = 3$ and $a = 2$ **b** $x = 7$ and $a = 4$ **c** $x = 4.5$ and $a = 3$
Work out the value of x when
d $y = 10$ and $a = 2$ **e** $y = 25$ and $a = 10$

3 Use the formula
$$P = 2l + 2w$$
where P is perimeter,
l is length and w is width,
to work out the perimeter
of each rectangle.

a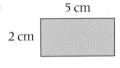
5 cm
2 cm

b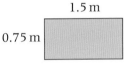
40 cm
25 cm

Be careful with the units.

c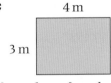
4 m
3 m

d
1.5 m
0.75 m

4 For each formula, work out the value of y when $x = 4$ and $c = 6$.
a $y = 3x + c$ **b** $y = 4x - c$ **c** $y = \dfrac{4c}{x}$ **d** $y = cx + 10$
e $y = x^2$ **f** $y = c^2$ **g** $y = x^3$ **h** $y = 2x^2 + c$

5 Use the formula $s = \dfrac{d}{t}$
where s = average speed, d = distance and t = time
to work out the average speed when

Be careful with the units.

a $d = 150$ miles, $t = 3$ hours **b** $d = 190$ km, $t = 2$ hours
c $d = 500$ metres, $t = 10$ seconds **d** $d = 60$ km, $t = 0.5$ hours

6 Jan uses the formula
$$s = ut + \tfrac{1}{2} at^2$$
to calculate s when $u = 0$, $t = 3$ and $a = 2$
Her working is shown on the right.

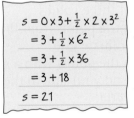

$s = 0 \times 3 + \frac{1}{2} \times 2 \times 3^2$
$= 3 + \frac{1}{2} \times 6^2$
$= 3 + \frac{1}{2} \times 36$
$= 3 + 18$
$s = 21$

Jan's answer is **wrong**.
Work out the correct value of s.
Explain which **two** mistakes Jan has made in her working.

7 An **equation** is an algebra statement with an unknown value (letter) to
be found.
It contains an equals sign.
$x + 6 = 10$ is an equation.
Sort the objects in the box into:
a equations
b expressions
c formulae

$x + 8 = 14$
$P = IV$
$x^2 + y^2$
$2x - 5 = 9$
$v^2 = u^2 + 2as$
$\dfrac{5x}{8}$

A03 **Problem**

Unit 2

235

Drawing conversion graphs

This spread will show you how to:
- Use and interpret conversion graphs
- Draw conversion graphs

Keywords
Conversion
Table of values

Joe is comparing data on heights of trees.
Some of the data is in feet and some is in metres.
He draws a conversion graph to help him convert from feet to metres easily.

From a ruler, Joe sees that 1 foot ≈ 30 cm = 0.3 m.

He uses this **conversion** to draw a **table of values**.

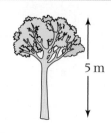

5 m

1 foot is approximately equal to 30 cm.

Metres	0	0.3	3.0
Feet	0	1	10

0 feet = 0 metres

1 foot = 0.3 m
↓ × 10   ↓ × 10
10 feet = 3 m

He writes the coordinate pairs from the table.

(0, 0) (0.3, 1) (3, 10)

To plot a straight line you only need to plot two points.

If you plot three, you can tell if you have made a mistake.

3 points correct   1 point must be wrong

Joe plots the points on a coordinate grid and joins them with a straight line.

- To draw a conversion graph
  - draw up a table of values with at least three values
  - plot the points from the table on a coordinate grid
  - join the points with a straight line
  - extend your line to the edges of the grid.

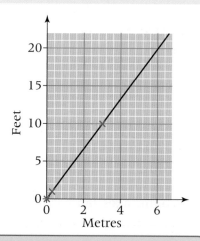

Feet / Metres

Example

Complete the table of values for a conversion graph for UK pounds to US dollars.

Pounds	0	1	10
US dollars		1.7	

···

Pounds	0	1	10
US dollars	0	1.7	17

1 pound = 1.7 dollars
↓ × 10   ↓ × 10
10 pounds = 17 dollars

0 pounds = 0 dollars

1 a Copy and complete this table of values for a grams-to-ounces conversion graph.

Ounces	0	1	10
Grams		28	

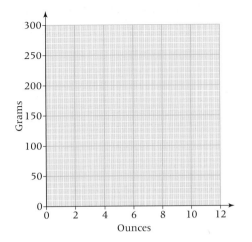

b Write three pairs of coordinates for the conversion graph.
Write them in this order
(number of ounces, number of grams)

c Copy these axes onto graph paper.

d Plot the points on the coordinate grid.
Join the points with a straight line.
Extend your line to the edge of the grid.

e Use your graph to convert
  i 4 ounces to grams   **ii** 200 g to ounces.

2 a Copy and complete this table of values for a kilometres-to-miles conversion graph.

Miles		5	10
Kilometres	0	8	

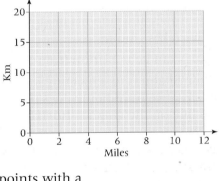

b Write three pairs of coordinates for the conversion graph.
Write them in this order
(number of miles, number of kilometres)

c Copy these axes onto graph paper.

d Plot the points on the coordinate grid and join the points with a straight line. Extend your line to the edge of the grid.

e Use your graph to convert
  i 6 miles to kilometres   **ii** 5000 metres to miles.

3 a Copy and complete this table of values for pounds to New Zealand dollars.

Pounds	0	1	10
NZ dollars		2.4	

b Write three pairs of coordinates for the conversion graph.

c Draw the graph by copying the axes and plotting the points.

d Use your graph to convert
  i £8 to NZ dollars   **ii** 12 NZ dollars to pounds.

e Use your graph to work out which is more
  i £6 or 12 NZ dollars?   **ii** 18 NZ dollars or £7?

This spread will show you how to:

- Draw, use and interpret distance–time graphs

Keywords
Distance
Horizontal
Time
Vertical

You can plot a graph for a journey.

- You plot **time** on the **horizontal** axis and **distance** on the **vertical** axis.

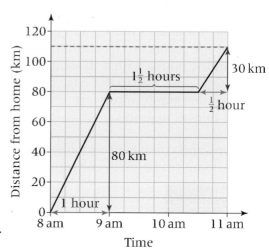

Shaun is a salesman.

- He leaves home at 8 am.
- He drives 80 km to his first meeting. This takes 1 hour.
- He arrives at 9 am.
- His meeting lasts $1\frac{1}{2}$ hours.
- At 10.30 am he sets off again.
- He drives 30 km to his next appointment. This takes $\frac{1}{2}$ hour.
- At 11 am he is 110 km from home.

While Shaun is in a meeting, he is not travelling. His distance from home does not change. The line on the graph is **horizontal**.

- A horizontal line on a distance-time graph shows a break in the journey.

Example

The graph shows Tristan's trip to the cinema and back again.

a What time did Tristan leave home?
b How far is the cinema from his home?
c How long was he at the cinema for?
d How long did he spend travelling home?

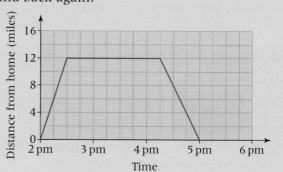

a He left home at 2 pm.
b 12 miles
c From 2.30 to 4.15 = $1\frac{3}{4}$ hours
d $\frac{3}{4}$ hour

On a journey going away from home, your distance from home is increasing. The graph slopes up.

On a journey back home, your distance from home is decreasing. The graph slopes down.

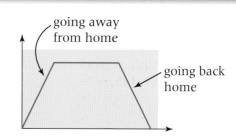

going away from home

going back home

A02 **Functional Maths**

1 Shona runs a corner shop.
The graph shows her trip from the shop to
the cash and carry.
   a What time did she set off to the cash and carry?
   b What time did she arrive at the cash and carry?
   c How long did the journey to the cash
   and carry take?
   d How long did she spend at the cash and carry?
   e How long did the journey home from the
   cash and carry take?
   f How far is the cash and carry from Shona's shop?
   g How many kilometres did she travel in total?

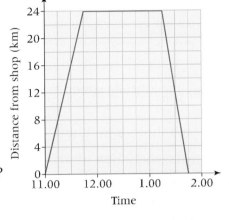

2 The graph shows a train journey.
   a How many stations did the train stop at?
   b How far did the train travel before it stopped
   for the first time?
   c How far did the train travel in total?
   d How long did the whole journey take?
   e At one station stop, the train had to wait for
   a connection.
   Which stop do you think this was?
   How long did it wait for?

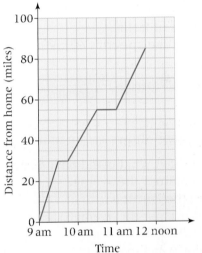

3 The graph shows Luke's trip to the shop.
   a How far is the shop from Luke's home?
   b How many minutes did it take Luke to walk to
   the shop?
   c How many minutes did he spend in the shop?
   d What time did he leave the shop?
   e Luke bought a magazine, and read it as he
   walked home.
   It took him 30 minutes to walk home.
   What time did he arrive home?
   f Copy the graph onto graph paper.
   Follow these steps to complete the graph for
   Luke's trip.
      i Mark the time that Luke arrived home on
      the time (horizontal) axis.
      ii Join this point to the graph where he left
      the shop.

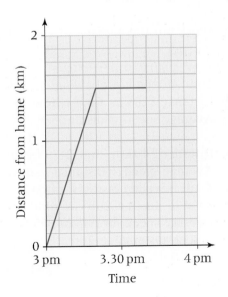

This spread will show you how to:

- Draw, use and interpret distance–time graphs
- Work out the average speed for a journey from a distance–time graph

Keywords
Average speed
Speed

You can work out speeds from a distance–time graph.

You use the formula **speed** $= \dfrac{\text{distance}}{\text{time}}$

This graph shows a car journey.

The car travels 120 km (distance) in 2 hours (time).

$\text{speed} = \dfrac{\text{distance}}{\text{time}} = \dfrac{120\,\text{km}}{2\,\text{hours}} = 60\,\text{km per hour}$

In real life, a car does not travel at exactly the same speed for 2 hours. It may have to slow down for junctions or traffic.

The **average speed** is 60 km per hour.

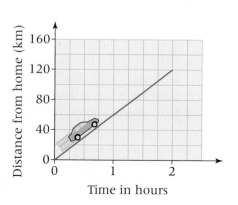

Distance from home (km)

Time in hours

- Average speed $= \dfrac{\text{total distance}}{\text{total time}}$

Example

The graph shows a train journey.

a Explain what could have happened at 2 pm.

b Work out the average speed for the first part of the journey.

c Work out the average speed for the second part of the journey.

d For which part of the journey was the train travelling fastest?

e Work out the average speed for the whole journey.

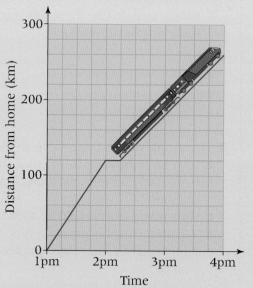

Distance from home (km)

Time

....

a Train stopped, probably at a station.

b Distance 120 km, time 1 hour.
  Average speed = distance ÷ time
  $= 120 ÷ 1 = 120\,\text{km per hour}$

c Distance 140 km, time 1.75 hours.
  Average speed = distance ÷ time $= 140 ÷ 1.75 = 80\,\text{km per hour}$

d Train travelled fastest for first part.

e Total distance is 260 km, total time is 3 hours.
  Average speed for whole journey
  $= \dfrac{\text{total distance}}{\text{total time}} = \dfrac{260}{3} = 86.6666\,\text{km per hour}$
  $= 87\,\text{km per hour (to the nearest km)}$

For speed in km per hour, the distance must be in km and the time must be in hours.

1 For each graph work out the average speed.

a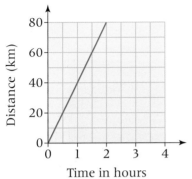

b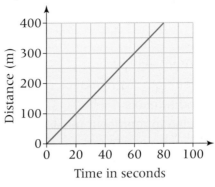

For part **a**, use km per hour.
For part **b**, use metres per second.

2 For each graph, work out
- the average speed for each part of the journey
- the average speed for the whole journey.

a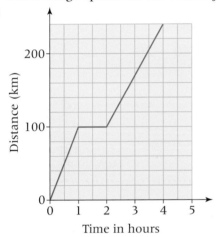

b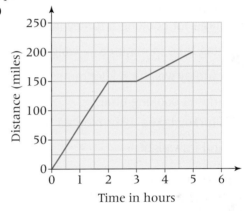

3 The graph shows Amit's car journey to Wales.

  a What distance does he travel in the first part of the journey?

  b What is the time taken for the first part of the journey? Write your answer in hours, as a decimal.

  c Use your answers from **a** and **b** to work out his average speed in km per hour for the first part of the journey.

  d Work out Amit's average speed in km per hour for the second part of the journey.

  e Work out his average speed in km per hour for the whole journey.

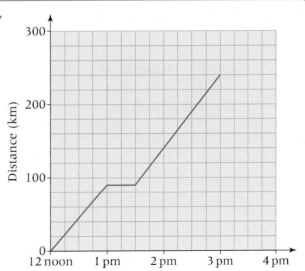

Summary

Check out

You should now be able to:

- Use formulae from mathematics and other subjects expressed in words and symbols
- Write formulae to represent real-life situations
- Substitute numbers into formulae
- Draw and interpret conversion graphs
- Draw and interpret distance-time graphs
- Work out the average speed from a distance-time graph

Worked exam question

The time for cooking a turkey is given by the formula

cooking time in minutes = weight in kilograms × 40 + 25

a A turkey weighs 6 kilograms.

Find its cooking time. (2)

b A turkey takes 165 minutes to cook.

Find its weight. (3)

(AQA, 2008)

a

cooking time = 6 × 40 + 25
= 240 + 25
= 265 minutes

Multiply comes before add.

b

165 = weight × 40 + 25
weight × 40 = 140
weight   = 140 ÷ 40
= 3.5 kg

Substitute 165 into the formula. Then treat it like an **equation**. Look ahead to page 264.

Exam questions

1 a A formula connecting the variables P, Q and R is given by
$$R = 6P + 7Q$$

    i Find the value of R when $P = 8$ and $Q = 11$ (2)

    ii Find the value of Q when $R = 38$ and $P = 4$ (2)

  b Simplify
$$2a + 8b + 3a - 2b$$
                                                (2)

                                       (AQA, 2008)

2 The Johnson family drove to Legoland.
They stayed for a few hours.
Then they drove home.
Here is the distance-time graph for their complete journey.

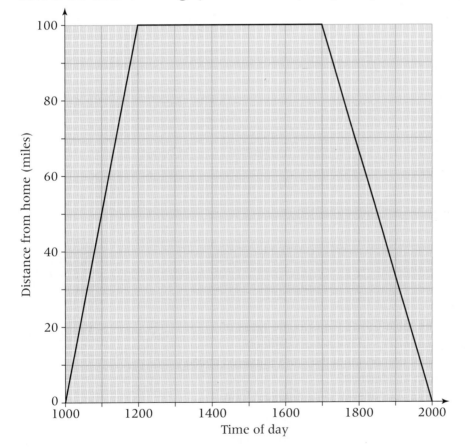

  a What is the distance from the Johnsons' home to Legoland?   (1)
  b For how many hours did they stay at Legoland?   (1)
  c Work out their average speed on their journey home from Legoland.
    Give your answer in miles per hour.   (2)

Introduction

People come in all shapes and sizes, but for hundreds of years artists and scientists have shown great interest in the average proportions of the human body. A classic example is Leonordo da Vinci's Vitruvian Man.

What's the point?
By understanding human proportions, artists can understand better how to represent the human form. Also, inventors can design objects that conform to these proportions.

Check in

1 The table shows the favourite types of sandwiches in the school canteen.
   What proportion of the class surveyed chose ham sandwiches?
   Write your answer in its simplest form.

Type	Frequency
Cheese	12
Salad	8
Ham	10
Total	30

2 10 litres of white paint cost £12.
   Work out the cost of 20 litres of paint.

3 Bart works for 4 hours. He gets paid £20.
   How much does he get paid per hour?

4 The exchange rate for pounds into Australian dollars is £1 = AU$2.
   How many Australian Dollars would you get for £5?

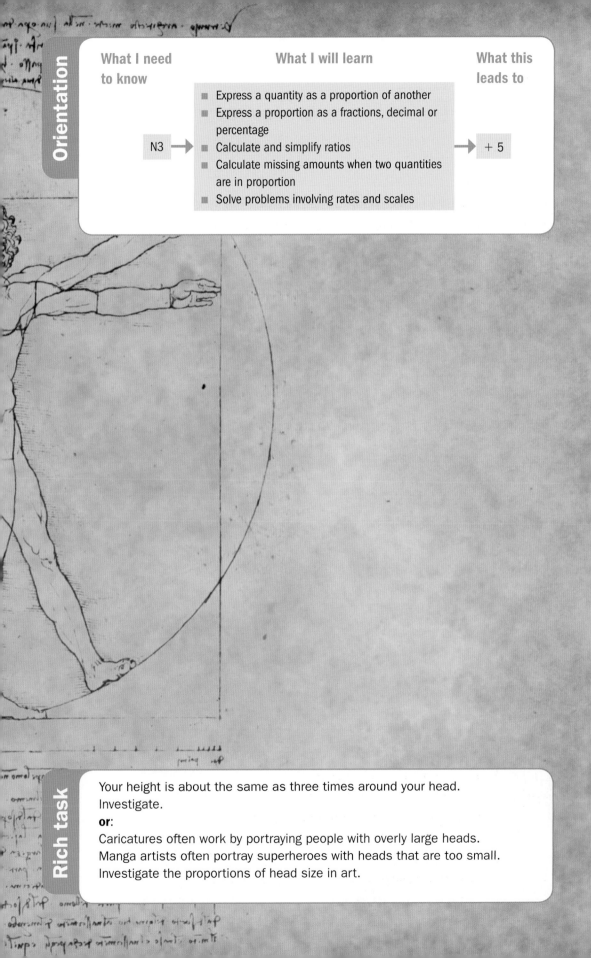

What I need to know	What I will learn	What this leads to
N3	■ Express a quantity as a proportion of another ■ Express a proportion as a fractions, decimal or percentage ■ Calculate and simplify ratios ■ Calculate missing amounts when two quantities are in proportion ■ Solve problems involving rates and scales	+ 5

Rich task

Your height is about the same as three times around your head.
Investigate.

or:

Caricatures often work by portraying people with overly large heads.
Manga artists often portray superheroes with heads that are too small.
Investigate the proportions of head size in art.

This spread will show you how to:

- Calculate missing amounts when two quantities are in proportion using the unitary method

Keywords

Ratio
Unitary method

You can find the value of one unit of a quantity using division.

Example

Three bags of crisps cost 93 pence. What is the price of 1 bag of crisps?

Total cost of crisps   = 93 pence
Number of bags of crisps   = 3

$$\text{The price of 1 bag of crisps} = \frac{\text{total cost of crisps}}{\text{number of bags of crisps}}$$

$$= 93 \div 3$$
$$= 31 \text{ pence}$$

- You can use the **unitary method** to solve proportion problems. In this method you find the value of 1 unit of a quantity.

Example

Here is a recipe for blackcurrant squash for 5 people.

Work out the number of grams of blackcurrants needed to make squash for 8 people.

Blackcurrant squash
(for 5 people)

400 g of blackcurrants
1200 ml of water
100 g sugar
250 ml blackcurrant juice

The recipe is for 5 people. First find the number of grams of blackcurrants needed for 1 person. Then multiply this by 8.

Number of people   Grams of blackcurrants

$$\div 5 \left(\begin{array}{c} 5 \\ 1 \end{array} \right) \qquad \left(\begin{array}{c} 400 \\ 80 \end{array} \right) \div 5$$

$$\times 8 \left(\begin{array}{c} 1 \\ 8 \end{array} \right) \qquad \left(\begin{array}{c} 80 \\ 640 \end{array} \right) \times 8$$

So for 8 people you need 640 g blackcurrants.

Example

15 boxes of chocolates cost £22.50. Each box of chocolates costs the same. What is the cost of 2 boxes of chocolates?

Number of boxes   Cost

$$\div 15 \left(\begin{array}{c} 15 \\ 1 \end{array} \right) \qquad \left(\begin{array}{c} £22.50 \\ £1.50 \end{array} \right) \div 15$$

$$\times 2 \left(\begin{array}{c} 1 \\ 2 \end{array} \right) \qquad \left(\begin{array}{c} £1.50 \\ £3.00 \end{array} \right) \times 2$$

So 2 boxes of chocolates will cost £3.

A02 Functional Maths

1 a 2 pizzas cost £6.00. What is the cost of 1 pizza?
  b 4 sweets cost 20p. What is the cost of 1 sweet?
  c 10 packets of seeds cost £18. What is the cost of 1 packet of seeds?
  d 4 tennis balls cost £2. What is the cost of 1 tennis ball?
  e There are 48 biscuits in 3 packets. How many biscuits are there in 1 packet?
  f 10 kg of apples cost £9.00. What is the cost of 1 kg of apples?
  g There are 320 MB of memory on 5 identical memory sticks. How much memory is there on each stick?

2 a There are 24 inches in 2 feet.
    How many inches are there in 1 foot?
  b There are 2000 ml in 2 litres.
    How many ml are there in 1 litre?
  c There are 24 pints in 3 gallons.
    How many pints are there in 1 gallon?
  d There are 120 hours in 5 days.
    How many hours are there in 1 day?

3 a Vince works for 4 hours. He gets paid £24.
    How much money is he paid each hour?
  b On average Barry fits 36 radiators in 3 days.
    How many radiators does he fit each day?
  c An athlete runs 240 metres in 30 seconds.
    How far does she run in 1 second?
  d Rashid drives his car 250 miles and uses 10 gallons of petrol.
    On average, how far does the car travel on each gallon of petrol?

4 a A recipe for cake uses 400 g of sugar for 5 people.
    What weight of sugar is needed for
      i 1 person   **ii** 8 people   **iii** 12 people
      iv 14 people   **v** 30 people?
  b A recipe for three bean chilli uses 840 g of beans for 7 people.
    What weight of beans is needed for
      i 3 people   **ii** 6 people   **iii** 17 people
      iv 24 people   **v** 100 people?
  c Frank works for 8 hours a day and earns £128.
    He is paid the same amount each hour.
    How much will he get paid for working
      i 40 hours   **ii** 35 hours   **iii** 168 hours
      iv 10 days   **v** 3 hours   **vi** $\frac{1}{2}$ hour?

Unit 2

This spread will show you how to:

● Calculate with rates and scales

Keywords
Rate
Ratio
Scale

● You can express a **ratio** in the form 1 : n using division. This is often called a **scale**.

Example

A photograph is 8 cm tall. An enlargement of the same photograph is 24 cm tall. What is the ratio of the height of the original to the height of the enlargement? Express your answer as a scale in the form 1 : n.

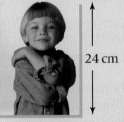

8 cm

24 cm

- -

Ratio of height of original : height of enlargement
   = 8 cm : 24 cm
   = 8 : 24

$$\frac{\text{enlargement height}}{\text{original height}} = \frac{24}{8} = 3$$

Scale = ratio of height of original : height of enlargement = 1 : 3

You will study more about enlargements in geometry on page 364.

● A rate is a way of comparing two quantities.

You can solve problems involving scales or rates by multiplying or dividing by the scale or rate.

Example

a Bill goes for a walk. On his map he travels 40 cm. The scale of his map is 1 : 2000. How far does he really walk?

b Sarah travels in her car. The petrol consumption of her car is 10 miles per litre. She travels 290 miles. How many litres of petrol does she use?

Petrol consumption is a **rate**.

- -

a Map scale

$\times 2000$

1 = 2000

$\div 2000$

40 cm = 40 × 2000 cm | Multiply by the scale.
   = 80 000 cm
   = 800 m
Bill walks 800 m.

b Petrol consumption

$\div 10$

10 miles = 1 litre

$\times 10$

290 miles = 290 ÷ 10 litres
   = 29 litres
Sarah uses 29 litres of petrol.

Divide by the rate.

A02 Functional Maths

1 Express each of these ratios as a ratio in the form 1 : *n* (a scale).

  a 2 : 6   **b** 3 : 12   **c** 10 : 20   **d** 8 : 40

  e 3 : 6   **f** 5 : 15   **g** 4 : 20   **h** 12 : 36

  i 30 : 60   **j** 9 : 45   **k** 45 : 90   **l** 20 : 120

2 In each of these questions work out the ratio and then express this as a ratio in the form 1 : *n* (a scale).

  a A photograph is 6 cm wide. An enlargement of the same photograph is 30 cm wide. What is the ratio of the width of the original to the width of the enlargement?

  b On a model plane the wing span is 2 m. In real life the wing span of the plane is 40 m. What is the ratio of the model wing span to the wing span of the real plane?

3 Work out the hourly rate for each of these people.

  a Wilf works for 3 hours. He gets paid £21. What is his hourly rate of pay?

  b Aaron works for 10 hours. He is paid £55. What is his hourly rate of pay?

  c Gary is a plumber. On average he fits 8 radiator valves every 4 hours. What is his hourly rate of fitting radiator valves?

> Work out how many pounds per hour.

> Work out how many radiators he fits each hour.

4 a Kerry has a plan of her house. On her plan she walks 40 cm. The scale of her plan is 1 : 20. How far does she really walk?

  b John makes a scale drawing of his kitchen. On his scale drawing the cooker is 6 cm wide. The drawing has a scale of 1 : 10. What is the real width of the cooker?

  c Gustav builds a model plane. The scale is 1 : 25. On his model the wing span is 40 cm. What is the real wing span of the plane?

5 Here is the nutritional information for a 500 g serving of pizza. Copy and complete the nutritional amount for every 100 g of pizza.

Typical values	Amount in a 500 g serving	Amount per 100 g
Energy	1500 kcal	
Protein	40 g	
Carbohydrate	150 g	
Fat	44 g	
Fibre	20 g	

Conversion and exchange rates

This spread will show you how to:
- Calculate conversion and exchange rates
- Solve problems using conversion and exchange rates

- A **conversion rate** is a way of converting between two different units of measurement.

Example

May was driving her car on holiday. The conversion rate for miles into kilometres is 1 mile = 1.6 kilometres.

a May travelled 300 miles in the UK. Work out the number of kilometres she travelled in the UK.

b May then travelled 1280 km in France. Work out the number of miles she travelled in France.

Conversion rate   5 miles = 8 kilometres

Examiner's tip
You are expected to remember the conversion from miles to km in the exam.

a 300 ÷ 5 = 60
  So 300 miles
      = 60 × 8
      = 480
  May travelled 480 km in the UK.

b 1280 ÷ 8 = 160
      = 1280 km
      = 160 × 5 miles
      = 800 miles
  May travelled 800 miles in France.

- An **exchange rate** is a way of comparing two currencies. It tells you how many units of one currency there are compared to one unit of another currency.

You can solve problems involving currency by multiplying or dividing by the exchange rate.

Example

Steve went to Austria.

a He changed £500 into euros. The exchange rate was £1 = €1.50. Work out the number of euros Steve got.

b He had €120 left at the end of the holiday. He changed them back into pounds. How many pounds did he get?

Exchange rate

$$\times 1.5$$
£1   =   €1.50
$$\div 1.5$$

a £500 = 500 × 1.5
        = €750
  Steve got €750.

b €120 = 120 ÷ 1.5
        = £80
  Steve got £80.

1 a There are 48 inches in 4 feet. How many inches are there in 1 foot?
  b There are 30 dl in 3 litres. How many dl are there in 1 litre?
  c There are 40 pints in 5 gallons.
    How many pints are there in 1 gallon?
  d There are 25 cm in 10 inches.
    How many centimetres are there in 1 inch?

2 a There are 1800 Rwandan francs in £2.
    How many Rwandan francs are there in £1?
  b There are 50 Canadian dollars in £25.
    How many Canadian dollars are there in £1?
  c There are 16 000 Belarussian rubles in £4.
    How many Belarussian rubles are there in £1?
  d There are 75 Ethiopian birrs in £5.
    How many Ethiopian birrs are there in £1?

3 Use the fact that **1 mile = 1.6 km** to answer each of these questions.
  a Convert these distances into kilometres.
    i 10 miles   **ii** 50 miles   **iii** 230 miles   **iv** 48 miles
  b Convert these distances into miles.
    i 32 km   **ii** 640 km   **iii** 512 km   **iv** 1352 km

> In reality,
> 1 mile is only
> **roughly** equal
> to 1 kilometre.

Unit 2

A02 Functional Maths

4 a David went to France. He changed £500 into €750.
    What was the exchange rate for pounds into euros?
  b Juan lives in Spain. He changes €400 into AUS$1000.
    What was the exchange rate for euros into Australian
    dollars?
  c There are approximately 50 squatches in 20 morcks.
    What is the conversion rate for changing squatches
    into morcks?

DID YOU KNOW?

The Chinese first used
paper money in the
7th century. Paper
money was not printed
in the UK until the
17th century.

5 Each of these people change amounts of money from
pounds into euros. The exchange rate is £1 = €1.60.
Work out the number of euros each person receives.

Person	Amount (£)	Exchange rate (£1 = €1.60)	Amount (€)
Basil	£10	£1 = €1.6	
Peter	£200	£1 = €1.6	
Clark	£80	£1 = €1.6	
Kathy	£150	£1 = €1.6	
Harry	£2300	£1 = €1.6	
Rudolph	£265	£1 = €1.6	

This spread will show you how to:

- Use a ratio to compare the size of two objects
- Use ratio notation and scales and express a ratio in its simplest form
- Divide a quantity in a given ratio

Keywords
Ratio
Scale

You can compare the size of two objects using a **ratio**.

Example

a Morrissey the kitten is 25 cm tall. Honey the puppy is 75 cm tall. What is the ratio of Morrissey's height compared to Honey's height? Express your answer in its simplest form.

b Loopy the dog is 100 cm (1 m) tall. Compare his height to Honey the puppy. Express your answer in its simplest form.

a Morrissey's height : Honey's height

$$= 25 \text{ cm} : 75 \text{ cm}$$
$$= 25 : 75$$
$$= 1 : 3$$

Honey is 3 times taller than Morrissey.

b Honey's height: Loopy's height

$$= 75 : 100$$
$$= 3 : 4$$

Honey's height is $\frac{3}{4}$ of Loopy's height.

Loopy's height is $\frac{4}{3} \times$ Honey's height.

You can simplify a ratio by dividing both parts of the ratio by the same number.

You can divide a quantity in a given ratio.

Example

Anne and Parvez share £200 in the ratio 3 : 7. How much money do they each receive?

Anne receives 3 parts for every 7 parts that Parvez receives.

Total number of parts = 3 + 7 = 10 parts
Each part = £200 ÷ 10 = £20

Anne will receive 3 parts = 3 × £20 = £60
Parvez will receive 7 parts = 7 × £20 = £140

This topic is extended to dividing with harder ratios on page 416.

£200 is divided into 10 parts.

- A **scale** is a ratio expressed in the form 1 : n.

Example

A map has a scale of 1 : 20 000. A distance on the map is 4.5 cm. What is this distance in real life?

Using the scale you can say:
Distance in real life = 20 000 × distance on the map
$$= 20 \, 000 \times 4.5 \text{ cm}$$
$$= 90 \, 000 \text{ cm}$$
$$= 900 \text{ m}$$

1 Write each ratio in its simplest form.
   a 4 : 6   **b** 6 : 10   **c** 10 : 25   **d** 16 : 24
   e 25 : 45   **f** 50 : 60   **g** 46 : 58   **h** 200 : 250

A02 Functional Maths

2 Express these pairs of objects as ratios in their simplest form.
   a There are 40 boys and 55 girls in Year 11.
   What is the ratio of boys to girls in Year 11?
   b In a batch of apples there are 8 bad apples and 52 good
   apples. What is the ratio of good apples to bad apples?
   c In a crowd of football supporters there are 12 000 men and
   8000 women. What is the ratio of women to men?
   d Hugh has 50p. Gwen has £3. What is the ratio of Hugh's
   money to Gwen's money?

3 Solve these problems.
   a In a batch of concrete the ratio of sand to cement is 5 : 2.
   How much sand is needed to mix with 10 kg of cement?
   b In a school the ratio of teachers to students is 2 : 25. If there
   are 500 students at the school, how many teachers are there?
   c In a metal alloy the ratio of aluminium to zinc is 3 : 4. How
   much aluminium is needed to mix with 20 kg of zinc?
   d For his vegetable beds, Paul mixes some sand and compost
   in the ratio 3 : 4. How much compost does he mix with
   72 kg of sand?

Hint for part **a**:
Amount of sand =
$\frac{5}{2}$ × amount of
cement

4 Use the scales to work out the measurements in each of these
   calculations.
   a A map has a scale of 1 : 500.
      i What is the distance in real life of a measurement of 10 cm on
      the map?
      ii What is the distance on the map of a measurement of 20 m in
      real life?
   b A map has a scale of 1 : 5000.
      i What is the distance in real life of a measurement of 4 cm on
      the map?
      ii What is the distance on the map of a measurement of 600 m in
      real life?

5 Solve these problems.
   a Divide £30 in the ratio 3 : 7.
   b Divide 250 kg in the ratio 7 : 3.
   c Divide 40 tonnes in the ratio 5 : 3.
   d Divide 135 litres in the ratio 5 : 4.

Unit 2

Summary

Check out

This spread will show you how to:

- Solve problems involving proportion
- Use ratio notation and express a ratio in its simplest form
- Divide a quantity in a given ratio

Worked exam question

Shampoo is on sale in three sizes of bottle.

Small

100 ml

79p

Medium

300 ml

£1.99

Large

$\frac{1}{2}$ litre

£3.49

Which size of bottle is best value?
You **must** show your working.

(4)

(AQA, 2009)

· ·

100 ml → 79 p
300 ml → 199 p
500 ml → 399 p

Medium: 100 ml costs 199 ÷ 3 = 66.333...p

Large: 100 ml costs 399 ÷ 5 = 69.8p

So the cheapest per 100 ml is the medium size.

Exam questions

1   Olivia goes on holiday to America.
   The exchange rate is £1 = $1.87 (dollars)

   a She changes £500 into dollars.
       How many dollars does she get? (2)

   b When she returns home she changes $200 back into pounds.
       How many pounds does she get back? (2)
       (AQA, 2008)

2   Two shades of pink paint are made by mixing red and white
   paint as shown.

Shade	red : white
BLUSHING PINK	3 : 1
DUSKY PINK	3 : 2

   a What percentage of Blushing Pink is red paint? (2)

   b How much red paint is needed to make 20 000 litres of Dusky Pink? (2)
       (AQA, 2008)

3   Divide £400 in the ratio 2:3.

Mathematics is used widely in sport, particularly when taking measurements and recording results.

Here are the results and reaction times (in alphabetical order) for the 100m Men's Final at the IAAF World Championships in Berlin in August 2009:

Use the photo to order Bailey and Thompson as well as Burns and Chambers. What degree of accuracy is shown here?

Name	Nationality	Time (s)	Reaction (s)
Bailey	ANT	9.93	0.129
Bolt	JAM	9.58	0.146
Burns	TRI	10.00	0.165
Chambers	GBR	10.00	0.123
Gay	USA	9.71	0.144
Patton	USA	10.34	0.149
Powell	JAM	9.84	0.134
Thompson	TRI	9.93	0.119

What degree of accuracy is reported for
a) the result times
b) the reaction times?

Draw a stem-and-leaf diagram to show the result times of this race.

Calculate the
a) range b) median c) mean
of the reported results, giving your answers to an appropriate level of accuracy.

Which average do you think best represents these results? Explain your answer.

Here are the results and reaction times for the 100m Women's Final at the same World Championships:

Name	Nationality	Time (s)	Reaction (s)
Fraser	JAM	10.73	0.146
Stewart	JAM	10.75	0.170
Jeter	USA	10.90	0.160
Campbell-Brown	JAM	10.95	0.135
Williams	JAM	11.01	0.158
Ferguson-McKenzie	USA	11.05	0.130
Sturrup	BAH	11.05	0.137
Bailey	BAH	11.16	0.173
	JAM		

Use diagrams and statistics to compare the Men's and Women's reported results.

File   Edit   View   History   Bookmarks   Window   Help

http://berlin.iaaf.org/results/racedate=08-16-2009/sex=M/discCode=100/combCode=hash/roundCode=f/results.html#detM_100_hash_f

Fastest ten all-time 100m Women's sprinters as of 20th September 2009

Google   Google Maps   OUP   Wikipedia

IAAF WORLD CHAMPIONSHIPS
BERLIN, AUGUST 2009

NEWS   PHOTOS   VIDEO   AUDIO

By Date   By Event   Entry List   Medal Table   Placing Table   Entry Standards

Any reaction time quicker than 0.1 seconds is considered to be a false start.
How close was the fastest reaction time in the
a) Men's final   b) Women's final
to the false start limit?

Do you think that the limit of 0.1 seconds is a suitable value?
Explain your answer.
Find the range of the reaction times for both the Men's and Women's races.
Draw a scatter diagram to show result time against reaction time for
a) the Men's final   b) the Women's final.

Do you think there is any link between the reaction times of the athletes and the results of these races?
Explain your answer.
Recalculate the result times for the athletes in
a) the Men's race   b) the Women's race
assuming that all of the athletes had a reaction time of 0.1 seconds.
Use diagrams and statistics to show what effect this would have on the results of each race.

Introduction

Formula 1 engineers use complex mathematical equations to predict the effect on performance of their cars when they make technical modifications. Mathematicians turn problems in the real world into mathematical equations which they know how to solve.

What's the point?

Learning how to solve equations allows complicated real life problems to be solved.

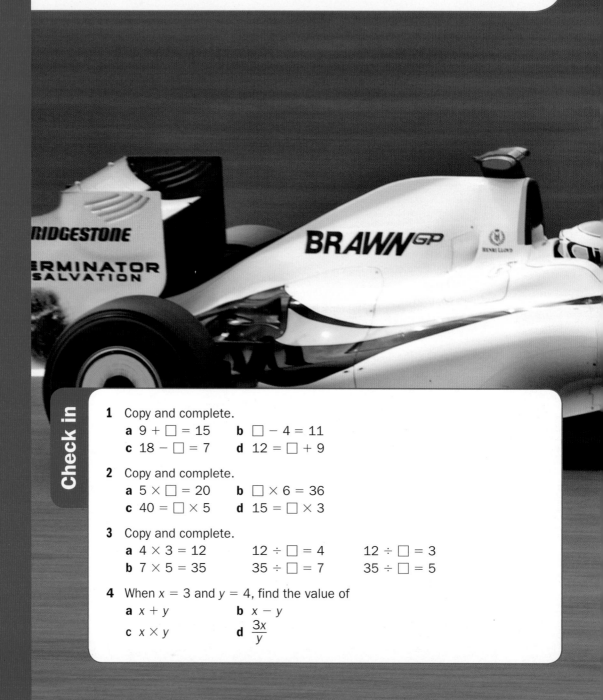

Check in

1 Copy and complete.
   a $9 + \square = 15$ **b** $\square - 4 = 11$
   c $18 - \square = 7$ **d** $12 = \square + 9$

2 Copy and complete.
   a $5 \times \square = 20$ **b** $\square \times 6 = 36$
   c $40 = \square \times 5$ **d** $15 = \square \times 3$

3 Copy and complete.
   a $4 \times 3 = 12$ $12 \div \square = 4$ $12 \div \square = 3$
   b $7 \times 5 = 35$ $35 \div \square = 7$ $35 \div \square = 5$

4 When $x = 3$ and $y = 4$, find the value of
   a $x + y$ **b** $x - y$
   c $x \times y$ **d** $\dfrac{3x}{y}$

What I need to know	What I will learn	What this leads to
A1 →	■ Understand and use inverse operations ■ Solve equations with whole number coefficients ■ Write equations for word problems ■ Check a solution by substitution	→ A6
N2 →		

Rich task

This grid of numbers uses each of the numbers from 1 to 9.

Every row, column, and diagonal adds up to 15. It is called a magic square.

4	9	2
3	5	7
8	1	6

Using the numbers from 1 to 9 invent your own magic square.

This spread will show you how to:

- Add, subtract, multiply and divide any number
- Use inverse operations

Keywords
Input
Inverse
Operation
Output

- You can write **calculations** using function machines.

A function machine has

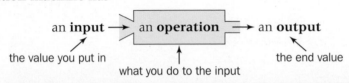

an **input** → an **operation** → an **output**

the value you put in

what you do to the input

the end value

p.176

p.374

Example

Work out the outputs for these function machines.

a 2 → +5 →

b 12 → ÷3 →

a 2 → +5 → 7

b 12 → ÷3 → 4

- Every operation has an **inverse** operation.
  The inverse operation 'undoes' the operation.

- You can work backwards through a function
  machine using inverse operations.

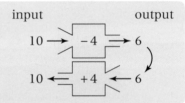

input   output

10 → −4 → 6

10 ← +4 ← 6

The inverse of
'add' is 'subtract'.
The inverse
of 'multiply' is
'divide'.

Example

Draw the inverse machines for these function machines.

a 3 → ×2 → 6   b 5 → +13 → 18   c 10 → ÷2 → 5

a 3 ← ÷2 ← 6   b 5 ← −13 ← 18   c 10 ← ×2 ← 5

- You can use function machines to solve 'think of a number' problems.

Example

I think of a number and
multiply it by 4.
My answer is 20.

What is my number?

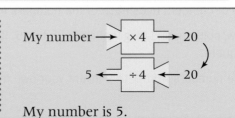

My number → ×4 → 20

5 ← ÷4 ← 20

My number is 5.

1 Work out the outputs for these function machines.

a 5 → ×4 →

b 8 → ×2 →

c 9 → +7 →

d 15 → −8 →

e 20 → ×3 →

f 18 → ÷3 →

g 14 → −6 →

h 19 → +12 →

i 27 → ÷9 →

2 Copy each machine and write the outputs for the inputs given.

a input   output   **b** input   output

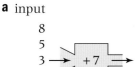

8   ___
5   ___
3 → +7 → ___
0   ___
−1   ___

4   ___
2   ___
1 → ×3 → ___
0   ___
−1   ___

3 Copy and complete these function machines.

a 7 → ×? → 21

b 5 → ×? → 35

c 4 → ×? → 24

d 7 → −? → 2

e 6 → +? → 11

f 4 → +? → 17

g 12 → ÷? → 4

h 24 → ÷? → 6

i 12 → ×? → 60

4 Write the inverse operation for each of these operations.

a ×2   **b** +4   **c** −3   **d** ÷6
e −7   **f** ×5   **g** ÷2   **h** +11

5 Copy and complete the tables for these function machines.

a → ÷2 →

Input	Output
6	
10	
24	
	15

b → −4 →

Input	Output
5	
13	
	11
20	

A03 Problem

6 Use function machines to solve these 'think of a number problems':
  a I think of a number and add 12.
  The answer is 25. What number did I think of?
  b I think of a number and divide it by 4.
  The answer is 5. What number did I think of?

This spread will show you how to:
- Use letters to represent numbers in algebra
- Understand and use the vocabulary of algebra
- Set up and solve simple equations

- An **expression** is made up of terms, containing letter symbols and numbers.

$3x + 2 \quad x - 4 \quad 2x \quad 4x + 1$
are all expressions.

- An **equation** includes letter and number terms and an equals sign.

$x + 2 = 5$ is an equation.

In an equation, the letter symbol represents one number value.
You can work out the value of a letter in an equation using number facts.

For example, $x + 2 = 5$ and $3 + 2 = 5$.
So $x = 3$ is the **solution** of the equation.
Working out the value of the unknown is called solving the equation.

- You can use function machines to **solve** equations.

Example

Solve these equations.

a $x + 5 = 12$ **b** $y - 6 = 10$

a

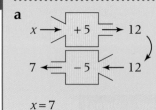

$x = 7$

b

$y = 16$

Draw the function machine for the equation.

Draw the inverse function machine.

- You can write an equation for a word problem and solve it.

Example

Tony had some pairs of socks.
For Christmas he got 4 more pairs of socks.
He counted all his socks and found he had 11 pairs altogether.
How many pairs of socks did he have to start with?

n pairs + 4 pairs = 11 pairs $n + 4 = 11$

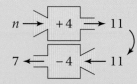

$n = 7$
Tony had 7 pairs of socks to start with.

Use the letter n to represent the number of pairs of socks Tony started with.

Write an equation to represent the problem.

Use function machines to solve the equation.

1 Use number facts to work out the missing numbers in these calculations.

a $6 + \square = 10$ **b** $2 + \square = 7$ **c** $5 + \square = 8$

d $3 + \square = 12$ **e** $6 + \square = 18$ **f** $7 = \square + 3$

g $9 = 4 + \square$ **h** $14 = \square + 6$ **i** $19 = 13 + \square$

2 Use number facts to work out the missing numbers in these calculations.

a $8 - \square = 2$ **b** $12 - \square = 6$ **c** $10 - \square = 3$

d $13 - \square = 2$ **e** $15 - \square = 8$ **f** $8 = 10 - \square$

g $5 = \square - 10$ **h** $7 = \square - 5$ **i** $20 = \square - 6$

3 Copy and complete these function machines to solve these equations.

a $x + 3 = 6$ **b** $a - 8 = 5$ **c** $b + 4 = 3$

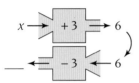 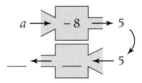 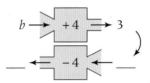

4 For each function machine, draw the inverse function machine and find the value of the unknown.

a $a \rightarrow \boxed{+8} \rightarrow 15$ **b** $b \rightarrow \boxed{+6} \rightarrow 23$ **c** $c \rightarrow \boxed{+7} \rightarrow 12$

d $d \rightarrow \boxed{+11} \rightarrow 20$ **e** $e \rightarrow \boxed{+15} \rightarrow 48$ **f** $f \rightarrow \boxed{+13} \rightarrow 21$

g $g \rightarrow \boxed{+27} \rightarrow 40$ **h** $h \rightarrow \boxed{+40} \rightarrow 100$ **i** $i \rightarrow \boxed{-5} \rightarrow 3$

j $j \rightarrow \boxed{-8} \rightarrow 4$ **k** $k \rightarrow \boxed{-3} \rightarrow 9$ **l** $l \rightarrow \boxed{-13} \rightarrow 9$

m $m \rightarrow \boxed{-25} \rightarrow 6$ **n** $n \rightarrow \boxed{-10} \rightarrow 90$ **o** $o \rightarrow \boxed{-15} \rightarrow 15$

5 Use function machines to solve these equations.

a $x + 3 = 7$ **b** $y + 6 = 10$ **c** $n - 1 = 6$

d $m + 9 = 14$ **e** $r - 3 = 10$ **f** $9 + v = 0$

g $y - 2 = 7$ **h** $x - 4 = 3$ **i** $z - 6 = 2$

j $m - 5 = 9$ **k** $z + 2 = 15$ **l** $p - 7 = 9$

m $q - 4 = 8$ **n** $n + 4 = 11$ **o** $a + 16 = 27$

6 Horace is three times older than his son, Homer.
In 10 years' time, Horace will be twice Homer's age.
How old is Homer?

A03 Problem

Solving multiplication and division equations

This spread will show you how to:

- Solve equations with whole numbers, including those involving multiplication and division

- You can use function machines to solve equations involving multiplication and division.

The equation $3x = 12$ means 'x multiplied by 3 = 12'.

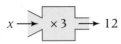

$x \longrightarrow \boxed{\times 3} \longrightarrow 12$

Solve the equation using an inverse machine.

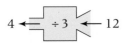

$4 \longleftarrow \boxed{\div 3} \longleftarrow 12$

$x = 4$

The equation $\dfrac{y}{4} = 6$ means 'y divided by 4 = 6'.

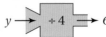

$y \longrightarrow \boxed{\div 4} \longrightarrow 6$

Solve the equation using an inverse machine.

$24 \longleftarrow \boxed{\times 4} \longleftarrow 6$

$y = 24$

Example

Solve these equations using number facts.

a $3s = 12$　　　　　　　　　**b** $\dfrac{t}{2} = 5$

....

a $3 \times s = 12$ and $3 \times 4 = 12$
So $s = 4$

b $t \div 2 = 5$ and $10 \div 2 = 5$
So $t = 10$

Example

Solve these equations using function machines.

a $6m = 30$　　　　　　　　　**b** $\dfrac{n}{7} = 3$

....

a

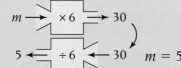

$m \longrightarrow \boxed{\times 6} \longrightarrow 30$

$5 \longleftarrow \boxed{\div 6} \longleftarrow 30 \quad m = 5$

b

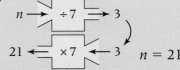

$n \longrightarrow \boxed{\div 7} \longrightarrow 3$

$21 \longleftarrow \boxed{\times 7} \longleftarrow 3 \quad n = 21$

Example

A pizza is cut into m slices. Ali and Kate share the pizza equally between them.

a Write an expression for the number of slices they have each.

b Ali and Kate have 6 slices each. Use your answer to part a to write an equation.

c Solve your equation to find the value of m.

....

a $\dfrac{m}{2}$　　　**b** $\dfrac{m}{2} = 6$　　　**c** $m \longrightarrow \boxed{\div 2} \longrightarrow 6$

$12 \longleftarrow \boxed{\times 2} \longleftarrow 6 \quad m = 12$

$\dfrac{m}{2}$ means 'm divided by 2'.

1 Use number facts to find the missing numbers.

a $3 \times \square = 15$ **b** $4 \times \square = 20$ **c** $5 \times \square = 25$ **d** $2 \times \square = 16$

e $8 \times \square = 32$ **f** $4 \times \square = 24$ **g** $6 \times \square = 30$ **h** $\square \times 3 = 12$

i $\square \times 5 = 30$ **j** $\square \times 8 = 24$ **k** $\square \div 2 = 4$ **l** $\square \div 5 = 5$

m $\square \div 3 = 5$ **n** $\square \div 4 = 6$ **o** $6 \times \square = 18$ **p** $18 \div \square = 6$

q $20 \div \square = 5$ **r** $\square \times 7 = 35$ **s** $\square \div 7 = 7$ **t** $\square \times \square = 36$

2 Copy and complete these function machines and their inverses to find the value of the unknowns.

a 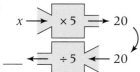   **b** 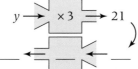   **c**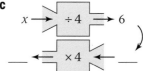

3 Match each function machine in set A with an equation in set B.

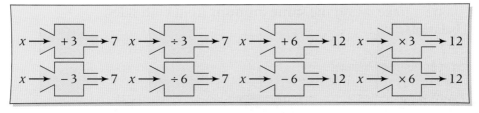

Set A

Set B

$3x = 12$ $6x = 12$ $x - 6 = 12$ $x + 6 = 12$

$\dfrac{x}{3} = 7$ $x + 3 = 7$ $x - 3 = 7$ $\dfrac{x}{6} = 7$

4 Draw function machines for these equations and use inverse machines to solve them.

a $4x = 20$ **b** $3y = 15$ **c** $5z = 30$ **d** $2r = 12$

e $4s = 28$ **f** $3t = 18$ **g** $2v = 22$ **h** $2w = 18$

i $\dfrac{x}{3} = 5$ **j** $\dfrac{y}{2} = 24$ **k** $\dfrac{z}{5} = 5$ **l** $\dfrac{r}{3} = 8$

5 Maisie has 5 boxes of pencils.
     Each box contains n pencils.

a Write an expression for the number of pencils Maisie has.

b Maisie counts the pencils. She has 40 in total.
     Use your expression from part **a** to write an equation.

c Solve your equation to find n, the number of pencils in a box.

The balance method

This spread will show you how to:
- Use the balance method to solve equations

Keywords
Balance
Inverse

In this set of scales, the two sides **balance**.

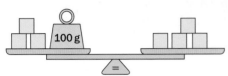

Add 2 boxes to each side.

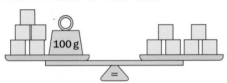

Still balanced.

Take 3 boxes from each side.

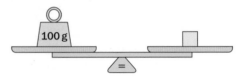

Still balanced.   1 box = 100 g

If you add or subtract (take away) the **same amount** from both sides, the scales still balance.

- The two sides of an equation balance.

Start with the equation
$x + 5 = 11$

Subtract 5 from each side
$x + 5 - 5 = 11 - 5$

The solution is $x = 6$.

The **inverse** of $+5$ is -5.
Use the inverse operation to get x on its own.

- You can use the **balance method** to solve an equation.
  You do the same to each side to keep the equation balanced.

Example

Use the balance method to solve these equations.
a $m + 4 = 15$ **b** $n - 3 = 8$

....

a $m + 4 = 15$ **b** $n - 3 = 8$
   $m + 4 - 4 = 15 - 4$ $n - 3 + 3 = 8 + 3$
          $m = 11$ $n = 11$

In **a** the inverse of $+4$ is -4.
Subtract 4 from both sides.

In **b** the inverse of -3 is $+3$.
Add 3 to both sides.

1 For each of these diagrams work out the weight of one box.

a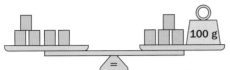

b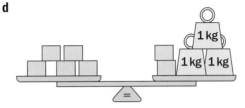

c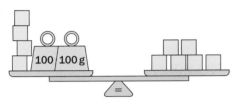

d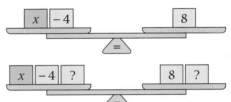

2 Copy and complete these balances to solve the equations.

    a $x + 6 = 19$ **b** $x - 4 = 8$

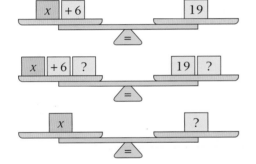

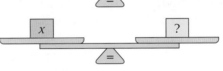

3 Copy and complete to solve these equations.

    a $m + 7 = 13$ The inverse of $+7$ is ___

      Subtract 7 from both sides:

                  $m + 7$ ___ $= 13$ _____

                        $m = $ _____

    b $n - 9 = 17$ The inverse of -9 is ___

      Add ____ to both sides:

                  $n - 9$ ___ $= 17$ ____

                      $n = $ _____

4 Solve these equations using the balance method.

    a $x + 5 = 8$ **b** $x + 3 = 14$ **c** $x + 8 = 13$ **d** $x + 3 = 18$

    e $x + 9 = 0$ **f** $5 + x = 11$ **g** $x - 4 = 7$ **h** $x - 9 = 6$

5 Match each equation in set A to its solution in set B.

    Set A: **Set B:**

$13 - x = 10$ $x - 4 = -3$ $x + 5 = 7$ $x + 17 = 21$ $x + 8 = 14$ $x + 6 = 15$ $x - 7 = 1$ $x - 3 = 4$ $22 + x = 27$	$x = 1$ $x = 2$ $x = 3$ $x = 4$ $x = 5$ $x = 6$ $x = 7$ $x = 8$ $x = 9$

Unit 2

A03 Problem

More solving equations

This spread will show you how to:

● Use the balance method to solve equations

● Check a solution is correct by substituting it back into the equation

Keywords
Balance
Substituting

These scales are **balanced**.

3 boxes weigh 300 g.

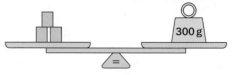

p.372

Double (×2) both sides.

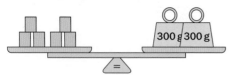

Divide both sides by 3.

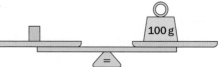

The scales still balance.
6 boxes weigh 600 g.

The scales still balance.
1 box weighs 100 g.

● You can solve equations using the balance method.
  To keep an equation balanced
  – You can add or subtract the same amount from both sides
  – You can multiply or divide both sides by the same number.

Example

Solve these equations using the balance method.

a $3x = 15$ **b** $\dfrac{x}{4} = 5$

....

a $3x = 15$

   Divide both sides by 3:

   $3x \div 3 = 15 \div 3$

       $x = 5$

b $\dfrac{x}{4} = 5$

   Multiply both sides by 4:

   $\dfrac{x}{4} \times 4 = 5 \times 4$

       $x = 20$

x is multiplied by 3. The inverse of ×3 is ÷3.

$\dfrac{x}{4} = x \div 4$.
The inverse of ÷4 is × 4.

● You can check that a solution is correct by **substituting** it back into the equation.

Example

Daisy solves the equation $\dfrac{x}{7} = 4$.

Her solution is $x = 28$. Is she correct?

....

Substitute $x = 28$ into $\dfrac{x}{7}$: $\dfrac{28}{7} = 28 \div 7 = 4$

                            So $x = 28$ is correct

The correct value of x will give the answer 4.

1 For each of these diagrams work out the weight of one box.

a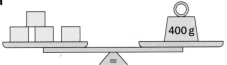

b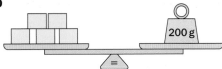

c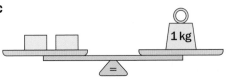

d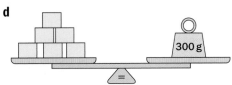

2 Copy and complete to solve these equations.

a $6m = 24$ The inverse of $\times 6$ is ____

Divide both sides by ___:

$$6m \div \underline{\hspace{0.5cm}} = 24 \div \underline{\hspace{0.5cm}}$$

$$m = \underline{\hspace{0.5cm}}$$

b $\dfrac{n}{5} = 1$ The inverse of $\div 5$ is ____

Multiply both sides by ___:

$$\dfrac{n}{5} \times \underline{\hspace{0.5cm}} = 11 \times \underline{\hspace{0.5cm}}$$

$$n = \underline{\hspace{0.5cm}}$$

3 Solve these equations using the balance method.

a $5x = 15$ **b** $3x = 21$ **c** $6x = 18$ **d** $4x = 36$
e $28 = 4x$ **f** $7x = 28$ **g** $50 = 25x$ **h** $4x = 10$

4 Use the balance method to solve these equations.

a $\dfrac{s}{5} = 5$ **b** $\dfrac{t}{12} = 3$ **c** $\dfrac{u}{2} = 4$ **d** $\dfrac{v}{7} = 3$

e $\dfrac{v}{5} = 9$ **f** $\dfrac{w}{3} = 8$ **g** $10 = \dfrac{x}{5}$ **h** $3 = \dfrac{y}{9}$

5 Solve these equations.
Check your answers using substitution.

a $a + 7 = 11$ **b** $g - 7 = 8$ **c** $\dfrac{c}{4} = 9$ **d** $d - 5 = -2$

e $3e = 21$ **f** $9 + f = 5$ **g** $4g = 0$ **h** $\dfrac{h}{4} = 2.5$

6 Tom and Anya both solve the equation $7x = 56$.

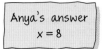

Tom's answer
$x = 9$

Anya's answer
$x = 8$

Who is correct? Explain how you worked it out.

Unit 2

A03 Problem

269

Summary

Check out
You should now be able to:

- Use letters to represent numbers in algebra
- Set up simple equations
- Solve simple equations using inverse operations
- Solve simple equations using the balance method
- Check a solution is correct by substituting it back into the equation

Worked exam question
Solve the equations.

a $9a = 45$ (1)

b $b - 3 = 7.2$ (1)

c $\dfrac{c}{2} = 7$ (1)

d $8d - 1 = 21$ (2)

e $5e + 13 = 7 - e$ (3)

(AQA, 2009)

a
$$9a = 45$$
$$a = \frac{45}{9} = 5$$

> ÷ 9 is the inverse operation to × 9.

b
$$b - 3 = 7.2$$
$$b = 7.2 + 3 = 10.2$$

> + 3 is the inverse operation to − 3.

c
$$\frac{c}{2} = 7$$
$$c = 7 \times 2 = 14$$

> × 2 is the inverse operation to ÷ 2.

d
$$8d - 1 = 21$$
$$8d = 21 + 1 = 22$$
$$d = \frac{22}{8} = 2\frac{3}{4}$$

> This involves **two** operations. + 1 is the inverse operation to − 1. Then ÷ 8 is the inverse operation to × 8.

e
$$5e + 13 = 7 - e$$
$$6e + 13 = 7$$
$$6e = 7 - 13 = -6$$
$$e = \frac{-6}{6} = -1$$

> Here the unknown appears on both sides. See page 422 for others like this.

Exam questions

1 The diagram shows a mathematical rule.

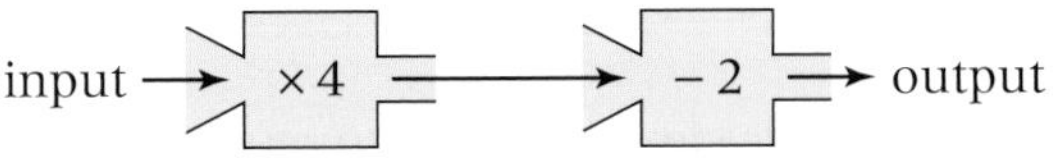

input → [× 4] → [− 2] → output

It multiplies a number by 4 and then subtracts 2.

a Copy and complete the diagram.

8 → [× 4] → [− 2] → ....

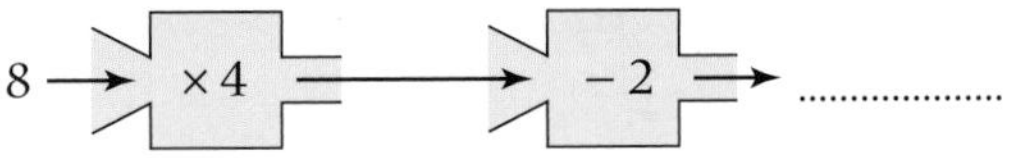

(1)

b Copy and complete the diagram.

.... → [× 4] → [− 2] → 14

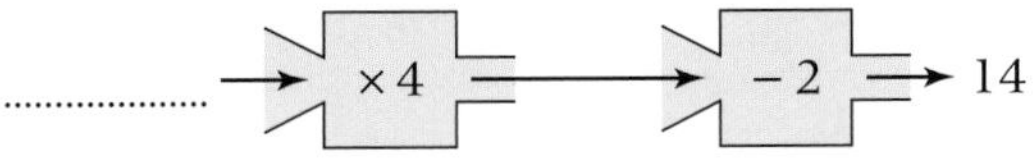

(1)

c Copy and complete the diagram.

.... → [× 4] → [− 2] → 126

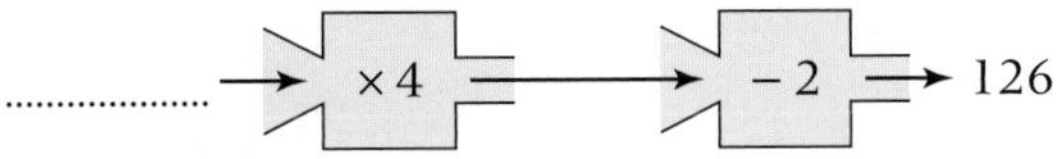

(1)

2 In the magic square, the rows, columns and diagonals add to the same number.

10	w	x
5	y	9
6	11	4

Work out the values of w, x and y.

(3)
(AQA, specimen)

3 Solve each of these equations.

a $2x = 12$ (1)

b $y - 1 = 9$ (1)

c $\dfrac{x}{3} = 8$ (1)

Introduction

The United Kingdom is not a very regular shape. However, cartographers have managed to work out its area as 244 820 km².

What's the point?

Cartographers use lines of latitude and longitude to divide countries into much smaller regular shapes, such as trapeziums. They can then calculate the area of each of these smaller pieces, and add them together to calculate the area of the country.

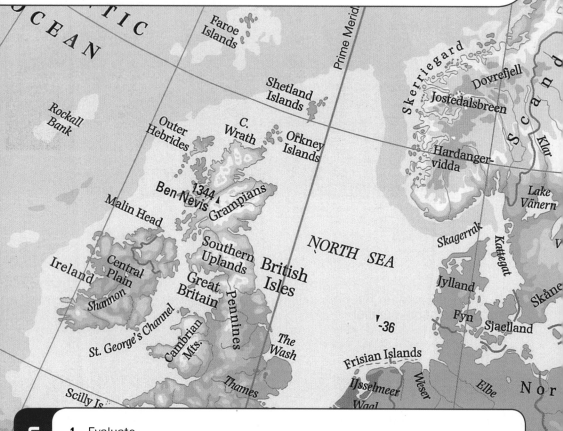

Check in

1 Evaluate
   a 4.2 + 3.6   **b** 3.8 + 5.6   **c** 2.5 + 3

2 Work out
   a 40 × 10   **b** 14 × 1000   **c** 3.1 × 10
   d 13.4 × 100   **e** 6.3 × 1000   **f** 400 ÷ 10
   g 6000 ÷ 100   **h** 430 ÷ 100   **i** 640 ÷ 1000
   j 3.1 ÷ 10

3 Measure this line

   _____

   a in millimetres
   b in centimetres.

What I need to know	What I will learn	What this leads to
Key stage 3 →	■ Make sensible estimates of measurements ■ Convert measurements ■ Know rough metric equivalents of imperial units ■ Find perimeters and areas of simple shapes ■ Find the surface area of cuboids	→ G2 + 7

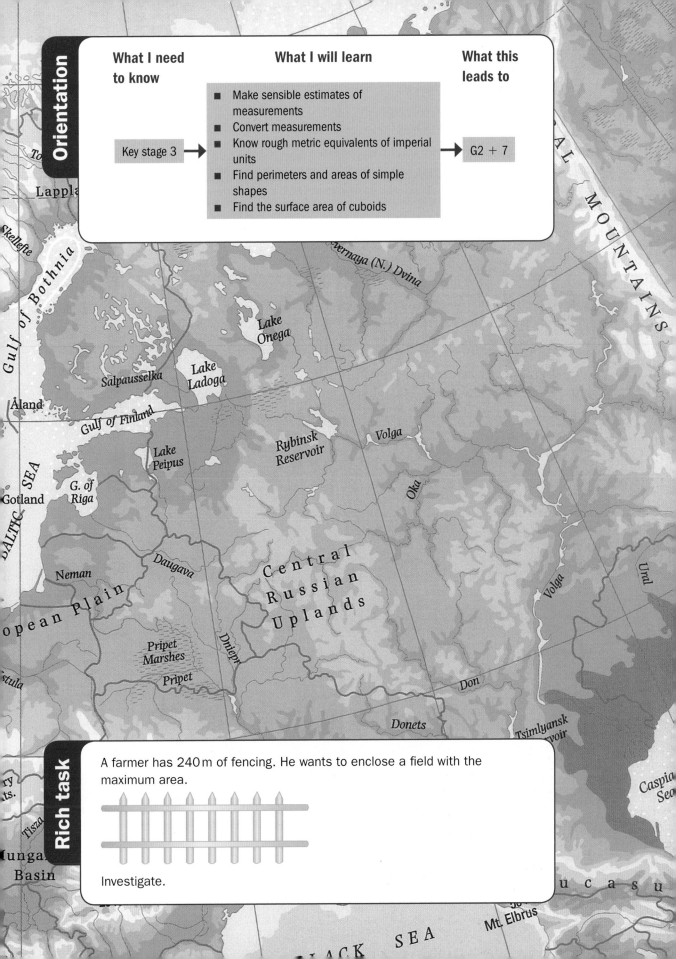

A farmer has 240 m of fencing. He wants to enclose a field with the maximum area.

Investigate.

This spread will show you how to:
● Make sensible estimates of measurements

Keywords
Capacity
Length
Mass
Measure
Metric

Metric units are based on the decimal system.

● You can **measure** length and distance using metric units.

millimetre (mm)   **centimetre (cm)**   **metre (m)**   **kilometre (km)**

   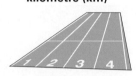

p.274

1 mm is $\frac{1}{10}$ of 1 cm
10 mm = 1 cm

The thickness of your little finger is about 1 cm.

The height of a door is about 2 m.

$2\frac{1}{2}$ times round the running track is about 1 km.

You use a ruler to measure short lengths.
You use a tape measure or trundle wheel to measure longer lengths.

Example

Give a sensible metric unit to measure

a the distance travelled on a car journey
b the mass of an apple
c the amount of water in a bath.

a kilometres (km)
b grams (g)
c litres

● You can measure **mass** using metric units.

Mass is linked to weight.

milligrams (mg)   **gram (g)**   **kilogram (kg)**   **tonne (t)**

1 mg is $\frac{1}{1000}$ of a gram
1000 mg = 1 g

A peanut weighs about 1 g.

A bag of sugar weighs 1 kg.

A small car weighs about 1 tonne.

● You can measure **capacity** or volume using metric units.

Capacity is the amount of liquid a container holds.

millilitre (ml)   **centilitre (cl)**   **litre (l)**

A teaspoon holds about 5 ml.

A can of drink holds 33 cl.

A carton of fruit juice holds 1 litre.

1 Four metric units for measuring distance are

> metre   kilometre   centimetre   millimetre

a Write them in order of size starting with the smallest.
b Write the correct abbreviations next to your answers.

2 Three metric units for measuring capacity are

> centilitre   litre   millilitre

a Write them in order of size, starting with the smallest.
b Write the appropriate abbreviation next to your answer.

DID YOU KNOW?

The world's tallest wooden house is around 43 m in height and extends to 13 floors. It was built by Nikolai Sutyagin in Arkhangelsk in Russia.

Unit 3

A02 Functional Maths

3 Which metric unit of length would you use to measure
  a the length of a swimming pool
  b the thickness of a coin
  c the distance from London to Paris
  d the height of a house?

4 Which of these measurements could be 2.5 cm?
  a height of a room   **b** height of a table
  c diameter of a coin   **d** length of a book

For questions 5–7 choose the most suitable answer.

5 The length of a car is about
  a 30 cm   **b** 300 mm   **c** 3 m   **d** 0.5 m

6 The length of a playing card is about
  a 9 mm   **b** 0.9 m   **c** 90 cm   **d** 9 cm

7 The width of a playing card is about
  a 60 mm   **b** 60 cm   **c** 0.6 m   **d** 6 m

8 Which metric unit of mass would you use to weigh
  a a person   **b** a bus
  c a banana   **d** a piece of paper?

For questions 9–11, choose the most suitable answer.

9 The weight restriction for baggage on an aircraft could be
  a 15 g   **b** 15 t   **c** 15 mg   **d** 15 kg

10 A tub of margarine could weigh
  a 500 kg   **b** 500 g   **c** 500 mg   **d** 500 t

11 The weight of flour used to make pastry could be
  a 200 mg   **b** 200 g   **c** 200 kg   **d** 200 t

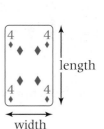

length

width

Metric measures

This spread will show you how to:

- Convert measurements from one unit to another

- **Metric** units are based on the decimal system.

 You can **convert** between units in the metric system, by multiplying or dividing by 10, 100, 1000, ...

Length

10 mm = 1 cm   100 cm = 1 m   1000 m = 1 km

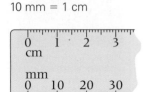  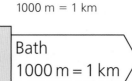

mm = millimetre
cm = centimetre
m = metre
km = kilometre

Bath
1000 m = 1 km

Mass

1000 mg = 1 g
1000 g = 1 kg
1000 kg = 1 t

Capacity

1000 ml = 1 litre
100 cl = 1 litre

mg = milligrams
g = gram
kg = kilogram
t = tonne

ml = millilitre
cl = centilitre
l = litre

Example

The height of a ceiling is 2.4 m.
Change 2.4 m to

a centimetres   **b** millimetres.

$$\text{metres} \xrightarrow{\times 100} \text{centimetres}$$
$$\text{metres} \xleftarrow{\div 100} \text{centimetres}$$

....

a   1 m = 100 cm
        2.4 m = 2.4 × 100 cm = 240 cm

$$\text{centimetres} \xrightarrow{\times 10} \text{millimetres}$$
$$\text{centimetres} \xleftarrow{\div 10} \text{millimetres}$$

b   1 cm = 10 mm
        240 cm = 240 × 10 mm = 2400 mm

Example

A bottle of wine holds 75 cl.
Change 75 cl to

a litres   **b** millilitres.

$$\text{litres} \xrightarrow{\times 100} \text{centilitres}$$
$$\text{litres} \xleftarrow{\div 100} \text{centilitres}$$

....

a   1 litre = 100 cl
        75 cl = 75 ÷ 100 litre = 0.75 litre

$$\text{litres} \xrightarrow{\times 1000} \text{millilitres}$$
$$\text{litres} \xleftarrow{\div 1000} \text{millilitres}$$

b   1 litre = 1000 ml
        0.75 litre = 0.75 × 1000 = 750 ml

1 Convert these measurements to millimetres.
  a 5 cm   **b** 8 cm   **c** 15 cm   **d** 6 cm 7 mm   **e** 19 cm 3 mm
  f 4.5 cm   **g** 4.3 cm   **h** 10.6 cm   **i** 80 cm   **j** 1 m

2 Convert these measurements to centimetres.
  a 60 mm   **b** 85 mm   **c** 240 mm   **d** 63 mm   **e** 4 mm
  f 4 m   **g** 10 m   **h** 3.5 m   **i** 1.6 m   **j** 1.63 m

3 Convert these measurements to metres.
  a 400 cm   **b** 450 cm   **c** 475 cm   **d** 470 cm   **e** 50 cm
  f 1 km   **g** 4 km   **h** 0.5 km   **i** 3.5 km   **j** 18 km

4 Convert these weights to kilograms.
  a 8000 g   **b** 7000 g   **c** 7500 g   **d** 500 g   **e** 200 g
  f 1 t   **g** 1.5 t   **h** 3.5 t   **i** 10 t   **j** 100 t

5 Convert these weights to grams.
  a 1 kg   **b** 4 kg   **c** 0.5 kg   **d** 4.5 kg   **e** 3 kg 500 g
  f 2 kg 400 g **g** 2.4 kg   **h** 1000 mg   **i** 500 mg   **j** 2500 mg

6 Convert these capacities to litres.
  a 1000 ml   **b** 3000 ml   **c** 500 ml   **d** 4500 ml   **e** 4750 ml
  f 100 cl   **g** 200 cl   **h** 50 cl   **i** 250 cl   **j** 70 cl

7 Write these lengths in order of size, smallest first.
  2.11 m   212 cm   2011 mm   209 cm

8 Write these heights in order of size, smallest first.
  173 cm   1.7 m   1.75 m   176 cm   171 cm

9 A lorry can carry a maximum load of five tonnes.
Crates are made up, each weighing 625 kg.
How many crates can the lorry take?

10 A glass holds 200 ml. How many glasses can
Dennis pour from a 1-litre bottle of lemonade?

11 One ream (500 sheets) of A4 paper weighs 0.5 kg.
Calculate the weight of one sheet of paper in grams.

12 Sarah buys a 0.5 kg bag of rice. Each portion of rice is 150 g.
How many complete portions can she get from the bag?

This spread will show you how to:

- Know rough metric equivalents to imperial units

Keywords
Capacity
Conversions
Equivalents
Imperial units
Length
Mass
Metric units

Most people in the world use **metric units**.
Some people still use **imperial units**.
It is useful to know the metric **equivalents** of imperial units.
The imperial to metric **conversions** that you need to learn for your
unit 3 assessment are highlighted in **bold**.

I'm 6 foot and
I weigh 170 lb.

I'm 1.7 m tall
and I weigh
60 kg.

≃ means
approximately
equal to.

lb is pounds.

oz is ounces.

A litre is more
than a pint.

- **Length** metric   imperial
  2.5 cm ≃ 1 inch
  30 cm ≃ 1 foot (12 inches)
  1 m ≃ 1 yard (3 feet)
  8 km ≃ 5 miles

- **Mass** **1 kg ≃ 2.2 lb**
  30 g ≃ 1 oz

- **Capacity**   metric   imperial
  600 ml ≃ 1 pint
  1 litre ≃ 1.75 pints
  4.5 litres ≃ 1 gallon

1 litre = 1 .75 pints

Example

In 2005 all Ireland's road signs were
changed from imperial to metric units.
Change 50 miles to kilometres.

Dublin
50 miles

....

$\times 10 \left(\begin{array}{l} 5 \text{ miles} = 8 \text{ km} \\ 50 \text{ miles} = 80 \text{ km} \end{array} \right) \times 10$

Dublin
80 kilometres

Example

Linda puts 8 gallons of petrol in her car.
Approximately how many litres is that?

....

1 gallon ≃ 4.5 litres

8 gallons ≃ $4\frac{1}{2} \times 8$ litres

≃ 36 litres

1 Convert these distances to miles.

a
| Madrid |
| 8 km |

b
| Valencia |
| 240 km |

c
| Benidorm |
| 96 km |

d
| Barcelona |
| 120 km |

e
| Granada |
| 32 km |

f
| Alicante |
| 104 km |

g
| Alicante |
| 104 km |

h
| Bilbao |
| 68 km |

2 Convert these distances to kilometres.

a
| Leeds |
| 20 miles |

b
| Sheffield |
| 40 miles |

c
| York |
| 100 miles |

d
| Manchester |
| 70 miles |

e
| Liverpool |
| 250 miles |

f
| London |
| 45 miles |

g
| Nottingham |
| 35 miles |

h
| Birmingham |
| 55 miles |

3 Convert these speeds to miles per hour.

a 64 km/h **b** 24 km/h **c** 16 km/h **d** 48 km/h **e** 80 km/h

km/h = kilometres per hour

4 Convert these speeds to kilometres per hour.

a 30 mph **b** 50 mph **c** 70 mph **d** 40 mph **e** 20 mph

5 Use 1 kg ≃ 2.2 lb, to convert these weights to pounds.
   a 2 kg   **b** 10 kg   **c** 8 kg   **d** 60 kg   **e** 50 kg

6 Use 1 kg ≃ 2 lb, to convert these weights to kilograms.
   a 4 lb   **b** 60 lb   **c** 100 lb   **d** 25 lb   **e** 11 lb

7 Use 1 litre ≃ 1.75 pints, to convert these capacities to pints.

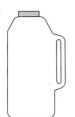
4 litres

3 litres

2 litres

1 litre

0.5 litres

8 Use 1 gallon ≃ $4\frac{1}{2}$ litres, to convert these capacities to litres.
   a 2 gallons   **b** 8 gallons   **c** 0.5 gallons
   d 2.5 gallons   **e** 40 gallons   **f** 500 gallons

Unit 3

This spread will show you how to:

- Interpret scales on a range of measuring instruments, including those for time and mass
- Recognise the possible inaccuracy of measurements

Measuring instruments use **scales** to show measurements.

The scales are divided into small divisions.

You need to work out what one division stands for.

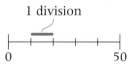

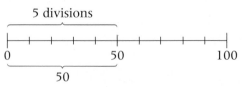

There are 5 divisions from 0 to 50.

$50 \div 5 = 10$

So each division stands for 10.

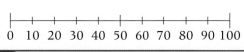

Example

Write the readings shown on the scales.

a

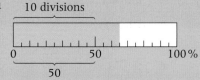

b

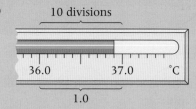

a There are 10 divisions from 0 to 50.

$50 \div 10 = 5$

Each division stands for 5%.
Reading shows
$50 + 5 + 5 + 5 = 65\%$.

b There are 10 divisions from 36.0 to 37.0.

$1.0 \div 10 = 0.1$

Each division stands for 0.1.
Reading shows
$36.0 + 0.9 = 36.9\ ^\circ C$.

The reading on this clock is only **accurate** to the nearest minute. The reading is not exact.

The reading shows 2 minutes past 12.

However, the time could be anywhere between 1.5 and 2.5 minutes past. The reading may be inaccurate by up to 30 seconds either way.

Two minutes past

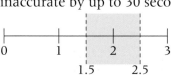

- Measurements given to the nearest whole unit may be inaccurate by up to one half in either direction.

1 For each scale, write what each division represents and the readings shown.

a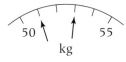

b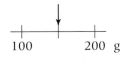

c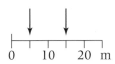

d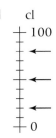

e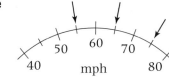

2 For each scale, write what each division represents and the readings shown.

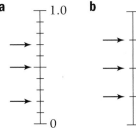 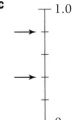 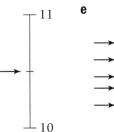 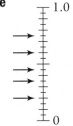

3 This scale shows how to convert from stones to kilograms.

Use the scale to convert these weights in stones to kilograms.

a 8 stones   **b** 3 stones   **c** 2.5 stones

d 5.5 stones   **e** 8.5 stones   **f** 0.5 stones

4 a Give the reading on the thermometer.

36.0°   37.0°   38.0°   °C

b Calculate how much the temperature is above 36.9 °C.

5 (**Challenge**) These measurements are given to the nearest centimetre. Give the lowest and highest measurements they could represent.

a 5 cm   **b** 8 cm   **c** 1 cm

d 10 cm   **e** 20 cm   **f** 0 cm

This type of question is indicative of grade C.

DID YOU KNOW?

The stone weight was established as 14 lb in 1352 during the reign of Edward III and hasn't changed since!

Unit 3

This spread will show you how to:
- Find the perimeter of a shape by counting squares and measuring

Keywords
Length
Perimeter
Rectangle
Unit
Width

- The **perimeter** is the distance all round a shape.
- You measure perimeter in units of **length**, for example centimetre (cm), metre (m).

Example

Find the perimeter of each shape. State the **units** of your answers.

p.402

a

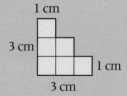

3 cm

1 cm

1 cm

3 cm

b

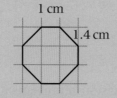

1 cm

1.4 cm

....

a Perimeter = 1 + 1 + 1 + 1 + 1 + 1 + 3 + 3
= 12 cm

b Perimeter = 1 + 1.4 + 1 + 1.4 + 1 + 1.4 + 1 + 1.4
= 9.6 cm

You can find the perimeter of a **rectangle** by counting lengths on a centimetre grid.

Perimeter = 3 + 2 + 3 + 2
= 10 cm

You can find the perimeter without a centimetre grid.

3

2   2

3

- For any rectangle

Perimeter = length + width + length + width
= 2 × length + 2 × width
Perimeter = $l + w + l + w$
= $2l + 2w$

width (w)

length (l)

Example

The length of a rectangle is 5.8 cm.
The perimeter of the rectangle is 19.4 cm.
Calculate the width of the rectangle.

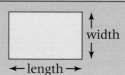

width

← length →

....

width + 5.8 + width + 5.8 = 19.4
2 × width + 11.6 = 19.4
2 × width = 19.4 − 11.6 = 7.8
width = $\frac{7.8}{2}$ = 3.9

So   width = 3.9 cm

Check:
5.8
5.8
3.9
+3.9
19.4

1 Find the perimeter of each shape. Each square represents 1 cm.

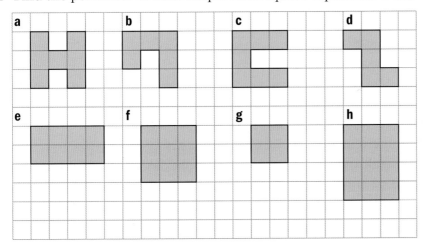

2 Calculate the perimeters of these shapes. State the units of
your answers.

 **a** 3 cm
7 cm

 b 5 m
10 m

 c 15 mm
5 mm

 d square
8 cm

e

10 m   8 m
6 m

f

6 cm   6 cm
6 cm

g

5 cm
8 cm   6 cm
3 cm

h
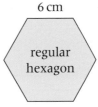
6 cm
regular hexagon

A regular hexagon has 6 equal sides.

3 A rectangular field is 80 m long and 35 m wide.
Calculate the perimeter of the field. State the units of your answer.

A03 Problem

4 a The perimeter of each rectangle is 24 cm. Calculate the unknown lengths.

i  ? cm
8 cm

ii ? cm
5 cm

iii ? cm
10 cm

iv square ? cm
? cm

b The perimeter of each rectangle is 36 cm. Calculate the unknown lengths.

i ? cm
14 cm

ii ? cm
15 cm

iii ? cm
17 cm

iv square ? cm
? cm

Unit 3

This spread will show you how to:
- Find the area of shapes by counting squares
- Find the area of a rectangle using the formula

Keywords
Area
Rectangle
Square
  centimetre
  (cm²)
Square metre
  (m²)

- **Area** is the amount of surface a shape covers.

You can find the area of a shape by counting the number of squares on a centimetre grid.
Each square is equal to an area of 1 cm².
The area of the circle is about 12 cm².

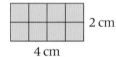
1 cm
1 cm
1 square centimetre or 1 cm².

You can find the area of a **rectangle** by counting squares.

2 cm

4 cm

Area = 4 × 2
     = 8 cm²

There are 2 rows of 4 squares.

This formula works for all rectangles.

- You can find the area of any rectangle by using the formula:

  Area of rectangle = length × width

width

length

Example

Calculate the area of this rectangle.
State the units of your answer.

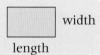
8 cm
12 cm

Area = 12 × 8 = 96 cm²

Example

I buy 12 square paving slabs. Each slab measures 1 metre by 1 metre.
I want to make a rectangle using all 12 slabs.

a What sizes of rectangles can I make?
b Calculate the area of each rectangle.

a

3 m

4 m

b Area = 3 × 4 = 12 m²

1 **square metre** = 1 m²
1 **square millimetre** = 1 mm²

2 m

6 m

Area = 2 × 6 = 12 m²

Factors of 12 are 1, 2, 3, 4, 6, 12

1 m

12 m

Area = 1 × 12 = 12 m²

1 Which is larger, one square centimetre or one square metre?

2 Find the area of each shape. Each square represents 1 cm².

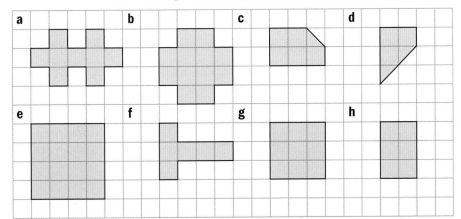

3 Calculate the areas of these rectangles. Remember to give the units of your answers.

a 3 cm, 5 cm

b 3 m, 9 m

c 10 cm, 20 cm

d square 9 cm

e 1.5 m, 6 m

f 3 m, 4.5 m

g 15 cm, 12 cm

h square 4.5 cm

A03 Problem

4 Calculate the missing lengths. Give the units of your answers.

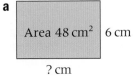

a Area 48 cm² 6 cm, ? cm

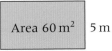

b Area 60 m² 5 m, ? m

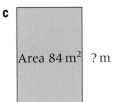

c Area 84 m² ? m, 7 m

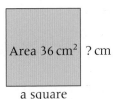

d Area 36 cm² ? cm, a square

e Area 10 cm² 4 cm, ? cm

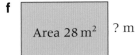

f Area 28 m² ? m, 8 m

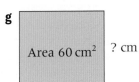

g Area 60 cm² ? cm, 8 cm

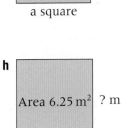

h Area 6.25 m² ? m, a square

Unit 3

Area of a rectangle and a triangle

This spread will show you how to:

- Calculate the area of rectangles and triangles and shapes made from rectangles and triangles

Keywords
Area
Diagonal
Perimeter
Rectangle
Right-angled
  triangle
Square
  centimetre

- The **area** is the amount of surface a shape covers.

You can find the area of a **rectangle** using the formula

- Area of rectangle = length × width

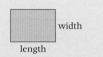

This formula also works for a square.

You can find the area of a **right-angled triangle** in several ways.
Area = 6 squares and 4 half squares
$$= 6 + 2$$
$$= 8 \text{ cm}^2$$

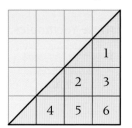

The **diagonal** line splits the square into two halves.

Area = $\frac{1}{2}$ of the area of the square
$$= \frac{1}{2} \text{ of } 16 \text{ cm}^2$$
$$= 8 \text{ cm}^2$$

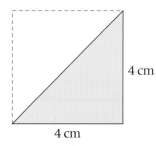

Area of the triangle is half the area of the square.

- Area of a right-angled triangle = $\frac{1}{2}$ × base × height

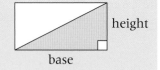

The height is perpendicular (at right angles) to the base.

This topic is extended to the area of a parallelogram and trapezium on page 428.

Example

Calculate the area of the triangle.
State the units of your answer.

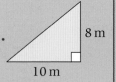

....

Area = $\frac{1}{2}$ × 10 × 8

$$= 40 \text{ m}^2$$

The units are square metres or m².

1 Find the area of each of these triangles. Each square represents one
square centimetre.

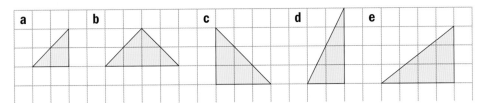

2 Calculate the area of each of these right-angled triangles. State the
units of your answers.

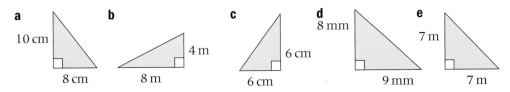

3 Calculate the area of each of these triangles. State the units of your
answers.

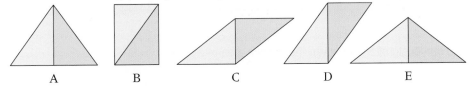

4 a Calculate the perimeter of this triangle.
   b Calculate the area of the triangle.

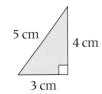

5 cm   4 cm
3 cm

c Two of these triangles are placed together to form five different shapes.

A   B   C   D   E

Copy and complete this table.

Shape	Perimeter (cm)	Area (cm²)
A		
B		
C		
D		
E		

Unit 3

A03 Problem

This spread will show you how to:
- Find the surface area of cuboids
- Find the length of a side of a cuboid, given the surface area

Keywords
Cuboid
Faces
Net
Surface area

A **cuboid** has six rectangular **faces**.

A cereal box is a cuboid.

You can unfold the cereal box to see its net.

When you unfold the cuboid, the six rectangles form the **net**.
The area of the net gives you the **surface area** of the cuboid.

- The surface area of a cuboid is the total area of its faces.

p.404 ▶

> There are two green rectangles, two red rectangles and two pink rectangles.

Example

Calculate the surface area of this cuboid.
State the units of your answer.

Area of one red rectangle $= 2 \times 4 = 8$ cm^2
Area of one pink rectangle $= 4 \times 8 = 32$ cm^2
Area of one green rectangle $= 2 \times 8 = \underline{16 \text{ cm}^2}$
56 cm^2

Total surface area $= 56 \times 2$
$ = 112$ cm^2

2 cm

4 cm

8 cm

> Units of area are cm^2.

- You can find the length of a side, given the surface area of a cube.

Example

The surface area of a cube is 150 cm^2.
Calculate the length of one side of the cube.

A cube has six square faces.

The area of one square $= 150 \div 6$
$ = 25$ cm^2

Length of one side $= \sqrt{25}$
$ = 5$ cm

x

Area 25 cm^2

x

x

x x

1 These nets make cuboids. Each square represents a 1 cm square.

a 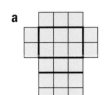 **b** 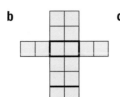 **c** 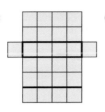 **d**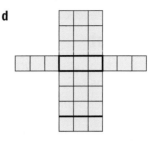

Calculate the surface area of each cuboid.
State the units of your answers.

2 A 3 cm by 4 cm by 5 cm cuboid is shown. Calculate
   a the area of the red rectangle
   b the area of the orange rectangle
   c the area of the green rectangle
   d the surface area of the cuboid.

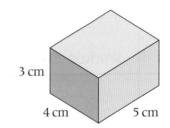

3 cm 4 cm 5 cm

3 Calculate the surface area of each of these cuboids.
State the units of your answers.

a 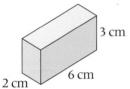 3 cm / 6 cm / 2 cm

b 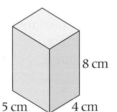 8 cm / 5 cm / 4 cm

c 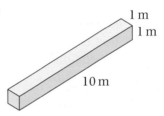 1 m / 1 m / 10 m

d 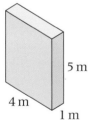 5 m / 4 m / 1 m

e  1 cm / 4 cm / 4 cm

f 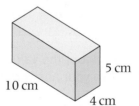 5 cm / 10 cm / 4 cm

4 Calculate the surface area of each of these cubes.
State the units of your answers.
   a length 5 cm   **b** length 8 m   **c** length 2.5 cm
   d length 15 mm   **e** length 0.5 m

length

5 Calculate the length of one side of a cube if the surface
area of the cube is
   a 600 cm^2 **b** 54 cm^2 **c** 294 cm^2
   d 9600 cm^2 **e** 37.5 cm^2

x

Unit 3

G1 Summary

Check out

You should now be able to:

- Make sensible estimates of measurements
- Convert measurements from one unit to another
- Know rough metric equivalents of imperial units
- Calculate the perimeter and area of shapes made from rectangles and triangles
- Calculate the surface area of cuboids

Worked exam question

Large areas can be measured in hectares.
1 hectare is $10\,000\,m^2$.

10 m   Not drawn
accurately

1 km

a Explain why the diagram represents 1 hectare. (1)

b This L–shape has an area of one hectare.
All lengths are a whole number of metres.

←30 m→

100 m

230 m

a

Work out the value of a.
Give your answer in metres. (3)

(AQA, specimen)

- -

a
$1\,km = 1000\,m$
Area of rectangle $= 1000\,m \times 10\,m$
$= 10\,000\,m^2$
$= 1$ hectare

> To **explain** something you need to present all the relevant facts clearly and in a logical order.

b
Area of rectangle A $= 100 \times 30$
$= 3000\,m^2$
Total area $= 1$ hectare $= 10\,000\,m^2$
So area of B $= 10\,000 - 3000$
$= 7000\,m^2$
$200 \times a = 7000$
$a = \dfrac{7000}{200} = 35\,m$

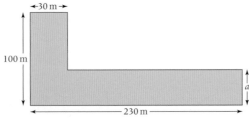

30 m

100 m   A

B a

200 m

> Split the L-shape into two rectangular areas.

Exam questions

1

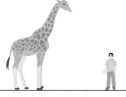

The picture shows a man standing next to a giraffe.
The giraffe and the man are drawn to the same scale.
Estimate the height, in metres, of the giraffe. (4)

2 Jill buys some potatoes.
The scales show the amount
she buys.
a What amount of potatoes does
she buy?
  i Give your answer in kilograms. (1)
  ii Give your answer in grams. (1)
b Explain how Jill can use the scales to weigh out
5 kilograms of flour. (1)

(AQA, 2009)

3 Copy and complete this table.
Write a sensible unit for each measurement.
Three have been done for you.

	Metric	Imperial
The length of a pencil	....	inches
The distance between England and France	kilometres	....
The weight of potatoes in a sack	....	pounds

(3)

4 The grids in this question are made of one
centimetre squares.
a Find the perimeter of the shaded shape. (1)

b On a copy of the grid, draw a rectangle
which has a perimeter equal to 10 cm. (2)

(AQA, 2009)

Introduction

In computer games 3D characters and objects are made from thousands of triangles. The triangles are then given different colours to create the illusion of three dimensions. Computer programmers can write a piece of computer code to represent a triangle and then repeat this over and over again to represent much more complex shapes.

What's the point?

Triangles are the most basic polygon. By using triangles in areas as diverse as computer graphics and architecture, we can create sophisticated shapes that we would otherwise not be able to create.

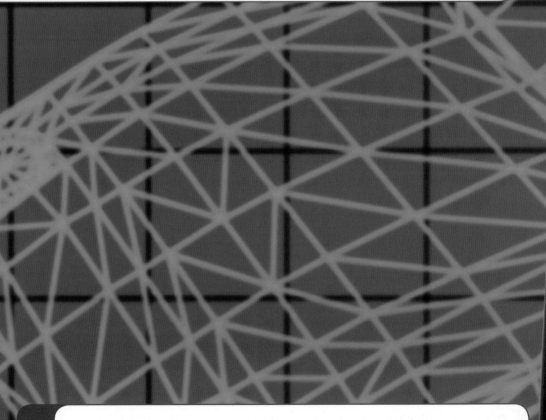

Check in

1 Measure this line in
   a millimetres   **b** centimetres.

_____

2 **Estimate** the size of these angles.
   a   **b**

What I need to know	What I will learn	What this leads to
Key stage 3 →	■ Identify types of angles ■ Recall and use properties of parallel and perpendicular lines ■ Recall and use properties of angles	→ G3
G1 →	■ Use angle properties of triangles ■ Measure lines and angles	

You will need a circular pinboard.

A triangle has been made on a circular geoboard. Measure its angles.
Investigate the angles in different triangles you can make on the pinboard.
Can you find some rules?

Measuring lines

This spread will show you how to:

- Measure and draw lines to the nearest millimetre

A ruler **measures length** in **millimetres** (mm) or **centimetres** (cm).

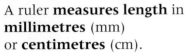

This line measures 2.5 cm or 25 mm.

10 mm = 1 cm

2.5 cm = $2\frac{1}{2}$ cm

This line measures 2.7 cm or 27 mm.

H	T	U	•	$\frac{1}{10}$	$\frac{1}{100}$
		2	•	7	

2.7 cm = $2\frac{7}{10}$ cm

To measure a line, line up the ruler so that the zero mark is at the start of the line.

You can construct shapes using a ruler and a protractor.

Example

Using a ruler and a protractor, construct a square of length 5 cm.
Draw and measure the diagonal in **a** centimetres
b millimetres.

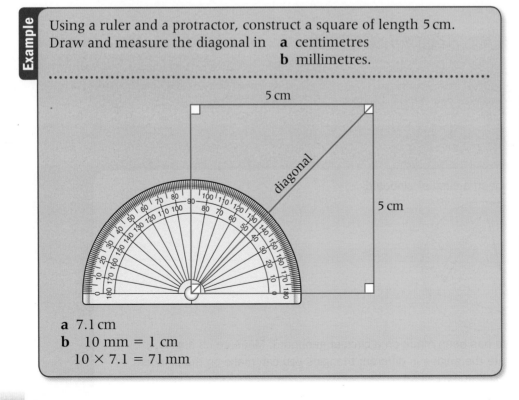

Use the ruler to draw the 5 cm lines.

Use the protractor to construct the 90° angles.

a 7.1 cm
b 10 mm = 1 cm
10 × 7.1 = 71 mm

1 Measure the lengths of these lines in
  a centimetres
  b millimetres.

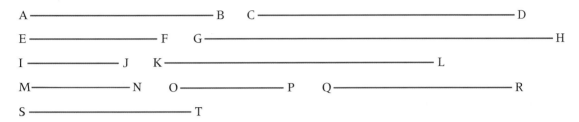

2 a Draw a line AB, so that AB = 9 cm.
  b Find the midpoint of AB and mark it with a cross.

3 a Draw a line CD, so that CD = 11.6 cm.
  b Find the midpoint of CD and mark it M.
  c Measure CM, stating the units of your answer.

4 Measure and state the diameter of each circle in centimetres.

a 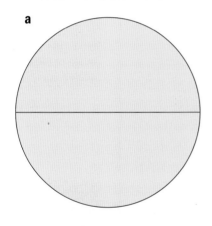 **b** 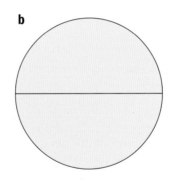 **c**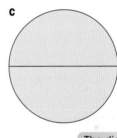

The diameter is the distance across a circle through the centre.

5 Measure and calculate the perimeter of this rectangle in
  a centimetres
  b millimetres.

The **perimeter** is the **distance** round the edge of a shape.

6 Using a ruler and protractor, construct a rectangle of length 7 cm and width 5 cm. Draw and measure the diagonal in
  a centimetres
  b millimetres.

5 cm

7 cm

Unit 3

Measuring angles

This spread will show you how to:
- Understand angle measure
- Measure and draw angles to the nearest degree
- Estimate the size of an angle in degrees

Keywords
Angle
Degrees (°)
Estimate
Measure
Protractor

You can **measure** and draw an **angle** in **degrees** with a **protractor**.
A protractor measures angles up to 180°.
There are 180° in a half turn.

180°   180°

° means degrees.

- There are 180° on a straight line.

Example

Measure the size of angle *p*.

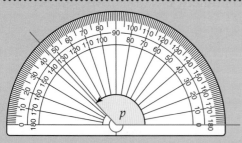

1 **Estimate** the size of angle *p*. (Guess 120°, as greater than 90°.)
2 Place the protractor over the angle.
3 The angle point should be at the cross in the protractor.
4 One arm of the angle should be along the zero line.
5 Start counting from this zero line.
$p = 134°$

You have to decide which scale to use, either the inner scale or the outer scale.

For this angle use the inner scale.

- You can measure a reflex angle by measuring the associated acute or obtuse angle.

A full turn is 360°.

Example

Measure the reflex angle AB̂C.

The acute angle AB̂C = 56°.
So the reflex angle AB̂C is
360° − 56° = 304°

Angles at a point add to 360°.

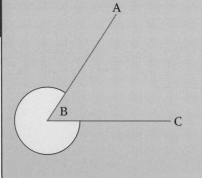

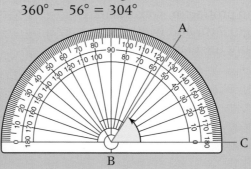

In questions **1–9**, for each angle state

a the type of angle – acute, right angle, obtuse or reflex
b your estimate in degrees
c the measurement in degrees.

Set out your answers like this:

Question	Type of angle	Estimate	Measurement
1	acute	40°	30°
2			

1

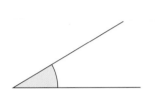

2

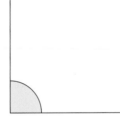

3

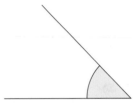

4

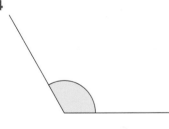

5

6

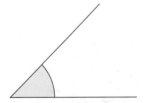

7

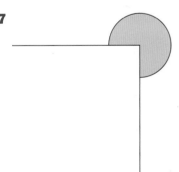

8

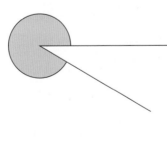

9

10 Draw and label these angles using a protractor.
State whether each angle is acute, obtuse,
reflex or a right angle.

a 40°	**b** 140°	**c** 90°	**d** 36°
e 144°	**f** 56°	**g** 124°	**h** 38°
i 142°	**j** 85°	**k** 300°	**l** 200°
m 320°	**n** 245°	**o** 265°	

Unit 3

Angles and lines

This spread will show you how to:
- Identify acute, obtuse, reflex and right angles
- Recall and use properties of parallel and perpendicular lines

Keywords
Acute
Angle
Degrees (°)
Intersect
Obtuse
Parallel
Perpendicular
Reflex
Right angle

- An **angle** is a measure of turn. You measure the turn in **degrees**.

Amount of turn	$\frac{1}{4}$ turn	$\frac{1}{2}$ turn	$\frac{3}{4}$ turn	full turn
		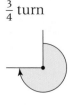		
Angle in degrees	90°	180°	270°	360°

° means degrees.

- You can describe an angle by its size.

an **acute** angle is less than 90°

a **right angle** is exactly 90°

an **obtuse** angle is between 90° and 180°

a **reflex** angle is more than 180°

  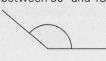

Example

What type of angle is shown by the letter
a x   **b** y?

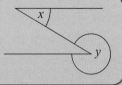

....

a x is acute.   **b** y is reflex.

- **Parallel** lines are always the same distance apart. Parallel lines are shown by sets of arrows.

Parallel lines never **intersect** (cross) each other.

- **Perpendicular** lines meet at a right angle.

Example

A line AB is drawn on a grid.
a Draw another line that is parallel to AB.
Label the line CD and mark with arrows (>).
b Draw another line that is perpendicular to AB.
Label the line EF and mark with a square (⌐).

....

CD is parallel to AB.
EF is perpendicular to AB.

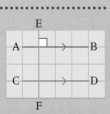

1 How many right angles make up the angle shown in each diagram?

a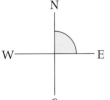

b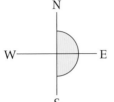

c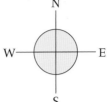

d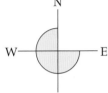

e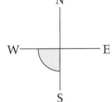

f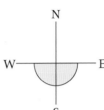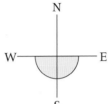

2 Choose one of these words to describe each angle.

acute	right angle	obtuse	reflex

a
b
c
d

e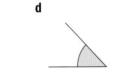
f
g
h

i
j
k
l

 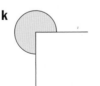

DID YOU KNOW?

Perpendicular and parallel lines are all around you!

3 Choose one of these words to describe each angle.

acute	right angle	obtuse	reflex

a 90°　　**b** 40°　　**c** 140°　　**d** 200°　　　**e** 270°　　**f** 36°
g 137°　**h** 248°　**i** 302°　**j** 33°　　　　**k** 96°　　**l** 239°

4　**a** Draw two lines that are parallel. Label them with >.
　　b Draw two lines that are perpendicular. Label them with ⌐.

Angle properties

This spread will show you how to:

- Recall and use properties of angles at a point, angles on a straight line, perpendicular lines and opposite angles at a vertex

Keywords
Angle
Degrees (°)
Point
Straight line
Vertically
  opposite

Knowledge of angles is useful for creating pie charts.

- These are 360° in a full turn at a **point**.

- There are 180° on a **straight line**. This is a half turn at a point.

- There are 90° in a quarter turn at a point.

Example

Calculate the values of p, q and r. Give a reason for each of your answers.

a
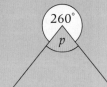

b

c

a $360° - 260° = 100°$
  $p = 100°$
  (angles at a point add to 360°)

b $76° + 65° = 141°$
  $180° - 141° = 39°$
  $q = 39°$
  (angles on a straight line add to 180°)

c $35° + 90° = 125°$
  $180° - 125° = 55°$
  $r = 55°$
  (angles on a straight line add to 180°)

When two lines intersect they make four angles.
The two acute angles are equal.
The two obtuse angles are equal.

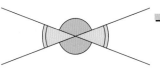

This topic is extended to alternate and corresponding angles on page 430.

- **Vertically opposite** angles are equal.

Example

Calculate the values of x and y.
Give a reason for each of your answers.

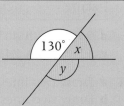

$x = 180° - 130° = 50°$ (angles on a straight line add to 180°)
$y = 130°$ (vertically opposite angles are equal)

1   Give the values in degrees of the coloured angles.

a

b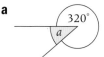

2   This diagram is wrong.
    Explain why.

3   Calculate the size of the angles marked by letters in each diagram.
    Give a reason for each answer. The diagrams are not accurately drawn.

a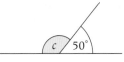

b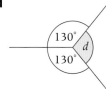

c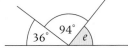

d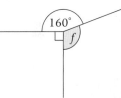

e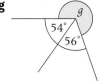

f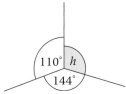

g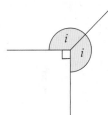

h

i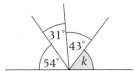

j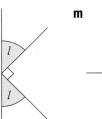

k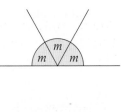

l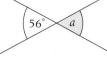

m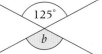

4   Calculate the size of the angles marked by letters in each diagram.
    Give a reason for each of your answers.

These diagrams are not drawn to scale.

a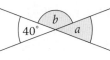

b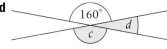

c

d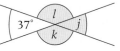

e

Unit 3

Angles in a triangle

This spread will show you how to:

• Use angle properties of equilateral, isosceles and right-angled triangles

Keywords
Angle
Degrees (°)
Equilateral
Isosceles
Right-angled
Scalene
Triangle

• There are 180° on a straight line.

You can draw any triangle ... tear off the corners ... and put them together to make a straight line.

• The angles in a **triangle** add to 180°.

Calculate the values of x, y and z. Give a reason for each of your answers.

a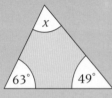

b

....

a $63° + 49° = 112°$
$180° − 112° = 68°$
$x = 68°$

(angles in a triangle add to 180°)

b $38° + 90° = 128°$
$180° − 128° = 52°$
$y = 52°$ (angles in a triangle add to 180°)
$180° − 52° = 128°$ (angles on a straight
$z = 128°$ line add to 180°)

• You should know these names for special triangles

| **Right-angled** | **Equilateral** | **Isosceles** | **Scalene** |

   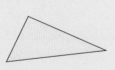

One 90° angle
marked ⌐

3 equal angles
3 equal sides

2 equal angles
2 equal sides

No equal angles
no equal sides

For an equilateral triangle each angle is 60° as $180° ÷ 3 = 60°$

Lines with the same mark are equal length.

Calculate the values of x and y.
Give reasons for your answers.

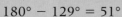

....

$180° − 129° = 51°$
$x = 51°$ (angles on a straight line add to 180°)
$51° + 51° = 102°$
$180° − 102° = 78°$
$y = 78°$ (angles in a triangle add to 180°)

As the triangle is isosceles, two of the angles are equal.

A03   **Problem**

1 a State the total of the three angles in this triangle.
  b Choose three of these angles that could be put
    together to make the angles in a triangle.

 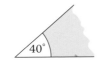

2 Calculate the size of the unknown angles in each diagram.
The diagrams are not drawn to scale.

a
b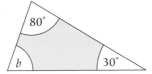
c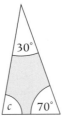

d
e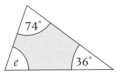
f

g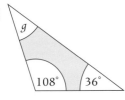
h
i

j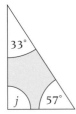
k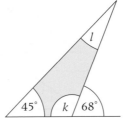
l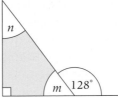

m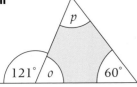
n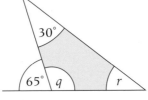
o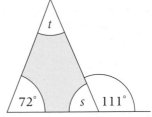

3 List any triangles in question **2** that are
  right-angled   isosceles.

Unit 3

This spread will show you how to:

- Know the properties of right-angled, equilateral, isosceles and scalene triangles
- Know that the angles in a triangle add to 180°
- Understand similarity and congruence

Keywords
Congruent
Equilateral
Isosceles
Right-angled
Scalene
Similar
Triangle

- The angles in a triangle add to 180°.

$\angle A + \angle B + \angle C = 180°$

You need to know the properties of these triangles.

p.318

You will learn about reflection and rotational symmetry on pages 312–315.

Triangle		Properties	Reflection symmetry	Rotational symmetry
Right-angled		One 90° angle marked ∟	No lines of symmetry	Order 1
Equilateral		3 equal angles 3 equal sides	3 lines of symmetry	Order 3
Isosceles		2 equal angles 2 equal sides	1 line of symmetry	Order 1
Scalene		No equal angles No equal sides	No lines of symmetry	Order 1

- **Similar** shapes are the same in shape but differ in size.

- **Congruent** shapes are the same size and shape.

Example

Here are two similar triangles.
a State the type of triangle.
b How many small congruent triangles will fit inside the large triangle?
c Draw the arrangement.

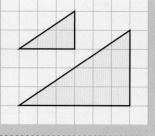

a Right-angled scalene triangle   b 4   c

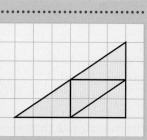

1 State the type of each triangle.

a   b   c   d

2 State the type of each triangle, if the sides of the triangle are
 a 8 cm, 8 cm, 8 cm
 b 6 cm, 7 cm, 8 cm
 c 3 cm, 5 cm, 5 cm

3 Calculate the third angle of the triangle and state the type of each of these triangles.
 a 30°, 60°
 b 70°, 40°
 c 60°, 60°
 d 35°, 65°
 e 45°, 45°

A03 Problem

4 How many equilateral triangles are in this pattern?

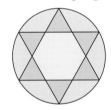

5 Plot and join up each set of points on a separate copy of this grid.
 a $(-2, -1), (-2, 2), (0, 2)$
 b $(-2, -3), (-1, 0), (0, -3)$
 c $(1, -2), (3, 2), (1, 3)$
 d $(1, -3), (3, -3), (3, -1)$
 In each case, state the type of triangle.

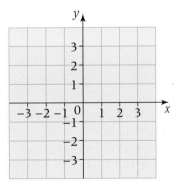

A03 Problem

6 Using three more congruent (identical) equilateral triangles, draw a larger similar equilateral triangle on isometric paper.

Unit 3

Summary

Check out

You should now be able to:

- Identify acute, obtuse, reflex and right angles
- Understand properties of parallel and perpendicular lines
- Understand and use properties of angles at a point, on a straight line and of opposite angles at a vertex
- Identify and use the properties of right-angled, equilateral, isosceles and scalene triangles
- Know that the angles in a triangle add to 180°
- Measure lines and angles

Worked exam question

a An isosceles triangle has one angle of 80°.
Write down the possible sizes of the other two angles. (2)

b Triangle *ABC* is a right-angled triangle.
BDC is an equilateral triangle.

Show that triangle *ABD* is an isosceles triangle.

(3)

(AQA, specimen)

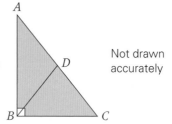

Not drawn accurately

· ·

a
Isosceles, so two angles the same.
If one is 80°, then the other must be:
$$180° - (80° \times 2) = 20°$$
If both unknown angles are the same, then:
$$180° - 80° = 100° \quad 100° \div 2 = 50°$$
So the two possibilities are:
$$80°, 80°, 20° \quad \text{and} \quad 80°, 50°, 50°$$

Show your **reasoning** to get full marks for quality of written communication.

b
△*BDC* is equilateral, so each angle is 60°.
So ∠*ABD* = 90° − 60° = 30°
and ∠*ADB* = 180° − 60° = 120° (angles on a straight line)
Therefore ∠*BAD* = 180° − (30° + 120°)
  = 180° − 150° = 30° (angles in a triangle)
So the three angles of △*ABD* are 30°, 30° and 120°
△*ABD* is isosceles because two angles are the same.

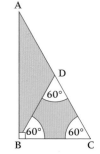

Exam questions

1 Viki is cutting angles out of paper to fit together exactly at a point as shown. She cuts out an acute angle, an obtuse angle and a reflex angle.

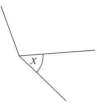

   a Measure the size of the acute angle, marked *x*, on the diagram.   (1)

   b Viki starts again using three different angles.

     Choose three different angles, one acute, one obtuse and one reflex, which fit together exactly at a point.   (3)

                        (AQA, specimen)

2 a *PQR* is a straight line.

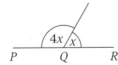

Not drawn accurately

   Explain why *x* = 36°.   (2)

   b The four lines shown below meet at a point.

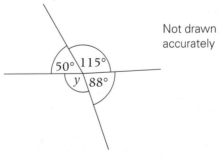

Not drawn accurately

   Work out the value of *y*.   (2)

                        (AQA, 2009)

3 The points *A* and *B* have coordinates (6, 2) and (2, 4) respectively. Write the coordinates of a third point *C* so that *ABC* is an isosceles right-angled triangle.

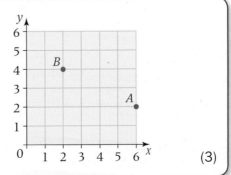

                        (3)

Mathematics can be used to explain how radio transmission works.

FlexiscreenS3000

Font   Tools   Table   Window   Work   Help   Mon 10:57

Document1

Radio transmitters use continuous sine waves to send and receive information such as music or speech.

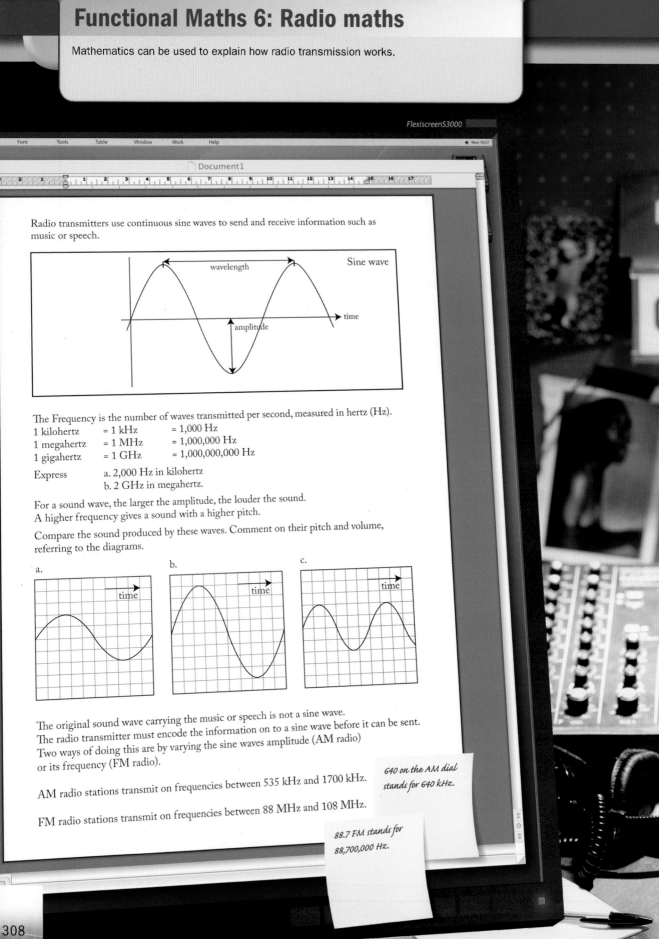

The Frequency is the number of waves transmitted per second, measured in hertz (Hz).

1 kilohertz	= 1 kHz	= 1,000 Hz
1 megahertz	= 1 MHz	= 1,000,000 Hz
1 gigahertz	= 1 GHz	= 1,000,000,000 Hz

Express   a. 2,000 Hz in kilohertz
           b. 2 GHz in megahertz.

For a sound wave, the larger the amplitude, the louder the sound.
A higher frequency gives a sound with a higher pitch.

Compare the sound produced by these waves. Comment on their pitch and volume, referring to the diagrams.

The original sound wave carrying the music or speech is not a sine wave.
The radio transmitter must encode the information on to a sine wave before it can be sent.
Two ways of doing this are by varying the sine waves amplitude (AM radio) or its frequency (FM radio).

AM radio stations transmit on frequencies between 535 kHz and 1700 kHz.

640 on the AM dial stands for 640 kHz.

FM radio stations transmit on frequencies between 88 MHz and 108 MHz.

88.7 FM stands for 88,700,000 Hz.

Wave speed (m/s) = frequency (Hz) × wavelength (m)

Maths FM transmits on the frequency 100.0 FM with a wavelength of 3 m.
a. What is the frequency of the radio station in
   i. MHz   ii. Hz?
b. Use the formula at the top of the page to calculate the speed of the waves that are being transmitted.
c. Rearrange the formula to give an equation for frequency in terms of wave speed and wavelength.
d. Use your answers from parts b and c to calculate the frequency (in Hz) of a radio station that transmits waves of wavelength 280 m.
e. Is the radio station in part d on the AM or FM dial?
   Justify your answer and write down its AM or FM frequency.

Mathematics can also be applied to plan and produce radio programmes.

DJ Cool uses this wheel diagram to plan his hour-long show:

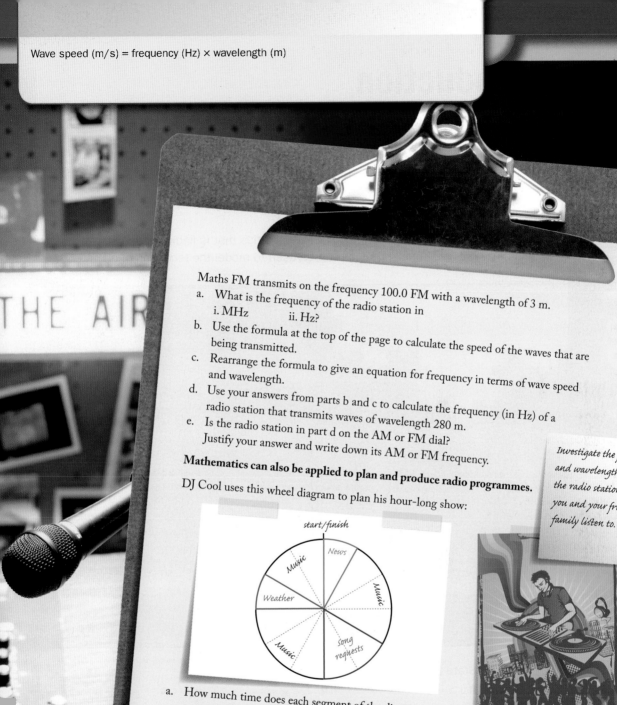

a. How much time does each segment of the diagram represent? Give your answer in minutes.
b. How many minutes of the show are taken up by
   i. news   ii. weather   iii. music (including requests)?
c. DJ Cool's show starts at 3pm. What time is the
   i. weather forecast   ii. news report   iii. requests slot?

The manager of the radio station decides that DJ Cool should include a 5-minute travel report at 3:20pm. The weather forecast and news report must not be moved.

d. Draw a wheel diagram to show how DJ Cool's show could look with the travel report included.

Investigate the frequency and wavelengths used by the radio stations that you and your friends and family listen to.

Consider some of the radio shows that you and your friends and family listen to. Do they use a format that could be shown on a wheel?

Introduction

A fractal is a geometrical shape that can be split into parts so that each part is a smaller copy of the whole shape. Here is an example of the Von Koch Snowflake. The Von Koch Snowflake fractal is constructed from an equilateral triangle. On the middle third of each side is built another equilateral triangle and the process is repeated over and over again.

What's the point?

Fractal geometry is a fairly new branch of mathematics that is finding new applications all the time. The Von Koch snowflake can be used to model the reception of an antenna.

1 State the sum of the three angles *x*, *y*, *z*.

a

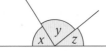

b

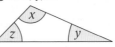

c

2 Find the value of each unknown angle.

a

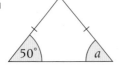

b

What I need to know

What I will learn

What this leads to

G2 →

- Understand symmetry
- Know the properties of quadrilaterals
- Find interior and exterior angles in triangles and quadrilaterals
- Know the names of parts of a circle
- Know the names and properties of 3D shapes

→ G7

A quadrilateral has been drawn on a 3 × 3 square dotty grid.

How many different quadrilaterals can you find?

Reflection symmetry

This spread will show you how to:
- Recognise reflection symmetry of 2D shapes

Keywords
Line of symmetry
Reflection
  symmetry
Regular polygon

A shape has **reflection symmetry** if

- the shape divides into two identical halves
- you can fold the shape so that one half fits exactly on top of the other

The dotted line
is the line of
symmetry.

mirror

- a mirror reflects half the shape to give the completed shape.

- A line of symmetry divides the shape into two identical halves, each of which is the mirror image of the other.

You can find symmetry in nature.
This butterfly has one line of symmetry.

Example

a Add one extra square so that the shaded shape has 1 line of symmetry.
b Draw the line of symmetry.

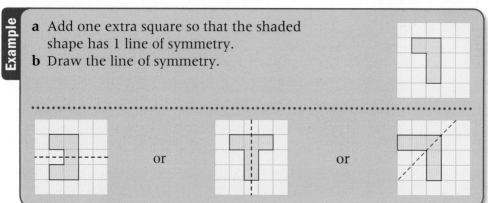

or   or

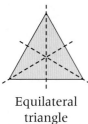

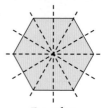

A shape can have more than one line of symmetry.

- A **regular polygon** with *n* sides has *n* lines of symmetry.

Regular polygons
have equal sides
and equal angles.

Equilateral triangle	Square	Regular pentagon	Regular hexagon
3	4	5	6

1 Copy these 2D shapes and draw in the lines of symmetry.

a b c d e

f g h i j

2 State the number of lines of symmetry for each of these regular polygons.

a b c d e

AO3 Problem

3 Draw these shapes on square grid paper. Add one square to give a shape with the required number of lines of symmetry. Draw the lines of symmetry for the new shape.

a b c d e

   2   1   2   1   4

f g 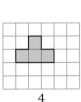 h i j

   0   4   1   1   2

4 Draw these shapes on isometric paper. Add one triangle to give a shape with the required number of lines of symmetry. Draw the lines of symmetry for the new shape.

a b c d e

   6   3   2   1   0

Unit 3

Rotational symmetry

This spread will show you how to:

- Recognise rotational symmetry of 2D shapes

Keywords
Order of rotational
   symmetry
Regular polygon
Rotational
   symmetry

- A shape has **rotational symmetry** if the shape looks like itself more than once in a full turn.

The **order of rotational symmetry** is the number of times a shape looks exactly like itself in a complete turn.

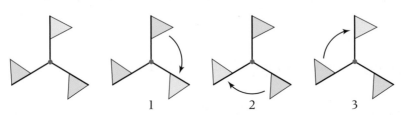

The order of rotational symmetry is 3.

Example

Add one extra square so that the shaded shape has rotational symmetry of order 2.

Example

Name these shapes. State the order of rotational symmetry for each one.

a   b   c   d

- -

a rhombus   **b** arrowhead   **c** rectangle   **d** regular
                                                                pentagon

   2   1   2   5

- A **regular polygon** with *n* sides has rotational symmetry of order *n*.

regular heptagon   **regular octagon**   **regular nonagon**   **regular decagon**
   order 7   **order 8**   **order 9**   **order 10**

Turn the page around to see the rotational symmetry.

314

Unit 3

1 Copy these 2D shapes and state the order of rotational symmetry for each shape.

a **b** **c** **d** **e**

f **g** **h** **i** **j**

2 State the order of rotational symmetry for these regular polygons.

a **b** **c** **d** **e**

3 Draw these shapes on square grid paper. Add one square to each to give a shape with the given order of rotational symmetry.

a 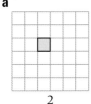 2 **b** 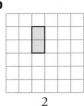 2 **c** 4 **d** 2 **e** 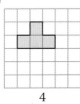 4

f 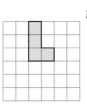 2 **g** 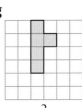 2 **h** 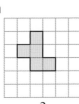 2 **i** 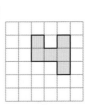 2 **j** 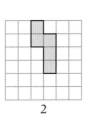 2

4 Draw these shapes on isometric paper. Add one triangle to give a shape with the given order of rotational symmetry.

a 6 **b** 2 **c** 2 **d** 3 **e** 2

Properties of quadrilaterals

This spread will show you how to:
- Know the properties of quadrilaterals

Keywords
Diagonal
Parallel
Quadrilateral
Rotational
  symmetry

A **quadrilateral** is a 2D shape with four sides and four angles.

You need to know the properties of these quadrilaterals.

Square	Rhombus	Parallelogram	Rectangle
4 equal angles 4 equal sides 2 sets parallel sides 4 lines of symmetry Rotational symmetry of order 4	2 pairs equal angles 4 equal sides 2 sets parallel sides 2 lines of symmetry Rotational symmetry of order 2	2 pairs equal angles 2 sets equal sides 2 sets parallel sides 0 lines of symmetry Rotational symmetry of order 2	4 equal angles 2 sets equal sides 2 sets parallel sides 2 lines of symmetry Rotational symmetry of order 2

The equal angles are colour-coded.

Trapezium	Isosceles trapezium	Kite	Arrowhead
Usually: No equal angles No equal sides Always has: 1 set of parallel sides 0 lines of symmetry Rotational symmetry of order 1	2 pairs equal angles 1 set equal sides 1 set parallel sides 1 line of symmetry Rotational symmetry of order 1	1 pair equal angles 2 sets equal sides No parallel sides 1 line of symmetry Rotational symmetry of order 1	1 pair equal angles 2 sets equal sides No parallel sides 1 reflex angle 1 line of symmetry Rotational symmetry of order 1

Example

The diagonals on this rhombus are drawn.
Say whether each of these statements is true or false.

a The diagonals are of equal length.
b The diagonals are perpendicular.
c The diagonals are the lines of symmetry.
d The diagonals bisect each other.
e The diagonals bisect the angles.

Perpendicular lines cross at 90°.

a false **b** true **c** true **d** true **e** true

A03 **Problem**

1 Cut out four congruent (identical) right-angled triangles.
Arrange all four triangles to make
  a square
  b an isosceles trapezium
  c a rectangle
  d a parallelogram
  e a rhombus.
Draw a sketch of each arrangement.

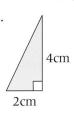

4cm

2cm

2 Give the mathematical name of each coloured quadrilateral in the regular octagon.

a 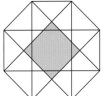   **b** 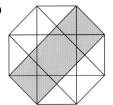   **c**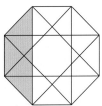

d 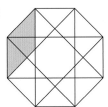   **e** 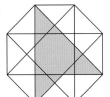   **f**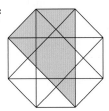

3 On separate copies of this grid, plot and join up each set of points.
  a (2, 3) (1, 0) (2, −3) (3, 0) (2, 3)
  b (2, −3) (2, 3) (0, 1) (0, −1) (2, −3)
  c (3, 2) (−2, 2) (−3, −1) (2, −1) (3, 2)
  d (0, −1) (2, 2) (0, 3) (−2, 2) (0, −1)
  e (2, 2) (−3, 3) (−1, 2) (−3, 1) (2, 2)
  f (1, 1) (−1, 3) (−3, 1) (−1, −1) (1, 1)
  g (−2, 3) (−3, 2) (1, −1) (2, 0) (−2, 3)
  h (3, −3) (0, −1) (−2, −1) (−3, −3) (3, −3)
In each case, state the type of quadrilateral.

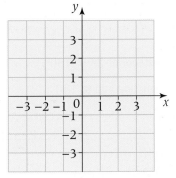

4 **a** Copy this shape and reflect it in the dotted line.
   b Give the mathematical name of the new shape.

Unit 3

G3.4 | Properties of triangles and quadrilaterals

This spread will show you how to:

- Use angle properties of equilateral, isosceles and right-angled triangles
- Use angle properties of quadrilaterals
- Find exterior angles in triangles and quadrilaterals

Keywords
Diagonal
Exterior
Interior
Quadrilateral
Triangle

- The angles in a triangle add to 180°.

A **quadrilateral** is a 2D shape with 4 sides and 4 angles.

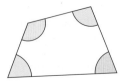

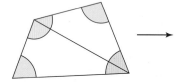 → 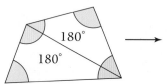 →

You can draw a **diagonal** on a quadrilateral to form 2 triangles.

The angles in each triangle add to 180°.

$2 \times 180 = 360°$

This works for any quadrilateral.

- The angles in a quadrilateral add to 360°.

The angles inside a shape are called **interior** angles.

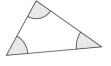

You find the **exterior** angles by extending each side of the shape in the same direction.

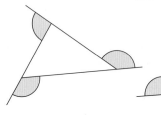 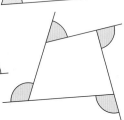

- Interior angle + exterior angle = 180°

  (angles on a straight line add to 180°)

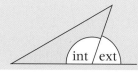

Example

Calculate the value of x and y.
Give a reason for each answer.

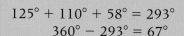

$125° + 110° + 58° = 293°$
$360° - 293° = 67°$
$x = 67°$ (angles in a quadrilateral add to 360°)
$180° - 67° = 113°$
$y = 113°$ (angles on a straight line add to 180°)

318

1 Give the mathematical name of each coloured shape in the regular hexagon.

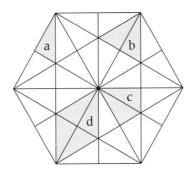

2 Calculate the value of the unknown angles.

a

b

c

3 Calculate the value of the unknown angles.

a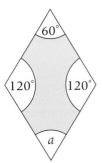

b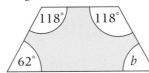

c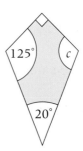

d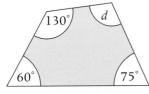

e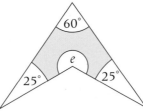

4 Calculate the value of the angles marked by a letter.

a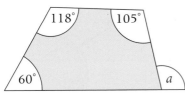

b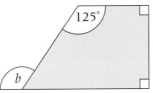

c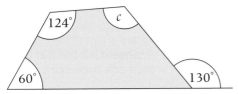

This spread will show you how to:

- Know the definition of a circle and the names of its parts
- Use a protractor and compasses to draw circles and sectors

Keywords
Arc
Centre
Chord
Circle
Circumference
Compasses
Diameter
Equidistant
Radius
Sector
Segment
Semicircle
Tangent

- A **circle** is a set of points **equidistant** from its **centre**.

Equidistant means 'the same distance from a fixed point'.

circumference

The **circumference** (*C*) is the distance around the circle.

radius

The **radius** (*r*) is the distance from the centre to the circumference.

p.402

diameter

The **diameter** (*d*) is the distance across the centre of the circle.

semi-circle

The diameter divides the circle into two **semicircles**.

Radii is the plural of radius.

Example

Draw a circle so that the line AB is the radius.

A———B

Put the point of the **compasses** at A or B and open the compasses to the length of AB. Draw the circle.

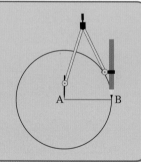

You also need to know these parts of a circle.

arc

chord

A **chord** is a line joining two points on the circumference.

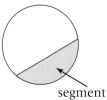

segment

A **segment** is the region enclosed by a chord and an arc.

sector

A **sector** is the region enclosed by an arc and two radii.

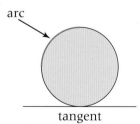

tangent

An **arc** is part of the circumference. A **tangent** is a line that touches the circle at a single point.

1 a Draw two circles that intersect at A and B.
  b Draw the diameters AC and AD.
  c Is CBD a straight line?

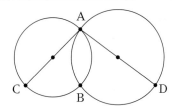

Intersect means **cross.**

The circle don't have to be the some size.

Unit 3

2 Measure
  a the diameter of the circle
  b the radius of the circle.

3 a Draw a circle with a radius of 4 cm.
  b Draw a chord of length 5 cm inside the circle.

4 Draw a circle with a diameter of 10 cm.

5 a Draw a 4 cm line AB.
  b Draw a circle so that AB is the diameter.
  c Find the radius of the circle.

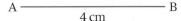
A ——————————— B
4 cm

6 Use a protractor and compasses to construct these sectors.

  a
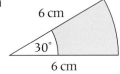
6 cm
30°
6 cm

  b
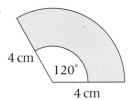
4 cm
120°
4 cm

7 Two circles have the same centre.
One has a radius of 3.5 cm and the other has a radius of 2.5 cm.
Construct and colour this diagram for the two circles.

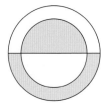

8 Explain why these circles are similar.

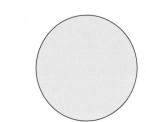

This spread will show you how to:
- Understand the terms face, edge and vertex
- Know the names of general 3D shapes

Keywords
Cube
Cuboid
Edge
Face
Prism
Pyramid
Solid
Three-dimensional (3D)
Vertex

A **solid** is a **three-dimensional (3D)** shape.

The three dimensions are length, width and height for a cuboid.

- In a 3D shape
  - a **face** is a flat surface of the solid
  - an **edge** is the line where two faces meet
  - a **vertex** is a point at which two or more edges meet. The vertex is a corner of the shape.

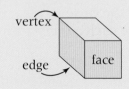

The plural of vertex is vertices.

A **cube** has 6 faces that are squares
12 edges
8 vertices.

p.404

A **cuboid** has 6 faces that are rectangles
12 edges
8 vertices.

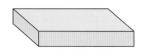

A **prism** has a constant cross-section.

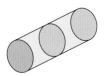
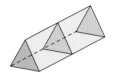
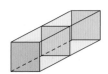

cylinder   triangular prism   square-based prism

You name a prism by the shape of the cross-section.

A **pyramid** has faces that meet at a common point.

square-based pyramid   triangular-based pyramid   cone

A tetrahedron is a pyramid made from four triangles.

Example

For this solid, write
a its mathematical name **b** the number of faces
c the number of edges **d** the number of vertices.

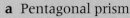

a Pentagonal prism **b** 7 faces
c 15 edges **d** 10 vertices (corners)

1 Decide whether these shapes are prisms, pyramids or neither of these.

a   b   c   d

e   f   g   h

i   j   k   l

m   n 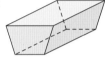 o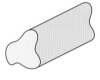

2 This solid is made from eight isosceles triangles and one octagon.
For this solid, write
a the mathematical name
b the number of faces
c the number of edges
d the number of vertices.

3 a Copy and complete this table.

Name of solid	Number of faces (*f*)	Number of edges (*e*)	Number of vertices (*v*)
pentagonal prism	7	15	10
cuboid			
pentagonal pyramid			
square-based pyramid			
cube			
hexagonal prism			
tetrahedron			
triangular prism			
hexagonal pyramid			
octagonal-based prism			

b Write a relationship between *f*, *e* and *v*.

Unit 3

A03 Problem

Volume

This spread will show you how to:
● Calculate the volume of cuboids

Keywords
Cube
Cubic centimetre
 (cm³)
Cubic metre (m³)
Cuboid
Volume

● The **volume** of a 3D shape is the amount of space it takes up.

You measure volume using **cubes**.

1 cm

1 cm
1 cm

One **cubic centimetre** is 1 cm³.

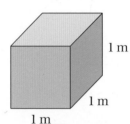

1 m

1 m
1 m

One **cubic metre** is 1 m³.

The ³ in cm³ shows there are 3 dimensions.

Example

Find the volume of these shapes made from centimetre cubes.
State the units of your answers.

a

b

....

a Volume
 = 5 cm³

b Volume
 = 6 cm³

The volume of a **cuboid** can be found by counting the number of layers.

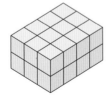

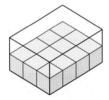

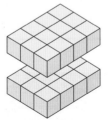

On the bottom layer, there are
3 × 4 = 12 cubes.

For 2 layers, there are
2 × 12 = 24 cubes.

● Volume of a cuboid = length × width × height

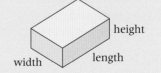

height
width   length

Example

Calculate the volume of this cuboid.
State the units of your answer.
....
Volume = 2 × 4 × 10
 = 80 m³

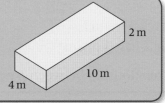

2 m
10 m
4 m

p.404

The units are cubic metres or m³.

1 a Calculate the volume, for each solid.
Each cube represents 1 cm³.

i ii iii iv

v  vi vii

b All these solids fit together to make a cube.
Find the volume of the cube.
c What are the dimensions of the cube?

2 Calculate the volume, in cm³, of each cuboid.

a b c d e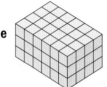

f 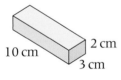 g h 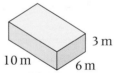 i 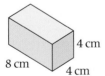 j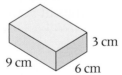

3 Calculate the volume of each cuboid. State the units of your answers.

a
10 cm   2 cm   3 cm

b
5 m   5 m   5 m

c
10 m   3 m   6 m

d
8 cm   4 cm   4 cm

e
9 cm   3 cm   6 cm

f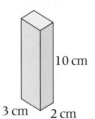
10 cm   3 cm   2 cm

4 A **prism** has a constant cross-section.
The cross-section of this prism is an L-shape.

- Volume of a prism = area of cross-section × length

Calculate the volume of this prism.

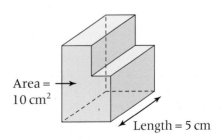

Area = 10 cm²

Length = 5 cm

This spread will show you how to:
- Use 2D representations of 3D shapes
- Calculate the surface area and volume of cuboids

Keywords
3D
Congruent
Cube
Cuboid
Isometric
Surface area
Volume

You can draw some **3D** shapes using **isometric** paper.

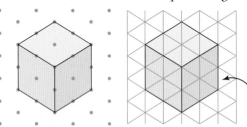

3D means 3-dimensional.

The paper must be this way round.

The equal edges of the cube are shown by lines of equal length.

Example

Add one cube to shape B
so that it is congruent to shape A.

A **B**

Congruent shapes are identical in size and shape. You will learn more about congruence on page 398.

- **Surface area** of a cuboid is the total area of its faces.

- **Volume** of cuboid = length × width × height

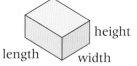
height
length width

p.404

Example

a On isometric paper, draw a cuboid with dimensions 2 cm by 3 cm by 4 cm.
b Calculate the surface area of the cuboid. State the units of your answer.
c Calculate the volume of the cuboid. State the units of your answer.

a
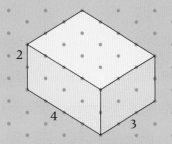
2
4
3

b Area of the 4 cm by 3 cm rectangle = 4 × 3 = 12 cm²
   Area of the 3 cm by 2 cm rectangle = 3 × 2 = 6 cm²
   Area of the 2 cm by 4 cm rectangle = 2 × 4 = 8 cm²
                                                 26 cm²

   Surface area = 26 × 2 = 52 cm²
c Volume = 2 × 3 × 4 = 24 cm³

There are three hidden faces you must account for when finding the total surface area. Opposite faces are congruent.

1 Draw these solids after the shaded cube is removed.

a   **b**   **c**   **d** 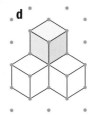 **e**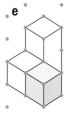

f **g** **h** 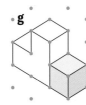 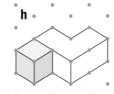 **i** **j**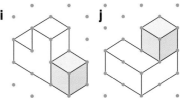

2 a State the dimensions of this cuboid.
   b Calculate the surface area of the cuboid.
   c Calculate the volume of the cuboid.

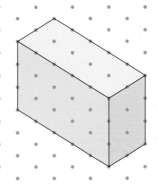

3 a Copy and complete the drawing of the
      1 cm by 2 cm by 5 cm cuboid on isometric paper.
   b Calculate the surface area of the cuboid.
   c Calculate the volume of the cuboid.

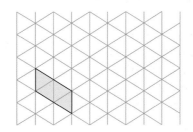

4 a On isometric paper, draw a cuboid with dimensions
      1 cm by 3 cm by 4 cm.
   b Calculate the surface area of the cuboid.
      State the units of your answer.
   c Calculate the volume of the cuboid.
      State the units of your answer.

5 On isometric paper, draw a cube with
   a volume of 27 cm³.

Volume
= 27 cm³

Unit 3

Problem

AO3

Summary

Check out

You should now be able to:

- Recognise reflection symmetry and rotational symmetry
- Know the properties of special types of quadrilaterals
- Use angle properties of triangles and quadrilaterals
- Know the definition of a circle and the names of its parts
- Use a protractor and compasses to draw circles and sectors
- Know the terms face, edge and vertex
- Identify and name common 3D shapes
- Find the volume of a cuboid

Worked exam question

1 The diagram shows a cuboid.

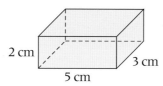

a Work out the volume of the cuboid. (2)

b On a copy of the centimetre grid complete a net of the cuboid.

(3)

c Work out the total surface area of the cuboid.
State the units of your answer. (4)

(AQA, 2009)

a $2 \times 5 \times 3 = 30\,cm^3$

b

c Surface area = $(2 \times 3) + (2 \times 3) + (2 \times 5) +$
$(2 \times 5) + (3 \times 5) + (3 \times 5)$
$= 62\,cm^2$

> A closed cuboid has six faces, so you need to add up six different areas.

Exam questions

1 Copy the diagram and draw arrows to match the properties of four different quadrilaterals.
The first one has been done for you.

● Only one pair of parallel sides	square
● Four right angles ● The sides are not all the same length	rectangle
● All sides are the same length ● No right angles	parallelogram
● Opposite angles are equal ● No right angles ● The sides are not all the same length	rhombus
	kite
	trapezium

(3)
(AQA, 2009)

2 Write down the mathematical name of each of these 3D shapes.

a 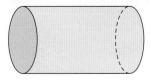 **b** **c**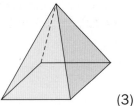

(3)

3 The diagram shows a tetrahedron.

Diagram NOT accurately drawn

Write down
a the number of faces
b the number of edges
c the number of vertices.

(3)

4 The volume of a cuboid is $84 \, \text{cm}^3$.
Give **two** different answers for the dimensions of this cuboid.

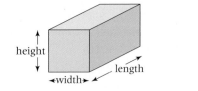

Diagram NOT accurately drawn

(4)

329

Introduction

The decimal system is based on the number 10, and is the universal number system used throughout the world. It is what the metric system of measurement is based on, as well as most countries' money systems including the euro. In the UK, decimalisation of the money system occurred on 15th February 1971.

What's the point?

A common number system allows different countries to appreciate and understand each others' measurements, quantities and calculations. In a world that is shrinking through enhanced travel and communication, the ability to communicate mathematically is increasingly important.

1 Calculate $5 \times 3 + 4 \times 8$

2 Calculate
   a $13 \div 10$ **b** 0.03×10

3 Round each of these numbers to 2 decimal places.
   a 3.5624   **b** 8.0392   **c** 0.0551

What I need to know	What I will learn	What this leads to
N2 + 4	■ Use approximation to estimate answers to decimal calculations ■ Multiply fractions ■ Calculate simple interest ■ Use calculators to carry out more complex calculations	→ +1 → +2 → +4

Rich task

Try to make the numbers 1 to 20 using up to four 4s and any of the operations $+$, $-$, $\times$ or $\div$. You may also use brackets and square roots, and 4 can appear as an index.

For example, $\dfrac{44 - 4}{4} = 10$

This spread will show you how to:

- Multiply and divide by powers of 10 and by decimals between 0 and 1
- Use checking procedures, including approximation to estimate the answer to multiplication and division problems

Keywords
Approximate
Estimate

- You can multiply or divide a number by a power of 10. Move the digits of the number to the left or to the right.

$$\times 10 \quad \text{or} \div 0.1$$
$$1.8 \quad 18$$
$$\div 10 \quad \text{or} \times 0.1$$

$$\times 100 \quad \text{or} \div 0.01$$
$$12.4 \quad 1240$$
$$\div 100 \quad \text{or} \times 0.01$$

$\times 0.1$ is the same as $\div 10$.
$\times 0.01$ is the same as $\div 100$.

$\div 0.1$ is the same as $\times 10$.
$\div 0.01$ is the same as $\times 100$.

- You can multiply and divide by any decimal between 0 and 1 using mental methods.

Example

Calculate   **a** 12×0.3 **b** $36 \div 0.04$ **c** $2 \div 0.05$

a $12 \times 0.3 = 12 \times 3 \times 0.1$
$= 36 \times 0.1$
$= 36 \div 10$
$= 3.6$

b $36 \div 0.04 = 36 \div (4 \times 0.01)$
$= 36 \div 4 \div 0.01$
$= 9 \div 0.01$
$= 9 \times 100$
$= 900$

c $2 \div 0.05 = \dfrac{2}{0.05}$
$= \dfrac{200}{5} = 40$
$= 40$

- You can **estimate** the answer to a calculation by first rounding the numbers in the calculation.

p.158

Example

Estimate the answers to these calculations.

a $\dfrac{8.93 \times 28.69}{0.48 \times 6.12}$

b $\dfrac{17.4 \times 4.89^2}{0.385}$

A good strategy is to round each number in the calculation to 1 significant figure.

a $\dfrac{8.93 \times 28.69}{0.48 \times 6.12} \approx \dfrac{9 \times 30}{0.5 \times 6}$
$= \dfrac{270}{3} = 90$

b $\dfrac{17.4 \times 4.89^2}{0.385} \approx \dfrac{20 \times 5^2}{0.4}$
$= \dfrac{20 \times 25}{0.4} = \dfrac{500}{0.4}$
$= \dfrac{5000}{4} = 1250$

1 Round each of these numbers to the nearest **i** 1000   **ii** 100   **iii** 10.
   a 1548.9   **b** 5789.47   **c** 17 793.8 kg
   d €35 127.35   **e** 236 872

2 Round each of these numbers to **i** 3 dp   **ii** 2 dp   **iii** 1 dp
   iv the nearest whole number.
   a 4.3563   **b** 9.8573   **c** 0.9373   **d** 19.4963
   e 26.8083   **f** 19.9999   **g** 0.004896   **h** 3896.6567

3 Calculate these.
   a 3×0.1 **b** $15 \div 0.1$ **c** 8×0.01 **d** 2.8×100
   e $3.8 \div 0.1$ **f** 0.4×0.1 **g** $9.23 \div 0.1$ **h** $44.6 \div 0.01$

4 Here are five number cards.

   | 0.1 | | 10 | | 0.01 | | 1000 | | 10^2 |

   Fill in the missing numbers in each of these statements using
   one of these cards.
   a $3.24 \times ? = 324$ **b** $14.7 \times ? = 0.147$
   c $6.3 \div ? = 630$ **d** $2870 \div ? = 2.87$
   e $0.43 \div ? = 4.3$ **f** $2.04 \div ? = 204$

5 Round each of these numbers to   **i** 3 sf   **ii** 2 sf   **iii** 1 sf.
   a 9.4837   **b** 27.73   **c** 46.73   **d** 387.63
   e 2.4058   **f** 4905.81   **g** 0.009 483   **h** 3489.7
   i 9.8765   **j** 25.1407   **k** 2314.17   **l** 237 415

6 Work out these calculations using a mental method.
   a 12×0.2 **b** 8×0.07 **c** $15 \div 0.3$
   d $3 \div 0.15$ **e** 1.2×0.4 **f** $28 \div 0.07$

7 Write a suitable estimate for each of these calculations.
   In each case clearly show how you estimated your answer.
   a 3.76×4.22 **b** 17.39×22.98
   c $\dfrac{4.59 \times 7.9}{19.86}$ **d** $54.31 \div 8.8$

8 Write a suitable estimate for each of these calculations.
   In each case clearly show how you estimated your answer.

   a $\dfrac{29.91 \times 38.3}{3.1 \times 3.9}$ **b** $\dfrac{16.2 \times 0.48}{0.23 \times 31.88}$

   c $\{4.8^2 + (4.2 - 0.238)\}^2$ **d** $\dfrac{63.8 \times 1.7^2}{1.78^2}$

   e $\sqrt{(2.03 \div 0.041)}$ **f** $\sqrt{(27.6 \div 0.57)}$

A03 Problem

Unit 3

This spread will show you how to:

- Use calculators to carry out more complex calculations
- Use checking procedures, including approximation to estimate the answer to multiplication and division problems
- Give answers to an appropriate degree of accuracy

Keywords
Appropriate
 · degree of
   accuracy
Brackets
Order of
 operations

You can use the bracket keys on a scientific calculator to do calculations where the **order of operations** is not obvious.

Example

a Use a calculator to work out the value of

$$\frac{21.42 \times (12.4 - 6.35)}{(63.4 + 18.9) \times 2.83}$$

Write all the figures on the calculator display.

b Put brackets in this expression so that its value is 45.908.

$$1.4 + 3.9 \times 2.2 \times 4.6$$

Estimate
$$\frac{20 \times (12 - 6)}{(60 + 20) \times 3}$$
$$= \frac{120}{240} = 0.5$$

....

a Rewrite the calculation as $(21.42 \times (12.4 - 6.35)) \div ((63.4 + 18.9) \times 2.83)$
Type this into the calculator:

$$(21.42\times(12.4-6.35))\div((63.4+18.9)\times2.83)$$ ➡ (21.42×(12.4− 0.556401856

So the answer is 0.556 401 856.

b By inserting a pair of brackets: $(1.4 + 3.9 \times 2.2) \times 4.6$
The calculator should display 45.908. ✓ This is the correct answer.

You can solve multi-step problems using a calculator. You will need to give your answer to an **appropriate degree of accuracy**.

Example

The diagram shows a box in the shape of a cuboid.
a Work out the volume, in m³, of the box.
b Saleem builds boxes of different sizes.
 He charges £7.89 for each m³ of a box's volume.
 Work out Saleem's charge for building this box.

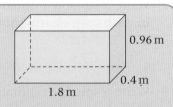

0.96 m
0.4 m
1.8 m

....

a Volume of a cuboid
 = length × width × height

Volume ≈ 2 × 1 × 0.4 = 0.8 m³
Volume = 1.8 × 0.4 × 0.96
   = 0.6912 m³
   = 0.7 m³

b Saleem's charge
 = cost for each m³ × number of m³

Estimate: Saleem's charge ≈ £8 × 0.8
   = £6.40
Type: Saleem's charge = £7.89 × 0.6912
   = £5.453 568
   = £5.45

1 Put brackets into each of these expressions to make them correct.

a $2.4 \times 4.3 + 3.7 = 19.2$

b $6.8 \times 3.75 - 2.64 = 7.548$

c $3.7 + 2.9 \div 1.2 = 5.5$

d $2.3 + 3.4^2 \times 2.7 = 37.422$

e $5.3 + 3.9 \times 3.2 + 1.6 = 24.02$

f $3.2 + 6.4 \times 4.3 + 2.5 = 46.72$

2 Use your calculator to work out each of these. Write all the figures on your calculator.

a $\dfrac{165.4 \times 27.4}{(0.72 + 4.32)^2}$

b $\dfrac{(32.6 + 43.1) \times 2.3^2}{173.7 \times (13.5 - 1.78)}$

c $\dfrac{24.67 \times (35.3 - 8.29)}{(28.2 + 34.7) \times 3.3}$

d $\dfrac{1.45^2 \times 3.64 + 2.9}{3.47 - 0.32}$

e $\dfrac{12.93 \times (33.2 - 8.34)}{(61.3 + 34.5) \times 2.9}$

f $\dfrac{24.7 - (3.2 + 1.09)^2}{2.78^2 + 12.9 \times 3}$

A02 Functional Maths

3 Work out each of these using your calculator. In each case give your answer to an appropriate degree of accuracy.

a Véronique puts carpet in her bedroom. The bedroom is in the shape of a rectangle with a length of 4.23 m and a width of 3.6 m. The carpet costs £6.79 per m².

  i Calculate the floor area of the bedroom.

  ii Calculate the cost of the carpet which is required to cover the floor.

b Calculate $\frac{1}{3}$ of £200.

4 Barry sees a mobile phone offer.

Vericheep Fone OFFER

Monthly fee £12.99

FREE – 200 texts every month

FREE – 200 voice minutes every month

Extra text messages 3.2p each

Extra voice minutes 5.5p each

Barry decides to see if the offer is a good idea for him.

His current mobile phone offers him unlimited texts and voice minutes for £22.99 per month.

a In February, Barry used 189 texts and 348 voice minutes. Calculate his bill using the new offer.

b In March, Barry used 273 texts and 219 voice minutes. Calculate his bill using the new offer.

c Explain if the new offer is a good idea for Barry.

Unit 3

This spread will show you how to:
- Solve percentage increase and decrease problems
- Calculate simple interest
- Use checking procedures involving estimation

Keywords
Decrease
Increase
Percentage
Simple interest

Banks and building societies pay **interest** on money in an account.
The interest is always written as a **percentage**.
4.5% interest means that the bank pays you an extra 4.5% of the
money you put into the bank account.

Example

Jamal puts £750 into a bank account. The bank pays interest of 4.5%
on any money he keeps in the account for one year. Calculate the
interest Jamal receives at the end of the year.

Estimate: 4.5% of £750 $\approx$ 5% of £700
$$= (10\% \text{ of } 700) \div 2$$
$$= 70 \div 2 = £35$$

Interest = 4.5% of £750 $= \frac{4.5}{100} \times 750$
$$= 0.045 \times 750$$
$$= 33.75$$
$$= £33.75$$

Always estimate
your answers
when working
with a calculator.

People sometimes choose to have the interest they earn at the end of
each year paid out of their bank account. This is called **simple interest**.

- To calculate simple interest you multiply the interest earned at the end of the year
  by the number of years.

This topic is
extended to
compound
interest on
page 414.

Example

Calculate the simple interest on £3950 for
a 4 years at an interest rate of 5%
b 10 years at an interest rate of 8%.

a Interest each year = 5% of £3950
$$= \frac{5}{100} \times 3950$$
$$= 0.05 \times 3950 = £197.50$$
Total amount of simple interest after 4 years = 4 × £197.50
$$= £790$$
b Interest each year = 8% of £3950
$$= \frac{8}{100} \times 3950$$
$$= 0.08 \times 3950 = £316$$
Total amount of simple interest after 10 years = 10 × £316
$$= £3160$$

Don't forget to
estimate.
5% of £3950
$\approx$ 5% of £4000
= 10% of
£4000 ÷ 2
= £400 ÷ 2
= £200

1 Calculate these amounts without using a calculator.
   a 10% of £5000   **b** 10% of $260   **c** 5% of £3900
   d 25% of €800   **e** 50% of £3.60   **f** 5% of $7500
   g 25% of £1240   **h** 20% of £780   **i** 15% of $8430
   j 1% of £560   **k** 15% of £230   **l** 25% of €1250

2 Calculate these percentages, giving your answer to two decimal places where appropriate.
   a 7% of £3200   **b** 12% of £3210   **c** 27% of €5400
   d 3.5% of £2200   **e** 0.3% of €4450   **f** 3.7% of £12 590

3 a Jane puts £3700 into a bank account. The bank pays interest of 4% on any money she keeps in the account for one year. Calculate the interest received by Jane at the end of the year.
   b Majid puts £30 000 into a savings account. The account pays interest of 8.1% on any money he keeps in the account for one year. Calculate the interest received by Majid at the end of the year.

4 Calculate the simple interest paid on £4580
   a at an interest rate of 4% for 3 years
   b at an interest rate of 11% for 5 years
   c at an interest rate of 4.6% for 4 years
   d at an interest rate of 8.5% for 3 years.

5 Calculate the simple interest paid on these amounts.
   a An amount of £4500 at an interest rate of 5% for 3 years
   b An amount of £8500 at an interest rate of 7% for 5 years
   c An amount of £320 at an interest rate of 2.5% for 8 years
   d An amount of £3900 at an interest rate of 7.5% for 11 years

6 Calculate these amounts.
   a Increase £250 by 10%   **b** Decrease £2830 by 20%
   c Increase £17 200 by 5%   **d** Decrease £3600 by 30%
   e Increase £3.60 by 17.5%   **f** Decrease £2500 by 20%

7 Calculate these amounts. Give your answer as appropriate to two decimal places.
   a Increase £740 by 8%   **b** Decrease £39 450 by 32%
   c Increase £107.80 by 5%   **d** Decrease $8230 by 34%
   e Increase $5900 by 4.5%.   **f** Decrease £2950 by 17.5%

Fraction of a fraction

This spread will show you how to:

- Use a fraction as an operator
- Multiply fractions
- Calculate a fraction of a fraction

Keywords
Denominator
Fraction
Numerator

Multiplying by $\frac{1}{5}$ is the same as dividing by 5.

For example, $3 \times \frac{1}{5} = \frac{3}{5}$ $3 \div 5 = \frac{3}{5}$

Multiplying by $\frac{1}{10}$ is the same as dividing by 10.

For example, $7 \times \frac{1}{10} = \frac{7}{10}$ $7 \div 10 = \frac{7}{10}$

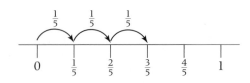

$\frac{1}{5}$ is the **reciprocal** of 5.
$\frac{1}{10}$ is the reciprocal of 10.

- You can multiply any **fraction** by a whole number using unit fractions.

Example

Calculate

a $\frac{2}{3} \times 8$

b $\frac{3}{5}$ of £220

- -

a $\frac{2}{3} \times 8 = 8 \times 2 \times \frac{1}{3}$

$= 16 \times \frac{1}{3}$

$= \frac{16}{3}$

$= 5\frac{1}{3}$

b $\frac{3}{5}$ of £220 $= \frac{3}{5} \times 220$

$= 3 \times \frac{1}{5} \times 220$

$= 3 \times 220 \times \frac{1}{5}$

$= 660 \times \frac{1}{5}$

$= \frac{660}{5} = 132$

So $\frac{3}{5}$ of £220 is £132.

Remember: You can find a fraction of an amount by multiplying.

- You can multiply a fraction by another fraction by multiplying the **numerators** together and multiplying the **denominators** together. $\frac{3}{4} \times \frac{7}{10} = \frac{3 \times 7}{4 \times 10} = \frac{21}{40}$

Example

Sarah saves $\frac{1}{3}$ of her weekly wage.
She puts $\frac{3}{4}$ of the money she saves into a pension.
What fraction of her weekly wage does Sarah put into a pension?

- -

Sarah's pension is $\frac{3}{4}$ of the money she saves;
she saves $\frac{1}{3}$ of her weekly wage.

Sarah's pension $= \frac{3}{4}$ of $\frac{1}{3}$ of her weekly wage.

$= \frac{3}{4} \times \frac{1}{3} = \frac{3 \times 1}{4 \times 3}$

$= \frac{3}{12} = \frac{1}{4}$ of her weekly wage

1 Calculate each of these, leaving your answer in its simplest form.

   a $3 \times \frac{1}{5}$ **b** $4 \times \frac{1}{7}$ **c** $11 \times \frac{1}{3}$

   d $18 \times \frac{1}{3}$ **e** $\frac{1}{7} \times 14$ **f** $\frac{1}{5} \times 20$

2 Calculate each of these, leaving your answer in its simplest form.

   a $4 \times \frac{1}{9}$ **b** $8 \times \frac{1}{3}$ **c** $9 \times \frac{1}{2}$

   d $10 \times \frac{1}{8}$ **e** $12 \times \frac{1}{6}$ **f** $\frac{1}{8} \times 13$

3 Calculate each of these amounts.

   a $\frac{1}{2}$ of 24 apples   **b** $\frac{1}{3}$ of 21 shops   **c** $\frac{1}{5}$ of 45 texts   **d** $\frac{1}{6}$ of 36 cups

4 Use an appropriate method for each of these calculations. The first
   question has been started for you using the multiplication method.

   a $\frac{3}{10}$ of €500 $= 3 \times \frac{1}{10} \times 500$

   $\qquad\qquad = 3 \times 500 \times \frac{1}{10}$

   $\qquad\qquad = 1500 \times \frac{1}{10}$ ($\times \frac{1}{10}$ is the same as $\div 10$)

   $\qquad\qquad = \overline{10}$

   $\qquad\qquad = €\_\_\_\_$

   b $\frac{3}{5}$ of £60   **c** $\frac{2}{3}$ of 120 kg   **d** $\frac{4}{5}$ of 250p

   e $\frac{7}{10}$ of 40 m   **f** $\frac{5}{6}$ of 54 cards   **g** $\frac{5}{12}$ of $84

5 Calculate each of these, leaving your answer in its simplest form.

   a $6 \times \frac{2}{3}$ **b** $9 \times \frac{1}{3}$ **c** $4 \times \frac{2}{3}$ **d** $\frac{2}{3} \times 12$

   e $4 \times \frac{3}{5}$ **f** $\frac{4}{5} \times 3$ **g** $\frac{2}{5} \times 10$ **h** $\frac{3}{8} \times 4$

6 Use a suitable method to calculate each of these amounts.
   Where appropriate round your answer to two decimal places.

   a $\frac{4}{15}$ of £390   **b** $\frac{7}{10}$ of 4500 m   **c** $\frac{3}{7}$ of 50 g   **d** $\frac{4}{9}$ of 639 mm

   e $\frac{7}{18}$ of 200 kg **f** $\frac{3}{17}$ of 360°   **g** $\frac{2}{25}$ of 775 miles   **h** $\frac{7}{15}$ of 345 m²

   i $\frac{14}{15}$ of £70   **j** $\frac{5}{6}$ of 18 hours

7 Calculate each of these, leaving your answer in its simplest form.

   a $\frac{1}{5} \times \frac{2}{3}$ **b** $\frac{2}{5} \times \frac{3}{4}$ **c** $\frac{2}{7} \times \frac{3}{4}$ **d** $\frac{2}{7} \times \frac{2}{5}$

   e $\frac{5}{6} \times \frac{3}{4}$ **f** $\frac{3}{8} \times \frac{5}{9}$ **g** $\frac{3}{5} \times \frac{4}{9}$ **h** $\frac{5}{6} \times \frac{2}{5}$

   i $\frac{3}{7} \times \frac{5}{6}$ **j** $\left(\frac{2}{5}\right)^2$ **k** $\left(\frac{2}{3}\right)^2$ **l** $\left(\frac{4}{9}\right)^2$

Unit 3

Summary

Check out
You should now be able to:

- Use rounding to estimate answers to calculations
- Use a calculator effectively and efficiently
- Multiply fractions
- Calculate simple interest

Worked exam question
The cost of sending airmail letters is shown

Weight not over	Europe cost (£)	Asia cost (£)
10 g	0.44	0.50
20 g	0.44	0.72
40 g	0.64	1.12
60 g	0.83	1.51
80 g	1.02	1.91
100 g	1.21	2.31

a Find the cost of sending one letter weighing 45 g to Europe. (1)

b Find the total cost of sending two letters, each weighing
82 g, one to Europe and one to Asia. (2)

c Find the total cost of sending three letters, each
weighing 26 g, to Europe. (2)

(AQA, 2008)

a   83p

b   1.21 + 2.31 = £3.52

c   0.64 × 3 = £1.92 ◄——— Use the 100 g amount, not the 80 g.

Exam questions

1 The table shows the cost of some items on the internet.
It also shows some of the postage and packing costs.
The total cost is the item cost plus the postage and packing cost.

Item	Item cost (£)	Postage and Packing cost (£)	Total cost (£)
Book	14.49	1.97	
DVD	9.99		10.94
Teddy Bear	12.50	2.08	

  a Work out the total cost for the book. (2)
  b Work out the cost of postage and packing for the DVD. (2)
  c Matty buys all three items.

    Work out the total cost for all three items including postage and packing. (3)

  d Georgina buys the same three items from a different supplier.
    She pays £10 for postage and packing.
    The item cost of the book and the DVD were both the same as shown
    in the table above.
    The teddy bear was 30% more expensive.

    How much more does Georgina pay than Matty? (4)
(AQA, 2009)

2 Estimate the value of 198×3.1 (2)
(AQA, 2008)

3 Use your calculator to work out
$$(1.4 + 2.8)^2 \times 3.12$$
(2)

4 Calculate the following.
  a $3 \times \dfrac{5}{6}$
  b $\dfrac{3}{4}$ of $28\,\text{kg}$
  c $\dfrac{5}{8} \times \dfrac{9}{15}$ (4)

Introduction

Transformations change points and shapes by moving them from one place to another. When you play a computer game your character is able to move around the screen because of mathematical transformations. Combinations of these transformations, often taking place in 3D worlds, allow the characters to move in many different ways.

What's the point?

Mathematicians use transformations not just to change shapes but also to change graphs and statistics. This helps them match the mathematics to real life situations.

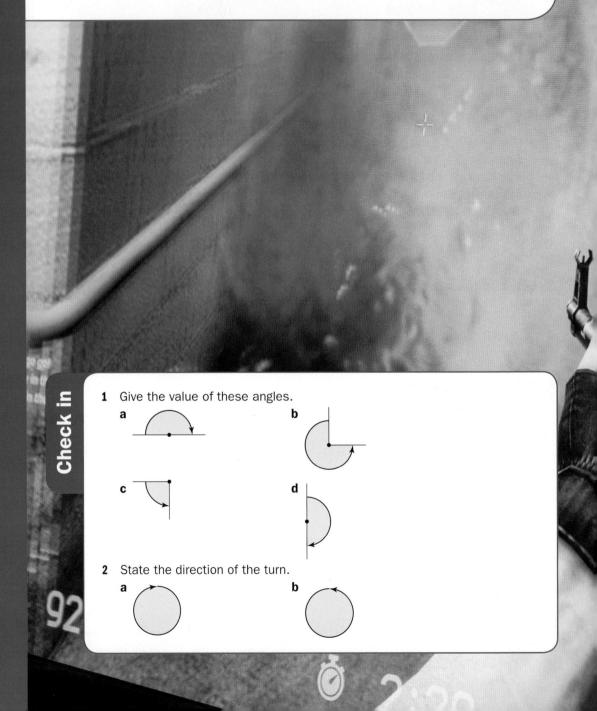

Check in

1 Give the value of these angles.

   a   b

   c   d

2 State the direction of the turn.

   a   b

Orientation

What I need to know	What I will learn	What this leads to
Key stage 3 →	■ Plot and locate coordinates ■ Transform shapes by reflection, rotation and translation	→ G5
G3 →	■ Recognise reflection symmetry of 2D shapes ■ Recognise rotation symmetry of 2D shapes	

Rich task

A shape (object) is reflected in the line $y = x$.

To find the new coordinates of each vertex of the shape (image), simply swap the x and y coordinates around.

Investigate rules for finding the image coordinates for this and other transformations.

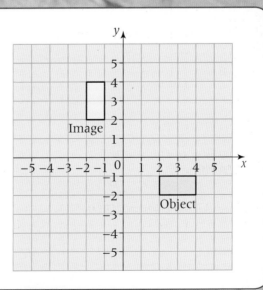

Reflections 1

This spread will show you how to:

- Recognise and visualise reflections
- Understand that reflections are specified by a mirror line
- Transform triangles and other shapes by reflection

Keywords

Mirror line
Reflection
Transformation

A **transformation** can change the size and position of a shape.

- A **reflection** flips the shape over.

When you look at yourself in a mirror, you are seeing a reflection.

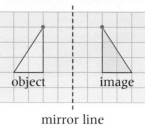

p.358

You specify a **mirror line** or reflection line to reflect the object.
To find the position of the reflection line you choose corresponding points on the object and the image.

object   image

mirror line

Each dot is 2 units from the mirror line.

- The image is the same distance from the mirror line as the object.

Example

Draw the mirror line so that shape B is a reflection of shape A.

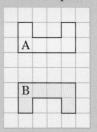

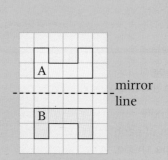

mirror line

You can rotate the page to make the mirror line vertical.

Example

Draw the reflection of the shape using the mirror line.

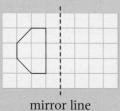

mirror line

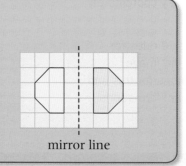

mirror line

1 Copy the

a  **e**

f 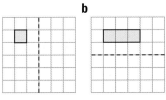 **j**

2 Copy and 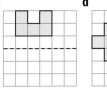 on of the shape in the m

a **b** **c** **d** **e**

f **g** **h** **i** **j**

3 Copy the diagrams.
Reflect the shapes in both mirror lines to create a pattern.

a 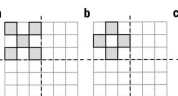 **b** **c** **d** **e**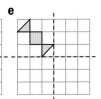

4 Give the equation of the mirror line for each reflection.

a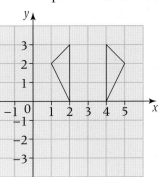

b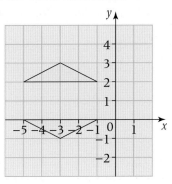

Rotations 1

This spread will show you how to:

- Recognise and visualise rotations
- Understand that rotations are specified by a centre of rotation and an angle and direction of turn

Keywords
Anticlockwise
Centre of rotation
Clockwise
Degrees (°)
Rotation
Turn

- A **rotation** turns a shape.

To describe a rotation you give
- the **centre of rotation** – the point about which it **turns**
- the angle or measure of turn
- the direction of turn – either **clockwise** or **anticlockwise**.

p.360

Clockwise

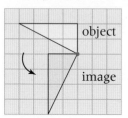

The dot is the centre of rotation.
The turn is 90° or $\frac{1}{4}$ of a turn.
The direction is anticlockwise.

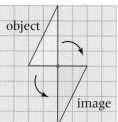

The dot is the centre of rotation.
The turn is 180° or $\frac{1}{2}$ a turn.
The direction is either clockwise or anticlockwise.

Anticlockwise

Example

a Draw the position of the green triangle after a rotation of 90° clockwise about the dot (•).

b What rotation would return the triangle to its starting position?

....

a
centre of rotation

b Rotation of 90° anticlockwise about the dot (•).

Use tracing paper to find the position of the blue triangle.

1   State the angle and direction of turn for each of these rotations
    (green shape to blue shape).

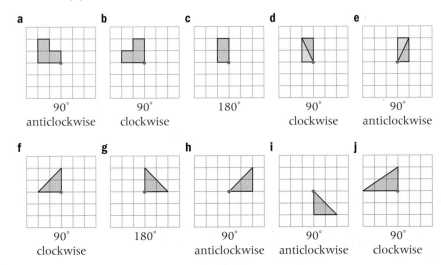

2   Copy these shapes onto square grid paper.
    Rotate the shapes through the given angle and direction about
    the dot (•).

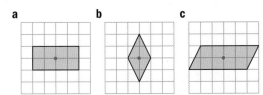

a	b	c	d	e
90° anticlockwise	90° clockwise	180°	90° clockwise	90° anticlockwise

f	g	h	i	j
90° clockwise	180°	90° anticlockwise	90° anticlockwise	90° clockwise

3   Copy the shapes onto square grid paper.

    a   b   c

    Rotate each shape through 180° about the dot (•).
    Describe your results.

4   Copy the triangles onto square grid paper.   **a**   **b**
    Rotate each triangle through 180° about
    the dot (•).

    Give the mathematical name of the new
    shape you have created.

This spread will show you how to:
- Recognise and visualise translations
- Understand that translations are specified by a distance and direction

Keywords
Left
Right
Slide
Translation

- A **translation** is a **sliding** movement.

p.362

To describe a translation you give:
- the distance moved **right** or **left**, then
- the distance moved **up** or **down**.

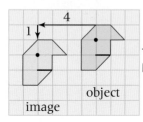

Translate the object 4 units left and 1 unit down.

object

image

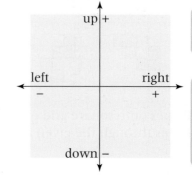

up +

left   right
  −   +

down −

Right and up are positive directions.

In your Unit 3 assessment, translations will be specified by a **vector**. This is explained on page 362.

You choose corresponding points on the object and image to work out the translation.

Example

Which triangles are translations of the black triangle?

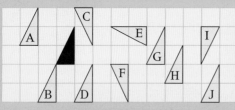

A, B, D, G, H, J because they are all in the same orientation.

Same orientation means the same way up.

Example

a Give the coordinates of the point marked by a dot (•) in triangle A.

b Describe the transformation that moves triangle A to triangle B.

c Give the coordinates of the point in triangle B that corresponds to the dot (•) in triangle A.

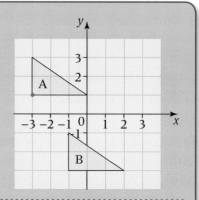

a (−3, 1)
b Translation, 2 units right and 4 units down.
c (−1, −3)

1 Which shapes are translations of the green shape?

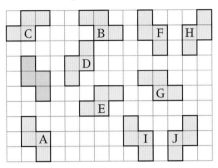

Unit 3

2 Describe these translations.

a E to D	**b** E to C
c A to B	**d** A to C
e B to D	**f** C to A
g C to E	**h** B to A
i E to A	**j** A to E

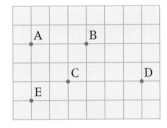

3 **a** Give the coordinates of point A.
   b Describe the transformation that moves the green shape to the blue shape.
   c Give the coordinates of the point in the blue shape that corresponds to point A in the green shape.

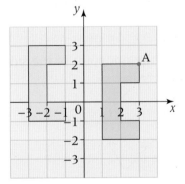

4 Describe these translations.

a D to B	**b** A to B
c A to C	**d** D to E
e B to E	**f** B to C
g E to D	**h** E to A
i B to D	**j** B to A
k E to B	**l** A to D
m C to B	**n** E to C
o C to A	**p** A to E
q C to D	**r** D to C
s C to E	**t** D to A

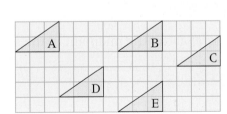

Tessellations

This spread will show you how to:

- Understand congruence and recognise congruent shapes
- Understand and create tessellations

Keywords
Congruent
Quadrilateral
Regular
Rotate
Scalene
Tessellation
Translate
Triangle

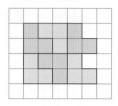

- **Congruent** shapes are exactly the same shape and size

You can make patterns with an L shape like this.

The L shapes fit together so that there are no gaps or overlaps. The L shape tessellates.

- A **tessellation** is a tiling pattern with no gaps.

p.398

Example

Draw at least five more trapezium shapes on the grid to show how the shape tessellates.

 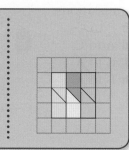

You are allowed to **rotate** or **translate** the shape.

- Any **triangle** tessellates.

Rotate the triangle about the midpoint of the sides.

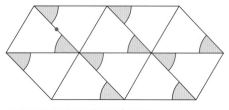

Even a **scalene** triangle tessellates.

- Any **quadrilateral** tessellates.

Rotate the quadrilateral about the midpoint of the sides.

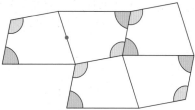

This means that all the special quadrilaterals also tessellate.

Only three regular shapes tessellate.

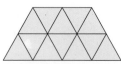

Equilateral triangles   Squares   Hexagons

A **regular** shape has equal sides and equal angles.

1 Copy these shapes onto square grid paper.
Show how each shape tessellates, using rotations and translations.

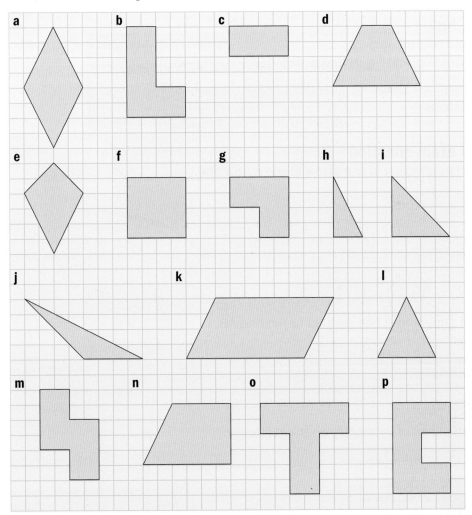

2 Draw a 4 by 2 rectangle on square grid paper.

Remove the triangle and translate it to the new position as shown.

Remove a second triangle and translate it to the new position as shown.

Cut out the shape and tessellate it using translations.

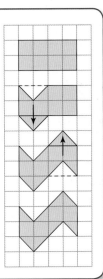

DID YOU KNOW?

Quilters make tessellating patterns out of fabric involving highly technical artwork.

Check out

You should now be able to:

- Recognise and visualise reflections, rotations and translations
- Transform 2D shapes using reflections, rotations and translations

Worked exam question

a Draw the reflection of the arrow in the mirror line.

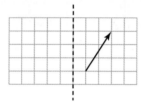

(1)

b On the grid, draw a line parallel to the line *AB*.

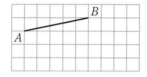

(1)

c Draw the lines of symmetry on the rectangle.

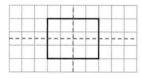

(2)

(AQA, 2009)

a

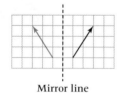

Mirror line

b

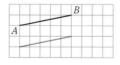

c

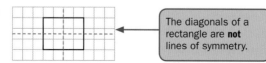

The diagonals of a rectangle are **not** lines of symmetry.

Exam questions

1

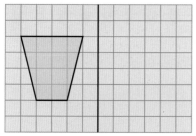

Mirror line

Copy the diagram on a square grid.
Draw the reflection of the shape in the mirror line.

(2)

(AQA, 2009)

2

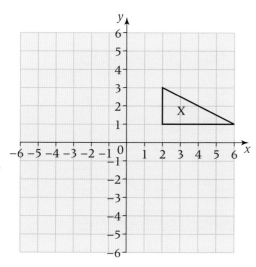

Triangle **X** has been drawn on the grid.
a Reflect triangle **X** in the *y*-axis.
  Label the new triangle **A**.

(1)

b Rotate triangle **X** by a half turn, centre O.
  Label the new triangle **B**.

(2)

Functional Maths 7: Business

One out of every two small businesses goes bust within its first two years of trading. Mathematics can be applied to reduce the risk of failure for a business as well as to maximise its profits.

A manager needs to know how much cash is coming into and going out of the business.

Accountants must set a suitable budget that includes realistic performance targets, and limits expenditure to what the business can afford.

Example

Annie sells hand made cards at a monthly craft fair.

The production costs and selling price per card are:

Cost of materials used	Production time	Wages paid	Selling price	Profit
£0.30	15 minutes	£1.00	£2.55	£1.25

This is Annie's cash flow budget for her first three craft fairs (some of the information is missing):

	January (£)	February (£)	March (£)
TOTAL SALES INCOME	56.10	71.40	63.75
Materials used	6.60	8.40	7.50
Wages			
Craft fair fees	10.00	10.00	10.00
Advertising	5.00	5.00	5.00
TOTAL EXPENDITURE	43.60		
NET CASH SURPLUS/DEFICIT	12.50		
CASH BALANCE BROUGHT FORWARD	-	12.50	
CASH BALANCE TO CARRY FORWARD	12.50		

How many cards did Annie sell in each of the three months?

Use this information to calculate the wages paid for each month.

Calculate the total expenditure for each month. During which month were Annie's expenses highest?

The net surplus (profit) or net deficit (loss) is calculated using the formula Balance = Income − Expenditure
Copy the table and complete the missing values.

On separate copies of the table template, show how the cash flow could change if
a) the craft fair fees were increased to £15
b) the cost of the materials used per card increased to £0.40
c) the selling price per card was increased to £2.75.

Investigate how other changes to costs/income might affect Annie's cash flow.

The breakeven point is when a company's expenditure is equal to its income. If the company can operate at levels above the breakeven point, it will make a profit. If sales fall below this point, the company will make a loss.

For Annie's cards:

Fixed costs = craft fair fees (£10) + advertising (£5) = £15;

Variable cost per card = material costs (£0.30) + wages (£1) = £1.30 per card;

Total costs = fixed costs + variable costs

To calculate total variable cost, multiply: variable cost per card × number of cards

To calculate revenue, multiply: sales price per card × number of cards

If 20 cards are sold, revenue = £2.55 × 20 = £51

Variable costs and revenue increase in direct proportion with the number of cards produced.

Fixed costs: £15, Variable costs:
£1.30 per card, Sales price: £2.55 per card

Make sure you understand where the plotted values come from. You may find it useful to draw up a table of values (showing number of cards, fixed costs, variable costs, total costs and revenue).

The fixed cost line is horizontal because the fixed costs do not change regardless of the number of cards produced.

What do you notice about the gradient and y-axis intercept of each line?

Annie must spend £30.60 to recover her expenses.

When no cards are sold the revenue is £0.

Annie would need to sell 12 cards at this price to break even.

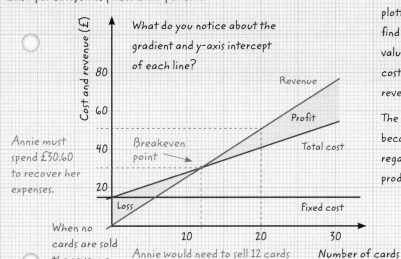

Plot your own charts to show the breakeven point if

a) the craft fair fees were increased to £15

b) the cost of the materials used per card increased to £0.40

c) the selling price per card was increased to £2.75.

Investigate how other changes to costs/income could affect Annie's profit/loss.

Introduction

Enlargements are mathematically similar to the original object – this means that the properties of the original shape, except the size, are retained. In practical terms when you enlarge a picture you want it to look like an exact copy of the original – just bigger!

What's the point?

From giant billboard posters to making model planes, enlarging (or reducing) an object is a very visible part of the modern world. Whether you are using a map or zooming in on a computer page, you are making use of enlargements.

Check in

1 State the equations of lines **a** and **b**.

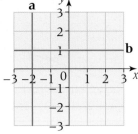

2 State the value of these angles.

a

b

c

What I need to know	What I will learn	What this leads to
G4 →	■ Transform 2D shapes by reflection, rotation, translation and enlargement ■ Understand the effect of enlargement on angles and lengths ■ Recognise similar and congruent shapes	→ +13

You can tessellate combinations of squares, hexagons and equilateral triangles.

Investigate which of the regular polygons tessellate, and which ones don't.

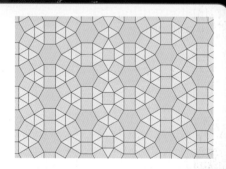

This spread will show you how to:
- Recognise and visualise reflections
- Understand that reflections are specified by a mirror line

Keywords
Congruent
Equidistant
Mirror line
Reflection
Transformation

A **transformation** changes the position of a shape.

- A **reflection** flips the shape over.

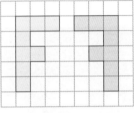

p.344 You specify the **mirror line** or reflection line.

The two shapes are **congruent** – they are exactly the same size and the same shape.

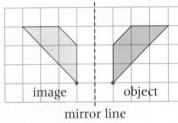

image | object

mirror line

The object and image are **equidistant** from the mirror line.

Each dot is 1 unit from the mirror line.

Example

a Draw the mirror line so that shape B is a reflection of shape A.

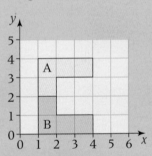

b Give the equation of the mirror line.

a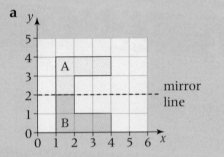

mirror line

b Each point on the mirror line has y-coordinate 2.
$y = 2$

You can rotate the page to make the mirror line vertical.

To reflect a shape, you choose a point on the object and find the position of the corresponding point in the image.

Example

Reflect this pattern using the y-axis as the mirror line.

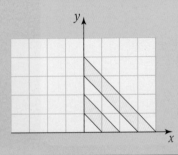

The equation of the y-axis is $x = 0$.

1 Copy the diagrams on square grid paper. Reflect each shape in the mirror line. Give the mathematical name of each new shape you have made.

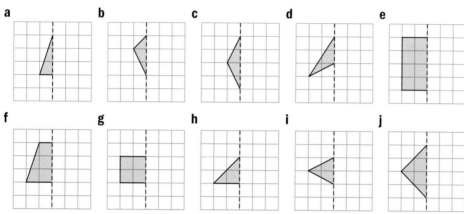

Explain why it is impossible to draw a parallelogram using this method.

2 Copy and complete the diagrams to show the reflections in both the *x*-axis and the *y*-axis.

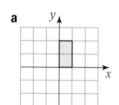 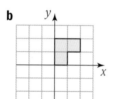 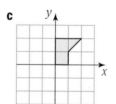 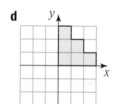

3 Copy and complete the diagrams to show the reflection of each triangle in the mirror line *x* = 3.

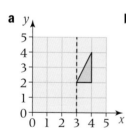 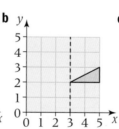 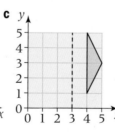 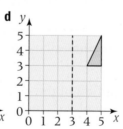

4 Give the equation of the mirror line for each reflection.

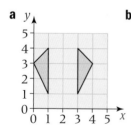 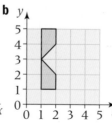 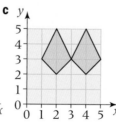 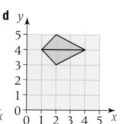

G5.2 Rotations 2

This spread will show you how to:
- Recognise and visualise rotations
- Understand that rotations are specified by a centre of rotation and an angle and direction of turn

 p.346

A **rotation** turns a shape.

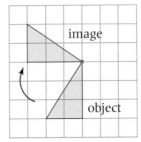

The turn is 90°. The direction is **clockwise**.

The dot is the **centre of rotation**.

The two shapes are **congruent**.

Keywords

Anticlockwise
Centre of rotation
Clockwise
Congruent
Origin
Rotation
Transformation

Example

Draw the pentagon after a rotation of 180° about the dot.

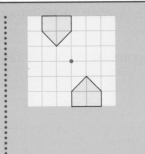

A rotation of 180° can be clockwise or anticlockwise.

You can use tracing paper to help rotate shapes.

- To describe a rotation you give
  - the centre of rotation – the point about which it turns
  - the angle of turn
  - the direction of turn – either clockwise or anticlockwise.

Example

a Give the mathematical name of the green shape.

b Draw the position of the green shape after a rotation of 90° clockwise about the origin.

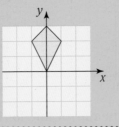

The **origin** is the point (0, 0).

a Kite

b

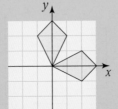

1 State the angle and direction of turn for each of these rotations, green shape to blue shape.

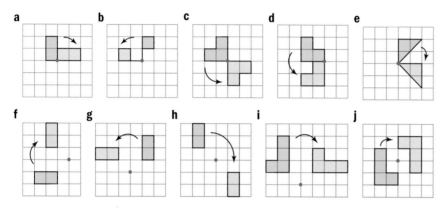

a   b   c   d   e

f   g   h   i   j

2 Copy these shapes on square grid paper. Rotate each shape through the given angle and direction about the dot (•).

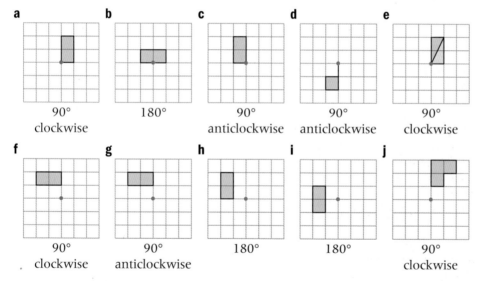

a   b   c   d   e

90°   180°   90°   90°   90°
clockwise   anticlockwise   anticlockwise clockwise

f   g   h   i   j

90°   90°   180°   180°   90°
clockwise   anticlockwise   clockwise

3 a Plot and join the points (0, 0) (1, 2) (0, 4) and (−1, 2) on a copy of this grid.
  b Give the mathematical name of this shape.
  c Rotate the shape through 90° anticlockwise about the origin.
  d Give the coordinates of the rotated points.
  e Are the two shapes congruent?

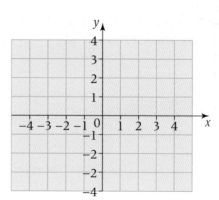

Unit 3

361

This spread will show you how to:

- Recognise and visualise translations
- Understand that translations are specified by a distance and direction

Keywords
Congruent
Slide
Translation

p.348
- A **translation** is a **sliding** movement.

You specify the distance moved
- right or left, then
- up or down.

Translate the object 4 units right and
1 unit up $\begin{pmatrix} 4 \\ 1 \end{pmatrix}$

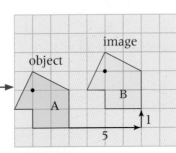

The two shapes are congruent.

You can write the translation in a column like this $\begin{pmatrix} \text{right} \\ \text{up} \end{pmatrix}$.

$\begin{pmatrix} 5 \\ 1 \end{pmatrix}$ means 5 right and 1 up.

Left and down are negative directions.

Shape B to shape A is $\begin{pmatrix} 5 \text{ left} \\ 1 \text{ down} \end{pmatrix}$ or $\begin{pmatrix} -5 \\ -1 \end{pmatrix}$.

Here are some other examples of translations.

2 units right and
1 unit down

 $\begin{pmatrix} 2 \\ -1 \end{pmatrix}$

4 units left and
1 unit down

 $\begin{pmatrix} -4 \\ -1 \end{pmatrix}$

Example

Describe fully the transformation that moves the shaded triangle to

a shape A

b shape B.

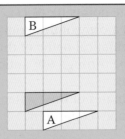

....

a A translation of 1 unit right and 1 unit down $= \begin{pmatrix} 1 \\ -1 \end{pmatrix}$.

b A translation of 0 units right and 4 units up $= \begin{pmatrix} 0 \\ 4 \end{pmatrix}$.

1 Which of these shapes are translations of the green shape?

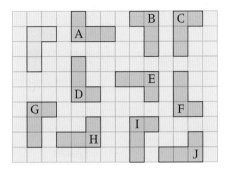

2 Describe these translations.

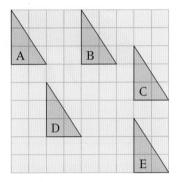

a A to B	**b** A to C
c A to D	**d** A to E
e B to C	**f** B to E
g C to E	**h** C to A
i D to C	**j** D to B
k B to A	**l** B to D

3 a Give the coordinates of the point A.

   b What is the mathematical name of the shape?

   c Copy the diagram. Draw the shape after a translation of 4 units left and 3 units down.

   d State whether the two shapes are congruent.

   e Give the coordinates of the point A after the translation.

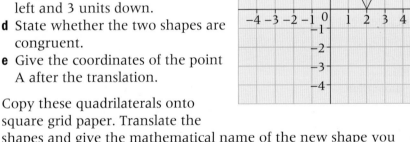

4 Copy these quadrilaterals onto square grid paper. Translate the shapes and give the mathematical name of the new shape you have made.

a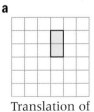

b

c

d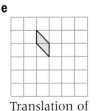

e

Translation of $\begin{pmatrix} 1 \\ 0 \end{pmatrix}$ Translation of $\begin{pmatrix} 0 \\ -1 \end{pmatrix}$ Translation of $\begin{pmatrix} 0 \\ -1 \end{pmatrix}$ Translation of $\begin{pmatrix} 2 \\ 0 \end{pmatrix}$ Translation of $\begin{pmatrix} 1 \\ -1 \end{pmatrix}$

Unit 3

This spread will show you how to:

● Understand that enlargements are specified by a centre of enlargement and a scale factor

Keywords
Enlargement
Multiplier
Proportion
Scale factor
Similar

In an **enlargement** the lengths change by the same **scale factor**.

● The scale factor is the **multiplier** in an enlargement.

p.388

The two bees are **similar** – the same shape but different sizes.

←— 3cm —→   ←——— 6cm ———→

The bee has been enlarged by a scale factor of 2.

3 cm × 2 = 6cm

The green rectangle is an enlargement of the yellow rectangle.

Corresponding lengths are multiplied by 2:

$$4 \times 2 = 8 \qquad 1 \times 2 = 2$$

The scale factor of this enlargement is 2.

● In an enlargement
   – the angles stay the same
   – the lengths increase in **proportion**.

Example

a Decide if these triangles are enlargements of the purple triangle. If so, calculate the scale factor.

b List the triangles that are similar to the purple triangle.

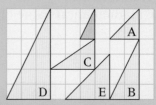

a A No, not an enlargement, as different shape.
   B Yes, enlargement. Each length is multiplied by 2. Scale factor 2.
   C No, not an enlargement, as a different shape.
   D Yes, enlargement. Each length is multiplied by 3. Scale factor 3.
   E No, not an enlargement, as a different shape.

b B and D are similar to the purple triangle.

1 a Decide if these rectangles are enlargements of the green rectangle.
If so, calculate the scale factor.

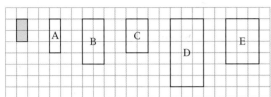

b List the rectangles that are similar to the green rectangle.

2 a Decide if these triangles are enlargements of the green triangle.
If so, calculate the scale factor.

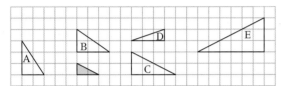

b List the triangles that are similar to the green triangle.

3 Find the kite that is similar to the green kite.

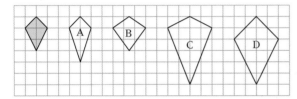

4 One rhombus is an enlargement of the green rhombus. State the
letter of this shape and calculate the scale factor of the enlargement.

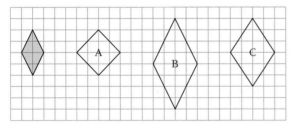

5 a Draw these triangles by plotting the
coordinates on a copy of this grid.

Green	(5, 5)	(7, 5)	(5, 6)
A	(6, 9)	(9, 9)	(6, 10)
B	(2, 7)	(8, 7)	(2, 10)
C	(8, 4)	(10, 4)	(8, 6)
D	(2, 2)	(10, 2)	(2, 6)
E	(1, 0)	(5, 0)	(1, 2)

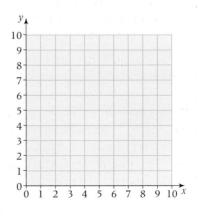

b State the triangles that are enlargements
of the green triangle. Calculate the scale
factor of the enlargement in each case.

Unit 3

Enlarging shapes

This spread will show you how to:

- Understand the effect of enlargement on the angles and lengths of shapes and how this relates to the scale factor of the enlargement
- Recognise similar shapes

- In an **enlargement**
  - the angles stay the same
  - the lengths increase in proportion.

The green triangle is an enlargement of the yellow triangle.

Corresponding lengths are multiplied by 3:
$2 \times 3 = 6$

The **scale factor** of this enlargement is 3.

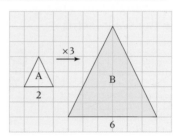

The two triangles are **similar** – the same shape but different sizes.

The scale factor of enlargement from B to A is $\frac{1}{3}$. You divide all the lengths by 3: $6 \div 3 = 2$.

- The scale factor is the multiplier in an enlargement.

Example

a Draw an enlargement of the yellow arrowhead with scale factor 2.

b Measure the length x. Measure the corresponding length y in your enlargement.

c Measure the angle at A. Measure the corresponding angle in your enlargement.

....

a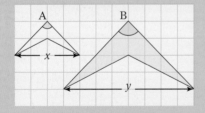

b $x = 4$ units
  $y = 8$ units

c Angle A = 90°
  Angle B = 90°

Check:
Scale factor is 2
$4 \times 2 = 8$.

Angles stay the same in enlargements.

Example

On the isometric paper draw an enlargement of the cuboid with scale factor 2.

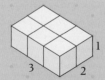

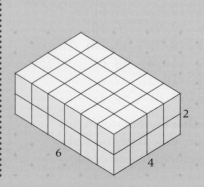

Check:
Scale factor is 2
$3 \times 2 = 6$
$2 \times 2 = 4$
$1 \times 2 = 2$

This topic is extended to similar shapes on page 432.

1 Copy each diagram onto square grid paper. Enlarge each shape by the given scale factor.

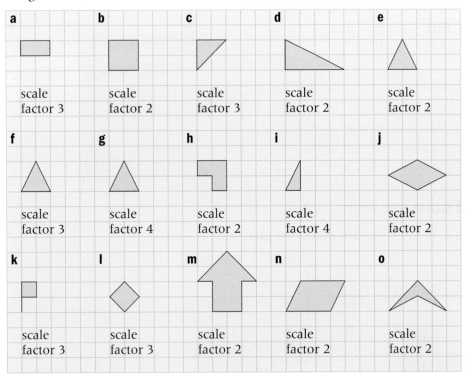

2 a Copy the 'L' shape onto square grid paper.
   b Calculate the perimeter of the shape.
   c Draw the shape after an enlargement of scale factor 3.
   d Calculate the perimeter of the enlarged shape.

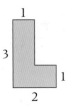

3 a Copy the triangle onto square grid paper.
   b Measure the shaded angle.
   c Draw the triangle after an enlargement of scale factor 2.
   d Measure the corresponding shaded angle in the enlargement.

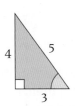

4 Copy each diagram onto isometric paper. Enlarge each shape by the given scale factor.

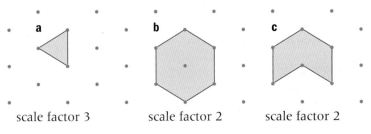

Summary

Check out

You should now be able to:

- Recognise and visualise reflections, rotations, translations and enlargements
- Describe and transform 2D shapes using reflections, rotations, translations and enlargements
- Identify shapes that are similar
- Identify congruent shapes

Worked exam question

Triangles A, B and C are shown on the grid.

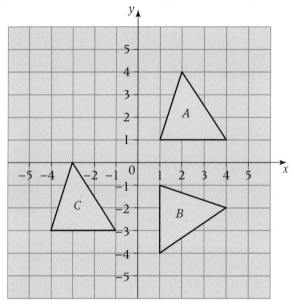

a   Describe fully the **single** transformation that maps triangle A onto triangle B.   (3)

b   Write down the vector which describes the translation of triangle A onto triangle C.   (1)

(AQA, 2009)

....

a   rotation of 90° clockwise about (0,0).

b $\begin{pmatrix} -5 \\ -4 \end{pmatrix}$ 5 units left and 4 units down, so − 5 and − 4

Exam questions

1 a Reflect the trapezium in the *x*-axis.

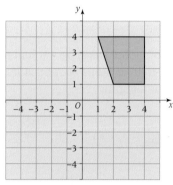

(1)

b Describe fully the **single** transformation which takes shape *A* to shape *B*.

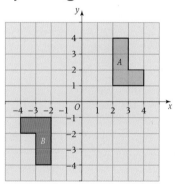

(3)

(AQA, 2009)

2 The diagram shows a triangle *A*, with vertices at $(-4, 3)$, $(-2, 3)$ and $(-2, 4)$.

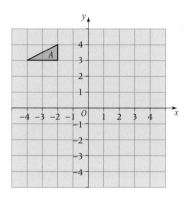

a Draw the image of triangle *A* when it is reflected in the line $y = 1$
Label your image *B*. (2)

b Draw the image of triangle *A* when it is rotated 90° clockwise
about the origin. Label your image *C*. (3)

(AQA, 2009)

Introduction

Scientists are currently trying to understand and respond to the effects of global warming on the environment. These effects are modelled by complex mathematical functions, and involve a large amount of data on a wide range of variables.

What's the point?

If we can understand the causes and effects of global warming, we can predict more accurately what is likely to happen, and begin to take steps to reduce its harmful effects. None of this would be possible without algebra.

1 State the inverse operation for each of these operations.
   a $+3$ **b** -6
   c $\times 5$ **d** $\div 4$

2 Simplify each of these expressions.
   a $x + x + y + y$ **b** $5 \times p + 2$
   c $\dfrac{m}{3 + 5}$

3 Calculate the value of each expression when $x = 4$ and $y = 3$.
   a xy **b** $2x + y$
   c $\dfrac{3x}{y}$ **d** $x + 3y$

4 Solve each of these equations.
   a $4x + 2 = 10$ **b** $3x - 6 = 9$
   c $2y \times 4 = 16$ **d** $\dfrac{y}{7} = 1$

Orientation

What I need to know	What I will learn	What this leads to

- Set up and solve linear equations
- Check a solution to an equation by substitution
- Write equations to represent real-life problems

A5 → → +8

Rich task

In this diagram the equation $3x + 2 = 17$ has been changed in different ways, but all of these ways still give the same solution of $x = 5$.

$$3x + 4 = 19$$

$$3x + 1 = 16 \qquad 3x + 5 = 20$$

$$3x + 2 = 17$$

$$3x - 1 = 14 \qquad 3x + 3 = 18$$

$$3x = 15$$

Describe each change to the equation.
Continue each change for at least one more step.
Invent a new starting equation of your own.

Solving simple equations

This spread will show you how to:

● Solve linear equations where the unknown appears on either side

Keywords
Balance method
Inverse
  operations
Solve

● You can **solve** equations using the **balance method**.

An equation remains balanced if you do the same to both sides.

p.262

You can

● add the same number to both sides

● subtract the same number from both sides

● multiply both sides by the same number

● divide both sides by the same number

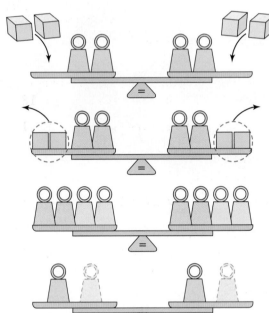

● You use **inverse operations** to get the letter on its own on one side of the equation.

Example

Solve
$\qquad$ **a** $x + 3 = 17$ $\qquad$ **b** $y - 5 = 27$
$\qquad$ **c** $3s = 24$ $\qquad$ **d** $\frac{t}{5} = 4$

a
$$x + 3 = 17$$
$$x + 3 - 3 = 17 - 3$$
$$x = 14$$

b
$$y - 5 = 27$$
$$y - 5 + 5 = 27 + 5$$
$$y = 32$$

c
$$3s = 24$$
$$3s \div 3 = 24 \div 3$$
$$s = 8$$

d
$$\frac{t}{5} = 4$$
$$5 \times \frac{t}{5} = 4 \times 5$$
$$t = 20$$

Example

Solve $15 - x = 18$

$$15 - x = 18 \qquad \text{subtract 15 from both sides}$$
$$15 - 15 - x = 18 - 15$$
$$- x = 3$$
$$x = -3$$

1 Work out the weight of one box on these balances.

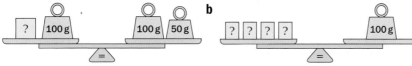

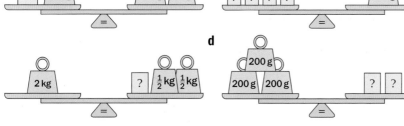

2 Solve these equations using the balance method.
a $x + 4 = 12$ **b** $y - 6 = 15$ **c** $18 = z + 9$

d $r - 89 = 27$ **e** $75 = 40 + s$ **f** $11 - t = 5$

3 Solve these equations.
a $8m = 40$ **b** $7n = 70$ **c** $25 = 5p$ **d** $42 = 6q$

e $9r = 72$ **f** $2t = 3$ **g** $15 = 2u$ **h** $4m = 48$

4 Solve these equations.
a $\frac{m}{5} = 11$ **b** $\frac{n}{6} = 8$ **c** $15 = \frac{p}{2}$ **d** $9 = \frac{q}{7}$

5 Solve these equations.
a $9 + r = 15$ **b** $11 - s = 14$ **c** $-15 = 3t$ **d** $\frac{u}{4} = -10$

e $v - 8 = -6$ **f** $6w = 8$ **g** $4 = \frac{x}{9}$ **h** $17 = 12 - y$

6 a Use these numbers and symbols.

Write all the correct equations you can make.

b Use these numbers and symbols.

Write the different equations you can make.
Solve each equation to find the value of x.

c Use these numbers and symbols.

Write the different equations you can make.
Solve each equation to find the value of x.

The x key is a symbol, not a multiply.

Problem

A03

Unit 3

373

Two-step function machines

This spread will show you how to:
- Set up functions equations with two steps

p.324

- You can draw a **function machine** for an equation.

$x + 7 = 20$

$x \longrightarrow \boxed{+7} \longrightarrow 20$

- Some functions have two operations or steps.

In number calculations with two steps, you follow the order of operations.

In the calculation $\qquad 3 \times 2 + 4 = 10$
You multiply first, then you add $\qquad 6 + 4 = 10$

BIDMAS helps you remember the order.

In algebra you follow the same order of operations.

The equation $\qquad 3n + 4 = 10$
means $\qquad 3 \times n + 4 = 10$

You multiply first, then you add.

So the function machine for $3n + 4 = 10$ is

$n \longrightarrow \boxed{\times 3} \longrightarrow \boxed{+4} \longrightarrow 10$

Draw a function box for each operation.
Two operations need a two-step function machine.

- To draw a function machine for a two-step function, follow the order of operations.

Example

For each function machine, work out the outputs for the inputs given.

a input $\qquad\qquad$ output $\qquad$ **b** input $\qquad\qquad$ output

$\begin{matrix} 0 \\ 3 \\ 7 \end{matrix} \longrightarrow \boxed{\times 4} \longrightarrow \boxed{-1} \longrightarrow \qquad\qquad \begin{matrix} 1 \\ 5 \\ 9 \end{matrix} \longrightarrow \boxed{\times 3} \longrightarrow \boxed{+2} \longrightarrow$

....

a $0 \times 4 - 1 = 0 - 1 \quad = -1$
$\quad 3 \times 4 - 1 = 12 - 1 = 11$
$\quad 7 \times 4 - 1 = 28 - 1 = 27$

b $1 \times 3 + 2 = 3 + 2 \quad = 5$
$\quad 5 \times 3 + 2 = 15 + 2 = 17$
$\quad 9 \times 3 + 2 = 27 + 2 = 29$

Example

Draw function machines for these equations.

a $4y + 2 = 26$ $\qquad\qquad$ **b** $2x - 5 = 7$

....

a
$y \longrightarrow \boxed{\times 4} \longrightarrow \boxed{+2} \longrightarrow 26$

b
$x \longrightarrow \boxed{\times 2} \longrightarrow \boxed{-5} \longrightarrow 7$

Multiplication then addition. $\qquad\qquad$ Multiplication then subtraction.

1 Here are some number machines. Work out the output for each input given.

a input   output   **b** input   output

0
2 → × 2 ⇒ + 1 ⇒
5

1
4 → × 3 ⇒ − 2 ⇒
7

c input   output   **d** input   output

1
3 → × 4 ⇒ − 3 ⇒
5

4
6 → × 2 ⇒ + 2 ⇒
8

2 Copy and complete the table of input and output values for each function machine.

a → × 2 ⇒ − 1 ⇒   **b** → × 3 ⇒ + 1 ⇒   **c** → × 2 ⇒ − 5 ⇒

Input	Output
1	
3	
5	
7	
9	

Input	Output
0	
2	
5	
7	
10	

Input	Output
20	
15	
	15
4	
1	

3 Draw function machines for these expressions.

   a $3x - 1$ **b** $4n + 2$ **c** $5m - 3$ **d** $6p + 1$

   e $3y + 5$ **f** $7z - 2$ **g** $4s - 9$ **h** $8t + 3$

4 A two-step function machine has input 4.

4 → ⇒ ⇒

Use any **two** of these function machines

 → + 5 ⇒   → × 3 ⇒   → − 6 ⇒   → ÷ 2 ⇒

to make a two-step machine that gives the output

   a 3   **b** 7   **c** 17

Make as many different outputs as you can. Draw the function machines you use each time.

5 Match each function machine to the expression it represents.

   A $3x - 2$ **B** $7x + 6$ **C** $2x + 4$ **D** $2x - 1$

   a → × 2 ⇒ + 4 ⇒   **b** → × 2 ⇒ − 1 ⇒

   c → × 7 ⇒ + 6 ⇒   **d** → × 3 ⇒ − 2 ⇒

Unit 3

Problem

A03

Inverse function machines

This spread will show you how to:
- Set up and solve equations using inverse operations

Keywords
Inverse
  operation

You can draw a function machine for a 'think of a number' problem.

You can work out the unknown number using the **inverse** function machine.

Example

Solve this 'think of a number' problem using a function machine.
    I think of a number.
    Half my number is 8.
    What is my number?

....

Draw a function machine

Work backwards, using **inverse operations**.
The number is 16.

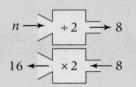

Use n for the unknown number.

This is the inverse function machine.

- To draw an inverse function machine, work backwards through the function machine, using inverse operations.

Example

I think of a number. I double my number and add 3.
The answer is 17. What is my number?

....

Function machine

Inverse function machine

The number is 7.

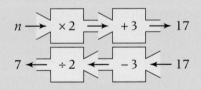

$17 - 3 = 14$
$14 \div 2 = 7$

You can use inverse function machines to solve equations.

Example

Solve these equations.
a $4x + 2 = 22$ **b** $3x - 5 = 13$

....

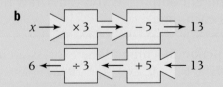

a

$x = 5$ **b** $x = 6$

Draw the function machine.
Draw the inverse machine.
$22 - 2 = 20$
$20 \div 4 = 5$

$13 + 5 = 18$
$18 \div 3 = 6$

1 Draw the inverse function machine for each of these function
machines.

a **b**

c **d**

2 For each of these 'think of a number' problems
  - Draw a function machine.
  - Draw the inverse function machine.
  - Use your inverse machine to work out the number.
  a I think of a number. I double it and add 3. The answer is 13.
  What is my number?
  b I think of a number. I double it and subtract 6. The answer is 0.
  What is my number?
  c I think of a number. I multiply it by 3 and add 3. The answer is 15.
  What is my number?
  d I think of a number. I multiply it by 4 and subtract 2. The answer
  is 26. What is my number?

3 Draw a function machine for each equation.
  Use the inverse function machine to solve the equation.
  a $3x + 4 = 16$ **b** $5x + 2 = 12$ **c** $4x + 3 = 19$ **d** $3x + 7 = 13$
  e $4x + 9 = 17$ **f** $8x + 5 = 21$ **g** $6x + 10 = 22$ **h** $9x + 3 = 30$

4 Use function machines to solve these equations.
  a $4x - 3 = 9$ **b** $6x - 4 = 20$ **c** $3x - 5 = 25$
  d $5x - 7 = 8$ **e** $2x - 10 = 12$ **f** $7x - 2 = 19$
  g $4x - 8 = 16$ **h** $5x - 7 = 43$

5 Solve these equations.
  a $2x + 7 = 5$ **b** $3x + 8 = 2$ **c** $4x + 15 = 3$
  d $2x - 5 = -9$ **e** $4x - 7 = -19$ **f** $2x + 3 = 8$
  g $4x + 2 = 0$ **h** $2x - 2 = 1$

AO3 Problem

6 Match each equation in box A
  with its solution in box B.

  There are four 'spare' solutions.
  Make up an equation with each
  of these spare solutions.

Box A	Box B	
$2x + 6 = 9$	$x = 1$	$x = -1$
$3x + 1 = 7$	$x = 2$	$x = -2$
$3x + 15 = 6$	$x = 3$	$x = \frac{1}{2}$
$4x - 3 = -5$		
$4x + 11 = 3$	$x = 4$	$x = \frac{3}{2}$
$4x + 7 = 19$	$x = 5$	$x = -\frac{1}{2}$
$5x - 12 = 13$	$x = 6$	$x = -\frac{2}{3}$
$7x + 8 = 15$		

The balance method for two-step equations

This spread will show you how to:

- Solve equations using the balance method
- Check a solution to an equation by substituting it back into the equation

You can work out the unknown weight on a balance by doing the same to both sides.

Take 3 weights off both sides

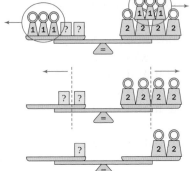

Divide both sides by 2

The unknown weight equals 4.

This topic is extended to equations with brackets and fractions on page 422.

You can work out the value of x in the equation $2x + 3 = 7$ by doing the same to both sides.

$$2x + 3 = 7$$

Subtract 3 from both sides.

Divide both sides by 2.

$$x = 2$$

First get the x term on its own on one side. This gives the value of $2x$.

Then divide to find the value of x.

- You can solve two-step equations using the **balance method**.

Example

Solve these equations.

a $4y + 2 = 18$ **b** $4x - 3 = 17$

....

a
$$4y + 2 = 18$$
$$4y + 2 - 2 = 18 - 2 \quad \text{Subtract 2 from both sides.}$$
$$4y = 16$$
$$4y \div 4 = 16 \div 4 \quad \text{Divide both sides by 4.}$$
$$y = 4 \qquad \text{This gives the value of } y.$$

b
$$4x - 3 = 17$$
$$4x - 3 + 3 = 17 + 3 \quad \text{Add 3 to both sides.}$$
$$4x = 20$$
$$4x \div 4 = 20 \div 4 \quad \text{Divide both sides by 4.}$$
$$x = 5$$

You can check using **substitution**. In part **b**
$$4x - 3 =$$
$$4 \times 5 - 3 =$$
$$20 - 3 = 17$$

- You can check a solution by **substituting** the value back into the equation.

1 Solve these equations using the balance method.
   a $2x + 3 = 13$ **b** $2x + 5 = 9$
   c $2x + 8 = 20$ **d** $2x + 1 = 21$
   e $2x + 3 = 15$ **f** $2x + 7 = 9$
   g $2x + 12 = 44$ **h** $2x + 5 = 23$
   i $2x + 13 = 21$ **j** $2x + 11 = 51$
   k $2x + 12 = 28$ **l** $2x + 36 = 40$

2 Solve these equations using the balance method.
   Check your answers by substitution.
   a $2m - 4 = 16$ **b** $3n - 5 = 10$
   c $5 = 2p + 9$ **d** $5 + 3r = 26$
   e $13 = 2s - 1$ **f** $4t + 1 = 1$
   g $25 - 3x = 10$ **h** $19 - 2y = 7$

3 Solve these equations.
   a $4m + 3 = 5$ **b** $4q - 2 = 2$
   c $8 - 6p = 5$ **d** $4r + 2 = 12$
   e $12 = 8q + 20$ **f** $6s - 6 = -3$

   Check your answers.

4 Tom and Sacha both solve the equation

   $5x - 7 = 43$

   Tom's solution is   Sacha's solution is

   $x = 8$ $x = 10$

   Check their solutions by substitution.
   Who is correct?

5 The formula for the perimeter of a rectangle is

   $P = 2l + 2w$

   where l = length and w = width.
   a Work out the perimeter of a rectangle where $l = 10$ cm and $w = 4$ cm.
   b Work out the length of a rectangle where $P = 40$ cm and $w = 7$ cm.
   c Work out the width of a rectangle where $P = 84$ cm and $l = 30$ cm.

6 Amos uses the formula

   $4.5s - 11.2t = r$

   a Work out the value of r when $s = 13$ and $t = 4$.
   b Work out the value of s when $t = 5$ and $r = 48$.
   c Work out the value of t when $s = 10$ and $r = 4.68$.

   Check your answers by substitution.

Challenge
Some equations are hard to solve exactly. For example, the equation $x^3 - x = 13$ has a solution somewhere between $x = 2$ and 3. Use a calculator and a **trial-and-improvement** method to find this solution to 1 d.p.

Writing and solving equations

This spread will show you how to:

- Check a solution to an equation by substituting it back into the equation
- Write equations to represent real-life problems

Jenny has *n* books in her school bag.
Her maths teacher gives her 4 more books for revision.
She now has 7 books in her school bag.
How many books did she have to start with?

You can write an equation for this problem

Jenny starts with	→	adds 4	→	total 7
n		$+ 4$	$=$	7

You can solve the equation $n + 4 = 7$ to find n.

$$n + 4 = 7$$
$$n + 4 - 4 = 7 - 4$$
$$n = 3$$

Subtract 4 from both sides.

Jenny had 3 books to start with.

- You can write an **equation** to represent a problem.

- You can solve the equation to find the **solution** to the problem.

Example

Marcus spends £r out shopping.
Pritesh spends twice as much as Marcus.
Tariq spends £6 more than Pritesh.

a Write an expression for the amount each person spends.

Tariq spends £50 in total.
b Write an equation for the amount Tariq spends.
c Solve your equation to find r.
d Work out how much Marcus and Pritesh spend.

....

a Marcus r
  Pritesh $2 \times r = 2r$
  Tariq $2r + 6$

b $2r + 6 = 50$

c $2r + 6 = 50$
  $2r + 6 - 6 = 50 - 6$
       $2r = 44$
        $r = 22$

Subtract 6 from both sides.
Divide both sides by 2.

d Marcus £22

  Pritesh $2 \times £22 = £44$

Substitute $r = 22$ into the original expressions.

1 For each of these 'think of a number' problems
  • write an equation
  • solve your equation to find the missing number.
  a I think of a number. I double it. Then I add 5. My answer is 17.
  b I think of a number. I multiply it by 4. Then I subtract 8. My answer is 8.
  c I think of a number. I multiply it by 7. Then I add 1. My answer is 50.
  d I think of a number. I multiply it by 3. Then I subtract 17. My answer is 13.

2 A pack of sausages costs £2.
  a Write an expression for the cost of x packs of sausages.

  For a barbeque, Charlotte spends £14 on sausages.
  b Write an equation for the sausages Charlotte buys.
  c Solve your equation to find the number of packs of sausages she bought.

3 Sarah, Josh and Millie bring sandwiches to a picnic.
  Sarah brings y sandwiches.
  Josh brings twice as many sandwiches as Sarah.
  Millie brings 4 less than Josh.
  a Write an expression for the number of sandwiches each person brings.

  Millie brings 12 sandwiches.
  b Write an equation for the sandwiches Millie brings.
  c Solve your equation to find y.
  d Work out the number of sandwiches each person brings to the picnic.

4 Four people go out for a meal.
  The meal costs £x each.
  The drinks cost £15.
  a Write an expression for the total bill for the meal.

  The total bill comes to £65.
  b Write an equation for the total bill.
  c Solve your equation to find x, the cost of one meal.

5 Rory buys four CDs at £y each and a DVD for £16.
  His total bill comes to £60.
  Write an equation for Rory's total bill.
  Solve your equation to find the cost of one CD.

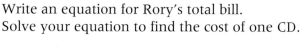

A02 Functional Maths

Unit 3

Summary

Check out
You should now be able to:

- Set up simple equations
- Solve linear equations where the unknown appears on either side of the equation
- Check a solution to an equation by substituting it back into the equation

Worked exam question
Solve the following equations.

a $x + 3 = 8$ (1)

b $3y + 4 = 16$ (2)

c $2(3z - 1) = 13$ (3)

(AQA, 2008)

....

a $x + 3 = 8$
$x = 8 - 3 = 5$

> The inverse operation of $+ 3$ is $- 3$

b $3y + 4 = 16$
$3y = 16 - 4 = 12$
$y = \dfrac{12}{3} = 4$

> The inverse operation of $+ 4$ is $- 4$.
> The inverse operation of $\times 3$ is $\div 3$.

c $2(3z - 1) = 13$
$6z - 2 = 13$
$6z = 13 + 2 = 15$
$z = \dfrac{15}{6} = 2\frac{1}{2}$

> You will learn about equations with brackets on page 422.

Exam questions

1 **a** Solve $\qquad$ $7x = 28$ $\qquad$ (1)

  b You are given that $6y = 48$

  Work out the value of $5y$. $\qquad$ (2)

  c Find the value of $3x + 5y$ when $x = 7$ and $y = -4$ $\qquad$ (2)

(AQA, 2009)

2 **a** Solve $\qquad$ $2x = 12$ $\qquad$ (1)

  b Solve $\qquad$ $9 = \dfrac{y}{5}$ $\qquad$ (1)

  c Solve $\qquad$ $6 - x = 2$ $\qquad$ (1)

3 **a** Solve $\qquad$ $5x + 1 = 11$ $\qquad$ (2)

  b Solve $\qquad$ $2y - 5 = 13$ $\qquad$ (2)

A03

4

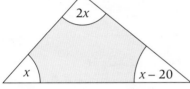

Diagram NOT accurately drawn.

The diagram shows a triangle.
The sizes of the angles, in degrees, are
  x
$2x$
  $x - 20$
Work out the value of x. $\qquad$ (3)

Introduction

When a ship sails across an ocean it sets course using a bearing. During a typical voyage, constant adjustments are made to the direction to allow for the effects of wind, currents, and other ships.

What's the point?

If you get lost in a town, you can often use landmarks to find your way. But there are some situations such as crossing an ocean where there are no landmarks to guide you! Understanding angles and bearings allows ships and planes to navigate their way around the world.

1 Convert these measurements to the units stated.

   a 10 mm =   cm   **b** 40 mm =   cm

   c 45 mm =   cm   **d** 100 cm =   m

   e 400 cm =   m   **f** 150 cm =   m

   g 1000 m =   km   **h** 6000 m =   km

   i 500 m =   km   **j** 1500 m =   km

2 **Estimate** these angles.

   a   **b**

   c   **d**

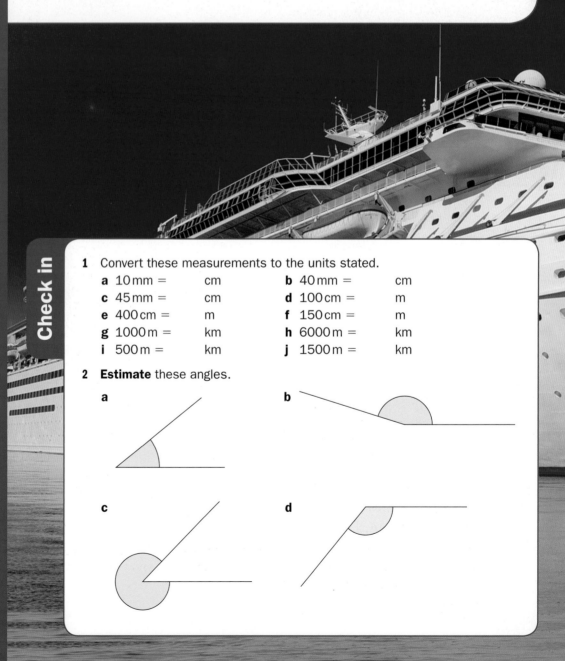

G1 + 2

- Draw triangles using a ruler and protractor
- Use and interpret scale drawings
- Give bearings accurately

Careers in technical drawing, graphic design and architecture

Rich task

Two ships, on the same line of latitude, are both travelling at a speed of 10km/h. The first ship is on a heading of 030° (angle *a*) and the second ship is on a heading of 330° (angle *b*)

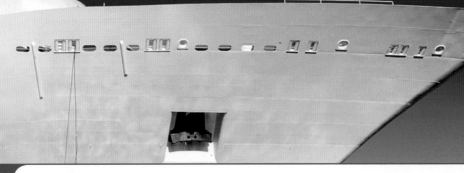

Construct a scale diagram to show where the two ships meet.

On the same diagram construct a diagram to show where the ships would have met if the first ship increased their bearing by 10° and the second ship decreased their bearing by 10°.

Investigate.

This spread will show you how to:
- Draw triangles and other 2D shapes using a ruler and protractor, given information about side lengths and angles

Keywords
Base
Construct
Protractor
Straight edge

Sunita and Emma were asked to **construct** a triangle with angles 50°, 40° and 90°. Here are their answers.

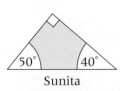
Sunita

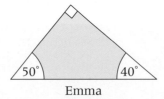
Emma

They are both correct!

They constructed different triangles because not enough information was given.

You will always construct identical triangles if you know:

two sides and the angle between them (SAS)　　or　　two angles and a side (ASA)

A = Angle
S = Side

5 cm
30°
6 cm

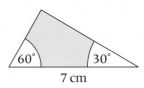
60°　30°
7 cm

A ruler is sometimes called a **straight edge**.

You will need a ruler and a **protractor** to construct SAS and ASA triangles.

Example

Construct triangle ABC with AB = 6 cm, BC = 4 cm and B̂ = 50°.
What is the length of AC?

••

Sketch the shape.　　Draw the **base** AB.　　Construct angle B　　Mark point C.
　　　　　　　　　　　　　　　　　　　　　using a protractor.　Join it to A.

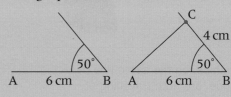

Measuring gives AC = 4.6 cm.

Example

Construct triangle PQR with angle P = 40°, angle Q = 40° and length PQ = 8 cm.
What sort of triangle is PQR?

••

Sketch the shape.　　Draw the base PQ.　　Measure angle P.　　Measure angle Q.

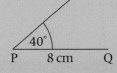

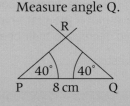

Triangle PQR is isosceles.

1 Make accurate drawings of these triangles (SAS).
  Measure the unknown length in each triangle.

a

4 cm
3 cm

b

3.5 cm
5.5 cm

c

3.5 cm
45°
6 cm

d

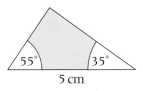

4 cm
120°
4 cm

e

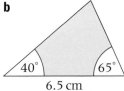

5 cm
60°
5 cm

2 Make accurate drawings of these triangles (ASA).
  Measure the two unknown lengths in each triangle.
  State the units of your answers.

a

55°   35°
5 cm

b

40°   65°
6.5 cm

c

70°   70°
4 cm

d

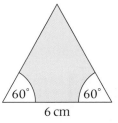

60°   60°
6 cm

e

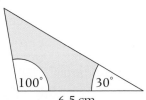

100°   30°
6.5 cm

3 Make accurate drawings of these triangles.
  Measure the unknown lengths in each triangle.

a

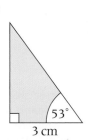

53°
3 cm

b

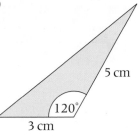

5 cm
120°
3 cm

c

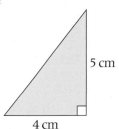

5 cm
4 cm

4 Make an accurate drawing of this parallelogram.

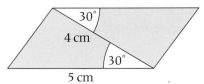

30°
4 cm
30°
5 cm

Unit 3

This spread will show you how to:
● Use and interpret scale drawings
● Understand the implications of enlargement for scale drawings

Keywords
Proportion
Reduced
Scale
Scale drawing

Real-life lengths are **reduced** in **proportion** to give a **scale drawing**.

p.364

Real-life

← 9 cm →

Scale drawing
Scale: 1 cm represents 2 cm

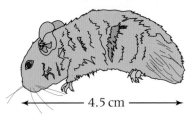

← 4.5 cm →

Scale: 1 cm represents 1 m

← 6 cm →

Length in scale drawing = 6 cm
Length in real life = 6 m

The scale of a drawing gives the relationship between the drawing and the real object.

Example

The scale for this drawing of a chessboard is 1 cm represents 10 cm.
a Calculate the dimensions of the real chessboard.
b Calculate the perimeter of the real chessboard.
c How many squares are on the real chessboard?

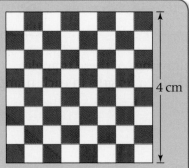

4 cm

....

a 1 cm represents 10 cm.
4 cm represents 4 × 10 cm = 40 cm.
Dimensions are 40 cm by 40 cm.
b Perimeter 40 + 40 + 40 + 40 = 160 cm.
c Number of squares = 8 × 8 = 64.

There are exactly the same number of squares on the scale drawing as on the real chessboard.

1 The scale on a drawing is 1 cm represents 5 cm.
Calculate the distance represented by

a 2 cm   **b** 4 cm
c 5 cm   **d** 10 cm
e 20 cm

2 The scale on a drawing is 1 cm represents 10 cm.
Calculate the distance represented by

a 2 cm   **b** 5 cm
c 2.5 cm   **d** 0.5 cm
e 4.1 cm

3 The scale on a drawing is 1 cm represents 50 cm.
Calculate the distance represented by

a 4 cm   **b** 5 cm
c 10 cm   **d** 0.5 cm
e 1.5 cm

4 The scale on a drawing is 1 cm represents 1 km.
Calculate the distance represented by

a 2 cm   **b** 2.5 cm
c 3.2 cm   **d** 10 cm
e 0.25 cm

5 The scale on a drawing is 1 cm represents 2 m.
Calculate the distance represented by

a 8 cm   **b** 7.5 cm
c 3.6 cm   **d** 10.8 cm
e 0.45 cm

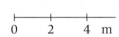

6 Using this scale drawing of the Eiffel Tower, calculate
  a the height
  b the width of the base.

Scale: 1 cm represents 60 m

This spread will show you how to:

- Understand angle measure using the associated language
- Give bearings accurately

You can give a **direction** using the compass points to describe P.

You use a 360° **scale** or a **bearing** to give a direction accurately.

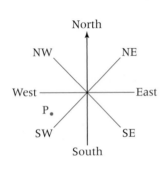

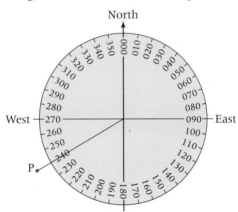

000° = North
090° = East
180° = South
270° = West

P is between SW and W.
This is not very accurate.

The bearing of P is 240°.
This is very accurate.

- To give a bearing accurately you
  - measure from North
  - measure clockwise
  - use three figures.

Example

a Write the bearing of Lincoln from Sheffield.
b Mark the position of Manchester on a bearing of 284° at a distance of 40 miles from Sheffield.

Scale: 1 cm represents 10 miles

From Sheffield means centre the protractor at Sheffield.

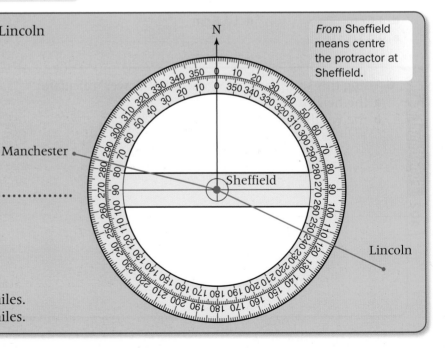

a Place the centre on Sheffield and 0° at North. Read off the direction of Lincoln as 115°.
b 1 cm represents 10 miles.
4 cm represents 40 miles.

1 a Use a protractor to draw an accurate diagram of the compass points.

b On your diagram, give the **three-figure bearings** of each of the compass points.

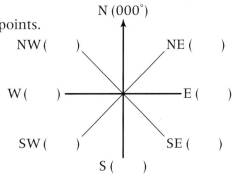

N (000°)

NW (   )   NE (   )

W (   )   E (   )

SW (   )   SE (   )

S (   )

A02 | Functional Maths

2 Measure the bearing of these places from the Lookout point.
  a Battlefield
  b Tower
  c Church
  d Castle
  e Buoy
  f Yacht
  g Needles rocks
  h Lighthouse

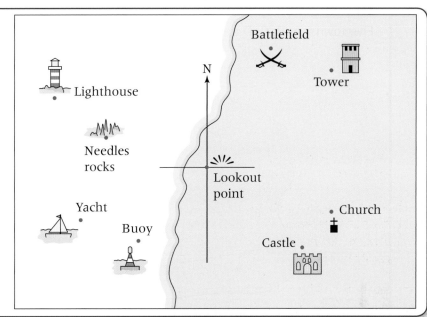

3 For each question, put a cross anywhere on your page.
Plot the points and join them to form a quadrilateral.
Name the shape, then measure and calculate the perimeter.

a

Bearing from the cross	000°	050°	180°	310°
Distance from the cross	5 cm	5 cm	5 cm	5 cm

b

Bearing from the cross	055°	145°	235°	325°
Distance from the cross	5 cm	5 cm	5 cm	5 cm

c

Bearing from the cross	000°	090°	180°	270°
Distance from the cross	5 cm	2.5 cm	5 cm	2.5 cm

d

Bearing from the cross	000°	135°	180°	225°
Distance from the cross	5 cm	5 cm	5 cm	5 cm

e

Bearing from the cross	040°	120°	240°	320°
Distance from the cross	4 cm	5 cm	5 cm	4 cm

Summary

Check out
You should now be able to:

- Understand and use bearings
- Construct triangles using a ruler and a protractor
- Use and interpret scale drawings

Worked exam question

Five towns, A, B, C, D and E on an island are joined by straight roads.

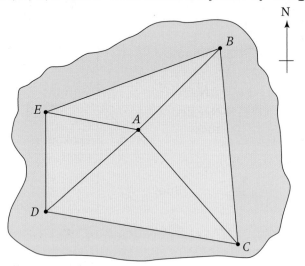

a Town D is due south of town E.
  What is the three-figure bearing of South? (1)
b Which town is North-East of town A? (1)
c Measure the bearing of town B from town E. (1)
d Measure the bearing of town C from town D. (1)

(AQA, 2009)

....

a

| 180° |

c

| 070° |

b

North-East is above and to the right.

d

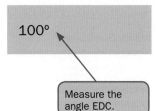

Measure the angle EDC.

Exam questions

1 This is a map of part of England.

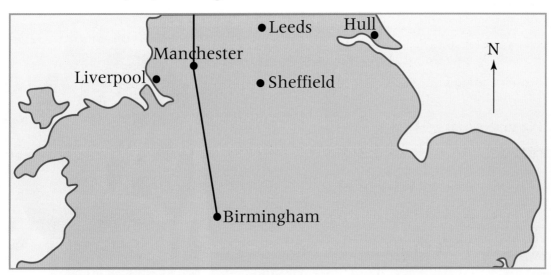

Scale: 1 cm represents 30 km

A plane flies in a straight line from Manchester to Birmingham.

a How far does it fly?
Give your answer in kilometres. (2)

b Measure and write down the bearing of Birmingham from Manchester. (1)

2 A helicopter flies from A to B.
The diagram shows the position of
A and B.
The diagram is drawn to scale.

a Use the diagram to find the actual
distance from A to B. (1)
b Measure and write down the three
figure bearing of B from A. (1)
c The helicopter then flies to C.
The bearing of C from A is 110°
The bearing of C from B is 080°
Mark the position of C on a copy of
the diagram. (3)

Scale: 1 cm represents 100 km

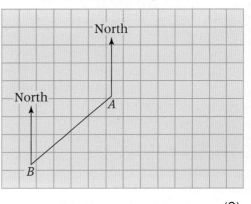

(AQA, 2008)

Functional Maths 8: Art

Graffiti artists often sketch their designs before projecting them onto the surface. They sometimes use grids or parts of their body as measuring tools to help them copy the proportions accurately.

1. A graffiti artist projects an image from a sketchpad of length 20cm and height 14.8cm onto a wall of length 6m.

   a. What scale factor is being used?
   b. What is the height of the graffiti wall?

   The artist's hand-span is 150mm.

   c. What are the dimensions of the wall in terms of hands?

Grid *method* ★★★★

The T is made up of a trapezium and a scalene triangle.
The coordinates of its vertices are

(-4, -1), (-4, 4.6), (-6, 4), (-4, 6), (4, 7), (-2.6, 5) and (-2.6, -1).

2. Describe
   a. the shapes used to make up   i. the A   ii. the G
   b. the coordinates of the vertices of   i. the A   ii. the G.

3. The dimensions of the sketch are 12cm × 10cm.
   a. What scale factor would you use to project this image onto a surface of dimensions 24cm × 20cm?
   b. What would the effect be on the area of the image?
   c. Calculate the area of
      i. the original sketch   ii. the enlarged image.
   d. Use a 2cm square grid to draw the enlarged image.

When a grid is being used, it is the shapes that make up the design and their borders that are important.

Here is a sketch of the word TAG drawn on a 1cm square grid. The artist's 'starting position', O, is the reference point (origin):

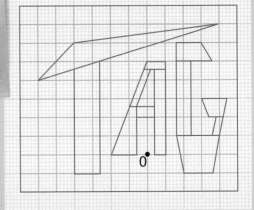

Sketch your own graffiti tags using geometric shapes. Use the grid method to create enlarged copies of your images.

Crop circles are geometric patterns that are displayed in crop fields.

CROP CIRCLES

This crop circle was found in Wiltshire in 2008. The design is based on an equilateral triangle.

You can recreate the pattern using these steps:

1. Use your compasses to draw a circle
2. Choose a point on your circle. Use your compasses (do not alter them) to step round the circle. Mark at each point your pencil touches the circle
3. Join three of the marks to form an equilateral triangle
4. Join the other three marks to form an equilateral triangle in the reverse direction
5. Alter your compasses. Draw a circle, with the same centre, passing through the six intersections of the two triangles
6. Alter your compasses again. Draw a circle, centred at a point of one of the triangles, so that it touches the second circle you drew
7. Construct two more circles as in step 6 at the other two points of that triangle
8. Erase your construction lines.

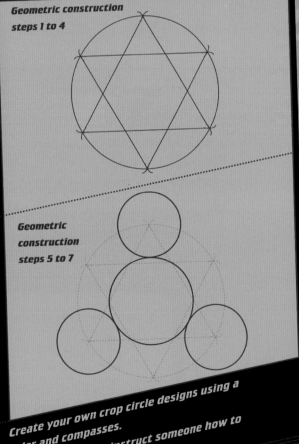

Geometric construction steps 1 to 4

Geometric construction steps 5 to 7

Create your own crop circle designs using a ruler and compasses.

Write the steps to instruct someone how to recreate your pattern.

395

Introduction

Many of the man-made shapes we see in everyday life are cuboids, particularly in packaging.

What's the point?

Cuboids are easy to assemble, and most importantly they stack up without leaving any gaps. This makes them more economical and practical for packaging and transporting goods.

Check in

1 Give the mathematical name for these distances in a circle.

a   b   c

2 Calculate the area of this rectangle. State the units of your answer.

4 cm

←— 7 cm —→

What I need to know

What I will learn

What this leads to

G3

■ Calculate the circumference and area of a circle
■ Calculate the volume and surface area of a cuboid
■ Use 2D representations of 3D shapes
■ Understand congruence
■ Find angles in polygons

Careers in manufacturing and industrial design

Rich task

A drinks company needs to design a container to hold exactly 360 ml. They are aware of environmental issues and want to minimise the surface area of the container.

a Design a container, in the shape of a cuboid, to hold exactly 360 ml, with the minimum possible surface area.

b Refine your design in the light of any practical considerations.

Congruent shapes

This spread will show you how to:
- Understand congruence

Keywords
Congruent
Corresponding
  angles
Corresponding
  sides

p.350 • **Congruent** shapes are exactly the same size and same shape.

Example

Which of these shapes are congruent?

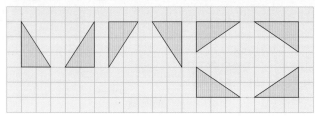

A and E are congruent.

Congruent shapes can be rotated or reflected if necessary.

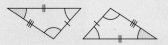

All these triangles
are congruent –
they fit exactly on
top of each other.

- In congruent shapes
  - corresponding angles are equal
  - corresponding sides are equal.

Example

This is triangle A.

Which triangle is congruent to triangle A?

Fill in the missing information.

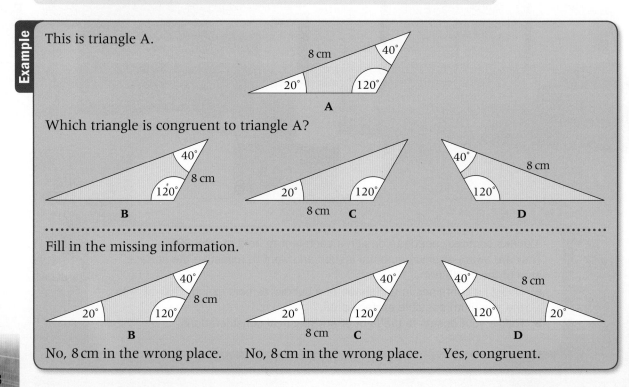

No, 8 cm in the wrong place.   No, 8 cm in the wrong place.   Yes, congruent.

1 State which are the congruent pairs.

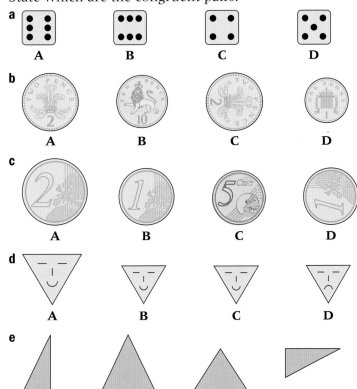

a   A   B   C   D

b   A   B   C   D

c   A   B   C   D

d   A   B   C   D

e   A   B   C   D

2 a Find **all** the pairs of quadrilaterals that are congruent.
   b Give the name of the shape for each pair.

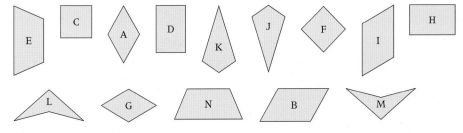

3 Here is triangle A.
Which of these triangles are
congruent to triangle A?

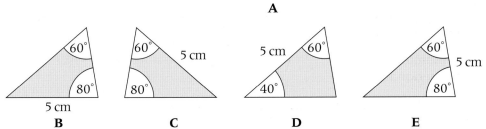

B   C   D   E

Unit 3

This spread will show you how to:
- Find exterior angles in triangles and quadrilaterals
- Know the names of general polygons
- Understand that regular polygons have equal sides and equal angles

Keywords
Isosceles
Polygon
Regular

- A **polygon** is a 2D shape with many sides and many angles.

You should know the names of these polygons.

Sides	Name
3	triangle
4	quadrilateral
5	pentagon
6	hexagon
7	heptagon
8	octagon
9	nonagon
10	decagon

- A **regular** shape has equal sides and equal angles.

Example

A regular octagon is drawn inside a circle.
There are 8 **isosceles** triangles.
Calculate the values of x and y.

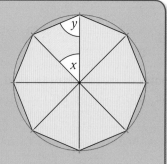

A regular pentagon has 5 equal sides and 5 equal angles.

$360° \div 8 = 45°$
$x = 45°$ (angles at a point add to $360°$)
$180° - 45° = 135°$
$2y = 135°$
$y = 67\frac{1}{2}°$ (angles in a triangle add to $180°$)

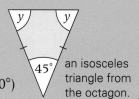

an isosceles triangle from the octagon.

p.318

- For any polygon
  - sum of exterior angles = $360°$
  - interior angle + exterior angle = $180°$

You can use the example to find the interior and exterior angles of an octagon.

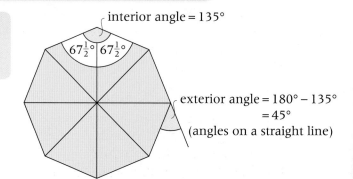

interior angle = $135°$

exterior angle = $180° - 135°$
$= 45°$
(angles on a straight line)

1 a Use a protractor and a ruler to draw a regular hexagon.

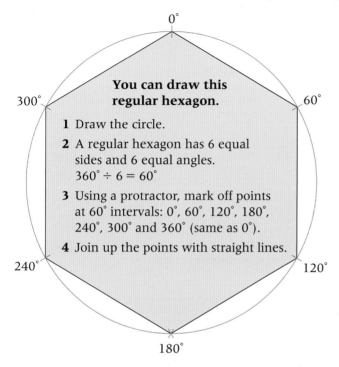

You can draw this
regular hexagon.

1 Draw the circle.

2 A regular hexagon has 6 equal
sides and 6 equal angles.
$360° ÷ 6 = 60°$

3 Using a protractor, mark off points
at 60° intervals: 0°, 60°, 120°, 180°,
240°, 300° and 360° (same as 0°).

4 Join up the points with straight lines.

2 A regular pentagon is made from five isosceles triangles.
   a Calculate the three angles in an isosceles triangle for a pentagon.
   b Use your protractor to measure and check these angles.
   c Use your results to work out the interior angle of a regular pentagon.

   d Work out the exterior angle of a regular pentagon.

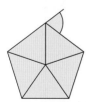

AO3 Problem

3 You can split a quadrilateral into two
triangles by drawing a diagonal.
Angle sum of quadrilateral = $2 × 180°$
$= 360°$
You can split a pentagon into triangles
by drawing diagonals.
   a How many triangles are formed?
   b What is the angle sum of a pentagon?
   c Find the angle sum of a hexagon in a similar way.

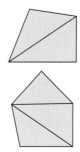

Circumference and area of a circle

This spread will show you how to:
- Use the vocabulary associated with circles
- Calculate the circumference and area of a circle

Keywords
Centre
Circle
Circumference
Diameter
Pi (π)
Radius

In a **circle**:
- the **radius** is r
- the **diameter** is d
- the **circumference** is C.

C, d and r are all measures of length.

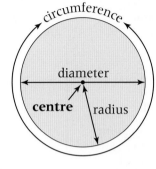

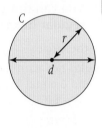

The perimeter of a circle is called the circumference.

p.320

- Diameter = 2 × radius

- $C = \pi \times$ diameter $= \pi d = 2\pi r$

$d = 2 \times r$

$\pi = 3.142 \ldots$

Example

Calculate the circumference of this circle.

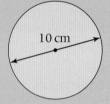

10 cm

$C = \pi \times d$
$= 3.142 \times 10$
$= 31.42 \, \text{cm}$

Remember to state the units.

- Area of a circle $= \pi \times$ radius $\times$ radius
  $= \pi \times r \times r$ or πr^2

r^2 means $r \times r$

Example

A circular lawn has radius 3 metres.
a Calculate the area of the lawn. State the units of your answer.
b Calculate the length of edging stones needed to fit all round the edge of the lawn.
Give your answer to a suitable degree of accuracy.

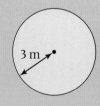

3 m

....

a Area $= \pi r^2$
$= 3.142 \times 3 \times 3$
$= 3.142 \times 9$
$= 28.28 \, \text{m}^2$ (2dp)
b Circumference $= \pi d$
$= 3.142 \times 6$
$= 18.852$
So 19 m of edging stones are needed.

Area is measured in square units.

Take $\pi = 3.142$ for all questions on this page.

1 Calculate the circumferences of these circles. State the units of your answers.

a   **b** 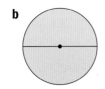 **c**   **d**

diameter = 10 cm diameter = 8 m diameter = 12 cm diameter = 20 m

e 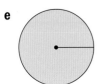 **f**   **g**   **h**

radius = 2 m radius = 8 cm radius = 1.5 m radius = 3.5 cm

2 Calculate the diameter of a circle, if its circumference is
  a 18.84 cm **b** 15.7 m **c** 28.26 cm **d** 47.1 m **e** 314 cm

3 Calculate the areas of these circles. State the units of your answers.

a   **b**   **c**   **d**

radius = 7 cm radius = 5 m radius = 4 cm radius = 3 m

e   **f**   **g**   **h**

diameter = 20 m diameter = 16 cm diameter = 12 mm diameter = 18 cm

DID YOU KNOW?

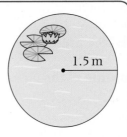

The world's largest tyre, in Michigan, USA, has a diameter of 24.4 m. That's a 76.6 m circumference!

4 A garden pond is circular.
  The radius of the pond is 1.5 m.
  a Calculate the diameter of the pond.
  b Calculate the circumference of the pond.
  c Calculate the area of the pond.
  Give your answers to a suitable degree of accuracy.

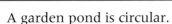

1.5 m

Functional Maths

A02

Cubes and cuboids

This spread will show you how to:
- Use nets to construct cuboids from given information
- Use 2D representations of 3D shapes

Keywords
Cube
Cuboid
Edge
Face
Net
Solid
Surface area
Three-dimensional (3D)
Vertex
Volume

p.322 A **solid** is a **three-dimensional (3D)** shape.

- A **net** is a 2D arrangement that can be folded to form a solid shape.

The net of a **cube** has 6 squares.

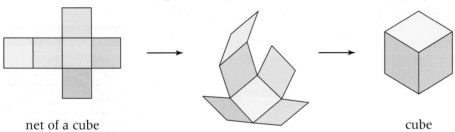

net of a cube   cube

There are many other possible nets of a cube.

The net of a **cuboid** has 6 rectangles.

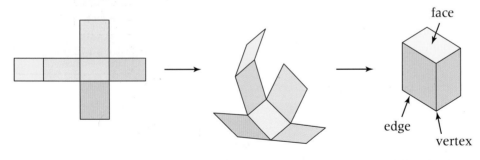

face

edge

vertex

A cuboid has
6 **faces**,
12 **edges**
and
8 vertices.

The plural of **vertex** is vertices.

Example

Here is the net of a cuboid.
a State the dimensions of the cuboid.
b Calculate the **surface area** of the cuboid.
c Calculate the **volume** of the cuboid.

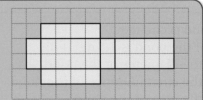

p.324

p.326

· ·

a 1 cm by 2 cm by 4 cm
b Surface area = (4 + 8 + 2) × 2
　　　　　　 = 28 cm²
c Volume = 2 × 4 × 1
　　　　 = 8 cm³

1 State whether each arrangement of squares is a net of a cube.

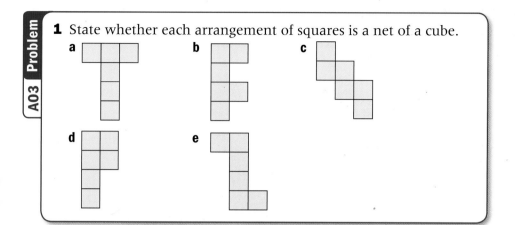

2 These nets make cuboids. Copy the nets onto centimetre squared paper and cut them out to make the cuboids. Write the dimensions and calculate the surface area and the volume of each cuboid.

a 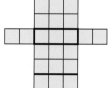   b   c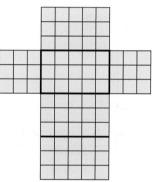

3 The volume of a cube is $27\,cm^3$.
On square grid paper, draw the net of this cube.

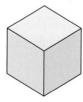

4 On square grid paper, draw the net for each cuboid.

a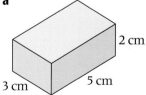

2 cm
5 cm
3 cm

b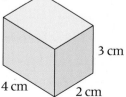

3 cm
4 cm   2 cm

c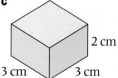

2 cm
3 cm   3 cm

d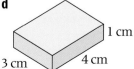

1 cm
3 cm   4 cm

e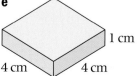

1 cm
4 cm   4 cm

Check out

You should now be able to:

- Calculate the circumference and area of circles
- Calculate the surface area and volume of cubes and cuboids
- Use 2D representations of 3D shapes
- Draw nets and show how they fold to make a solid
- Recognise congruent shapes
- Find interior and exterior angles in polygons

Worked exam question

a Calculate the area of a semicircle of radius 12 cm.

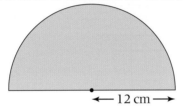

←— 12 cm —→

(2)

b The area of another semicircle is 40 000 cm².
Show clearly that this is equal to 4 m².

(2)

(AQA, 2009)

··

a

Area of circle	$= 3.14 \times 12^2$
	$= 452.16 \, \text{cm}^2$
Area of semicircle	$= 452.16 \div 2$
	$= 226.08 \, \text{cm}^2$

> Take the value of π to be 3.14 unless otherwise stated.

b

$$1 \, \text{m} = 100 \, \text{cm}$$
$$\text{So } 1 \, \text{m}^2 = 100 \, \text{cm} \times 100 \, \text{cm}$$
$$= 10\,000 \, \text{cm}^2$$
$$4 \, \text{m}^2 = 4 \times 10\,000$$
$$= 40\,000 \, \text{cm}^2$$
$$\text{So } 4 \, \text{m}^2 = 40\,000 \, \text{cm}^2$$

> You could use a sketch diagram to support your argument if you wish.

Exam questions

1 The diagram shows a square and two quarter circles.
The square has sides of 6 cm.
The radius of each circle is 3 cm.

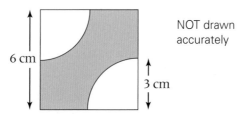

NOT drawn accurately

a Find the area of the shaded region. (3)

b Jane says that because a square has four lines of symmetry, the shaded area also has four lines of symmetry.

Is Jane correct?
Give a reason for your answer. (1)

(AQA, 2009)

2

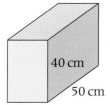

Diagram NOT accurately drawn

The diagram shows a cuboid.

The length of the cuboid is 50 cm.
The width of the cuboid is 10 cm.
The height of the cuboid is 40 cm.

Work out the volume of the cuboid. (2)

3

Diagram NOT accurately drawn

The radius of this circle is 5 cm.

Work out the circumference of the circle.
Give your answer correct to 2 decimal places. (2)

Rounding decimals

This spread will show you how to:

- Round numbers to a given number of decimal places
- Round numbers to a given number of significant figures
- Use approximation to estimate an answer

Keywords
Approximate
Decimal places
Estimate
Rounding
Significant figures

You can round a decimal number to a given accuracy.

To round 718.394 to 2 **decimal places**, look at the **thousandths** digit.

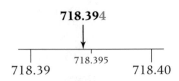

718.394

718.39   718.395   718.40

The **thousandths** digit is **4**, so round down to 718.39.

718.394 = 718.39 (to 2 decimal places).

You can also round numbers to a given number of **significant figures**.

- The first **non-zero digit** in a number is called the **1st significant figure** – it has the highest value in the number.

You only need to know how to round to 1 significant figure for your exam.

Example

Round 54.76 to 2 **significant figures.**

Look at the 3rd significant figure.

Tens	Units	•	tenths	hundredths
5	4	•	7	6

The **3rd significant** figure is **7**, so the number is rounded up to 55.

54.76 ≈ 55 (to 2 significant figures).

- When **rounding numbers** to a given degree of accuracy, look at the next digit. If it is 5 or more then round up, otherwise round down.

You can **estimate** the answer to a calculation by rounding the numbers.

Example

Estimate the answer to $\dfrac{6.23 \times 9.89}{18.7}$.

You can round each of the numbers to 1 significant figure.

$$\frac{6.23 \times 9.89}{18.7} \approx \frac{6 \times 10}{20} = \frac{60}{20} = 3$$

1 Round each of these numbers to the
  i nearest 10   **ii** nearest 100   **iii** nearest 1000.
  a 3487   **b** 3389   **c** 14 853 m
  d £57 792   **e** 92 638 kg   **f** £86 193
  g 3438.9   **h** 74 899.36

2 Round each of these numbers to the nearest whole number.
  a 3.738   **b** 28.77   **c** 468.63
  d 369.29   **e** 19.93   **f** 26.9992
  g 100.501   **h** 0.001

3 Round each of these numbers to the nearest
  i 3 dp   **ii** 2 dp   **iii** 1 dp.
  a 3.4472   **b** 8.9482   **c** 0.1284
  d 28.3872   **e** 17.9989   **f** 9.9999
  g 0.003 987   **h** 2785.5555

4 Round each of these numbers to the nearest
  i 3 sf   **ii** 2 sf   **iii** 1 sf.
  a 8.3728   **b** 18.82   **c** 35.84
  d 278.72   **e** 1.3949   **f** 3894.79
  g 0.008 372   **h** 2399.9   **i** 8.9858
  j 14.0306   **k** 1403.06   **l** 140 306

5 Write a suitable estimate for each of these calculations.
  In each case, clearly show how you estimated your answer.
  a 4.98×6.12 **b** $17.89 + 21.91$

  c $\dfrac{5.799 \times 3.1}{8.86}$ **d** $34.8183 - 9.8$

  e $\dfrac{32.91 \times 4.8}{3.1}$ **f** $\{9.8^2 + (9.2 - 0.438)\}^2$

C Booster

This spread will show you how to:

- Add and subtract fractions

Keywords

Cancel
Common
  denominator
Equivalent
Fraction

It is easy to add or subtract **fractions** when they have the same denominator.

   +      =

$\frac{3}{8}$ + $\frac{1}{8}$ = $\frac{4}{8}$

- You can add or subtract fractions with different denominators by first writing them as **equivalent** fractions with the same denominator.

Example

Calculate   **a** $\frac{3}{5} + \frac{1}{3}$ **b** $1\frac{3}{4} - \frac{5}{7}$

a $\frac{3}{5} + \frac{1}{3}$

$$\frac{3}{5} + \frac{1}{3} = \frac{9}{15} + \frac{5}{15}$$
$$= \frac{9+5}{15}$$
$$= \frac{14}{15}$$

$$\overset{\times 3}{\frac{3}{5}} = \underset{\times 3}{\frac{9}{15}} \qquad \overset{\times 5}{\frac{1}{3}} = \underset{\times 5}{\frac{5}{15}}$$

The lowest **common denominator** is the least common multiple of 5 and 3, which is 15.

b $1\frac{3}{4} - \frac{5}{7}$

Change the mixed number to an improper fraction:

$$1\frac{3}{4} = \frac{7}{4}$$
$$1\frac{3}{4} - \frac{5}{7} = \frac{7}{4} - \frac{5}{7}$$
$$= \frac{49}{28} - \frac{20}{28}$$
$$= \frac{49 - 20}{28}$$
$$= \frac{29}{28} = 1\frac{1}{28}$$

$$\overset{\times 7}{\frac{7}{4}} = \underset{\times 7}{\frac{49}{28}} \qquad \overset{\times 4}{\frac{5}{7}} = \underset{\times 4}{\frac{20}{28}}$$

The lowest common denominator is the least common multiple of 4 and 7, which is 28.

- You can compare and order fractions by writing them as **equivalent fractions** with the same denominator.

Example

Which is bigger: $\frac{3}{7}$ or $\frac{4}{9}$?

You need an equivalent fraction for both $\frac{3}{7}$ and $\frac{4}{9}$.

$\frac{27}{63} < \frac{28}{63}$ so $\frac{3}{7} < \frac{4}{9}$ $\frac{4}{9}$ is bigger.

$$\overset{\times 9}{\frac{3}{7}} = \underset{\times 9}{\frac{27}{63}} \qquad \overset{\times 7}{\frac{4}{9}} = \underset{\times 7}{\frac{28}{63}}$$

The common denominator of these equivalent fractions will be $7 \times 9 = 63$.

1 Work out

a $\frac{1}{3} + \frac{1}{3}$ **b** $\frac{3}{8} + \frac{2}{8}$ **c** $\frac{8}{11} - \frac{3}{11}$

d $\frac{8}{17} + \frac{5}{17}$ **e** $\frac{14}{23} - \frac{11}{23}$ **f** $\frac{5}{27} + \frac{8}{27}$

2 Work out each of these, leaving your answer in its simplest form.

a $\frac{2}{3} + \frac{1}{3}$ **b** $\frac{8}{9} - \frac{2}{9}$ **c** $\frac{8}{11} + \frac{5}{11}$ **d** $\frac{15}{13} - \frac{8}{13}$

e $\frac{14}{9} + \frac{1}{9}$ **f** $\frac{17}{12} - \frac{9}{12}$ **g** $1\frac{2}{3} + \frac{2}{3}$ **h** $4\frac{2}{7} - \frac{5}{7}$

3 Work out

a $\frac{1}{3} + \frac{1}{2}$ **b** $\frac{1}{4} + \frac{3}{5}$ **c** $\frac{3}{5} - \frac{1}{3}$ **d** $\frac{4}{5} - \frac{2}{7}$

e $\frac{5}{8} + \frac{1}{3}$ **f** $\frac{4}{9} + \frac{2}{5}$ **g** $\frac{7}{9} - \frac{2}{11}$ **h** $\frac{7}{15} + \frac{3}{7}$

> Write both fractions as equivalent fractions with the same denominator.

4 Work out each of these, leaving your answer in its simplest form as appropriate.

a $\frac{2}{5} - \frac{1}{15}$ **b** $\frac{1}{2} - \frac{1}{3}$ **c** $\frac{2}{5} + \frac{7}{20}$ **d** $\frac{1}{2} - \frac{1}{6}$

5 Work out each of these, leaving your answer in its simplest form.

a $\frac{4}{5} + \frac{2}{3}$ **b** $1\frac{1}{2} + \frac{3}{5}$ **c** $1\frac{1}{3} + 1\frac{1}{4}$ **d** $1\frac{2}{7} + \frac{3}{5}$

e $2\frac{2}{5} - \frac{1}{3}$ **f** $3\frac{3}{8} - 1\frac{1}{2}$ **g** $4\frac{1}{3} - 2\frac{3}{4}$ **h** $3\frac{4}{7} - 2\frac{8}{9}$

6 Work out each of these problems, leaving your answer in its simplest form.
  a Pete walked $3\frac{2}{3}$ miles before lunch and then a further $2\frac{1}{4}$ miles after lunch. How far did he walk altogether?
  b A bag weighs $2\frac{3}{16}$ lb when it is full. When empty the bag weighs $\frac{3}{8}$ lb. What is the weight of the contents of the bag?
  c Henry and Paula are eating peanuts. Henry has a full bag weighing $1\frac{3}{16}$ kg. Paula has a bag that weighs $\frac{4}{5}$ kg. What is the total mass of their two bags of peanuts?
  d Simon spent $\frac{2}{3}$ of his pocket money on a computer game. He spent $\frac{1}{5}$ of his pocket money on a ticket to the cinema. Work out the fraction of his pocket money that he had left.

7 Write if each of these statement are true or false.

a $\frac{9}{2} < 3$ **b** $\frac{17}{24} > \frac{5}{8}$ **c** $\frac{11}{12} > \frac{8}{9}$ **d** $\frac{2}{3} < \frac{5}{7}$

e $\frac{3}{5} > \frac{4}{7}$ **f** $\frac{26}{25} > \frac{16}{15}$ **g** $\frac{5}{4} < \frac{12}{7}$ **h** $\frac{7}{4} > \frac{12}{10}$

> $<$ means less than
> $>$ means more than.

This spread will show you how to:

● Express a number as the product of its prime factors
● Recognise and use the HCF and LCM of two numbers

Keywords
Factor
HCF
LCM
Prime factor
Prime number

● A **prime factor** is a prime number that is also a factor of another number.
  Factors of 28 are {1, 2, 4, 7, 14, 28}.   Prime factors are {2, 7}.

● Every whole number can be written as the product of its prime factors.

Here are two common methods to find prime factors.

Factor trees

Split the number into a **factor** pair. Continue splitting until you reach a prime factor.

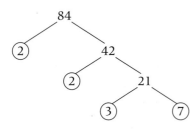

$84 = 2 \times 2 \times 3 \times 7 = 2^2 \times 3 \times 7$

Division by prime numbers

Divide the number by the smallest **prime number**. Repeat dividing by larger prime numbers until you reach a prime number.

2	84
2	42
3	21
⑦	

$84 = 2 \times 2 \times 3 \times 7 = 2^2 \times 3 \times 7$

● You can find the **highest common factor (HCF)**
  of a set of numbers by using prime factors.

For example, the HCF of 30 and 135:
$30 = 2 \times 3 \times 5 \qquad = 2 \times 3 \times 5$

$135 = 3 \times 3 \times 3 \times 5 = 3 \times 3 \times 3 \times 5$

$HCF = 3 \times 5 = 15$

2	30
3	15
	5

3	135
3	45
3	15
	5

● Write each number as the product of its prime factors.
● Pick out the common factors 3 and 5.
● Multiply these together to get the HCF.

● You can find the **least common multiple (LCM)**
  of a set of numbers by using prime factors.

For example, the LCM of 28 and 126:
$28 = 2^2 \times 7 = 2 \times 2 \times 7$

$126 = 2 \times 3^2 \times 7 = 2 \times 3 \times 3 \times 7$

$HCF = 2 \times 7 = 14$
$LCM = 2 \times 3 \times 3 \times 14 = 252$

2	28
2	14
	7

2	126
3	63
3	21
	7

● Write each number as the product of its prime factors.
● Pick out the common factors 2 and 7.
● Multiply these together to get the HCF (14).
● Multiply the HCF by the remaining factors – the remaining factors are 2, 3 and 3.

1 Work out the value of each of these expressions.

a 3×5^2 **b** $2^3 \times 5$ **c** $3^2 \times 7$

d $2^2 \times 3^2 \times 5$ **e** $3^2 \times 7^2$

2 Express these numbers as products of their prime factors.

a 18   **b** 24   **c** 40   **d** 39

e 48   **f** 82   **g** 100   **h** 144

i 180   **j** 315   **k** 444   **l** 1350

3 In each of these questions, Jack has been asked to write each of the numbers as the product of its prime factors.

i Mark his work and identify any errors he has made.

ii Correct any of Jack's mistakes.

a 126   **b** 210   **c** 221

2	126
3	63
3	21
	7

Answer: $126 = 2 \times 3^2$

2	210
3	105
3	21
	7

Answer: $2 \times 3^2 \times 7$

221

Answer: 221

4 The number 18 can be written as $2 \times 3 \times 3$.

You can say that 18 has three prime factors.

a Find three numbers with exactly three prime factors.

b Find five numbers with exactly four prime factors.

c Find four numbers between 100 and 300 with exactly five prime factors.

d Find a two-digit number with exactly six prime factors.

5 Find the HCF of

a 9 and 24   **b** 15 and 40   **c** 18 and 24

d 96 and 144   **e** 12, 15 and 18   **f** 425 and 816.

6 Find the LCM of

a 9 and 24   **b** 15 and 40   **c** 18 and 24

d 20 and 30   **e** 12, 15 and 18   **f** 48, 54 and 72.

7 Cancel these fractions to their simplest forms using the HCF of the numerator and denominator to help.

a $\frac{6}{8}$ **b** $\frac{12}{18}$ **c** $\frac{60}{96}$

d $\frac{36}{54}$ **e** $\frac{117}{169}$ **f** $\frac{26}{65}$

Keywords
Decrease
Increase
Percentage

This spread will show you how to:

● Calculate percentage increase and decrease using a range of methods

Percentages are used in real life to show how much an amount has increased or decreased.

● **Percentage increase** is often used in the contexts of wages and price inflation, also population increases.

● **Percentage decrease** is often used in the contexts of **depreciation** of goods, or sale discounts.

WORKERS DEMAND A 6% INCREASE

MARKET NEWS

Shares fall by record 35% over 6 months

Example

a Alan is paid £940 a month. His employer increases his wage by 3%. Calculate the new wage Alan is paid each month.

b A new car costs £19 490. After one year the car depreciates in value by 8.7%. What is the new value of the car?

....

a Calculate 3% of the amount.
Add to the original amount.
Increase in wage = 3% of £940 = $\frac{3}{100} \times$ £940

$$= \frac{3 \times 940}{100} = \frac{2820}{100}$$

Increase in wage = £28.20 per month
Alan's new wage = £940 + £28.20 = £968.20

b Calculate 8.7% of the amount.
Subtract from the original amount.
Depreciation = 8.7% of £19 490

$$= \frac{87}{100} \times £19\ 490$$

$$= 0.087 \times £19\ 490$$

Price reduction = £1695.63
New value of car = £19 490 − £1695.63 = £17 794.37

The percentage calculation has been worked out using a written method.

The percentage calculation has been worked out using a calculator.

Money saved in a bank account usually earns **interest**.

To calculate **compound interest** you work out the amount of money in the bank account at the end of each year. At the end of the next year the interest is paid on **all** the money.

You will not need to know about compound interest for the Foundation exam. However it is important to know about for your own financial responsibility.

Example

Ben puts £1200 into a bank account. Each year the bank pays a rate of interest of 10%. Work out the amount of money in Ben's bank account after 3 years.

Year 1 amount	Year 2 amount	Year 3 amount
= (100 + 10)% of £1200	= 110% of £1320	= 110% of £1452
= 110% × £1200	= 1.1 × £1320	= 1.1 × £1452
= 1.1 × £1200 = £1320	= £1452	= £1597.20

1 Calculate these amounts using an appropriate method.
   a 25% of 18 kg   **b** 20% of 51 m
   c 15% of 360°   **d** 2% of 37 cm
   e 65% of 510 ml   **f** 17.5% of 360°
   g 28% of 65 kg   **h** 31% of 277 kg
   i 3.6% of 154 kg   **j** 0.3% of 1320 m²

2 Calculate each of these using a mental or written method.
   a Increase £350 by 10%
   b Decrease 74 kg by 5%
   c Increase £524 by 5%
   d Decrease 756 km by 35%
   e Increase 960 kg by 17.5%

3 Calculate these. Give your answers to 2 decimal places as appropriate.
   a Increase £340 by 17%
   b Decrease 905 kg by 42%
   c Increase £1680 by 4.7%
   d Decrease 605 km by 0.9%
   e Increase $2990 by 14.5%

AO2 Functional Maths

4 These are the weekly wages of five employees at Suits-U clothing store. The manager has decided to increase all the employees' wages by 4%. Calculate the new wage of each employee.

Employee	Original wage	Increase	New wage
Hanif	£350	350 × 1.04 = ?	
Bonny	£285.50		
Wilf	£412.25		
Gary	£209.27		
Marielle	£198.64		

Give your answers to 2 decimal places as appropriate.

5 a Patricia puts £8000 into a bank account. Each year the bank pays a compound interest rate of 5%. Work out the amount of money in Patricia's bank account after 2 years.
   b Simone puts £12 500 into a savings account. Each year the building society pays a compound interest rate of 6%. Work out the amount of money in Simone's bank account after 2 years.
   c Antonio invests £3400 into a Super Saver account. Each year the account pays a compound interest rate of 6%. Work out the amount of money in Antonio's account after 3 years.

Compound interest will not appear in your exam. However it is a good example of maths in everyday life.

C Booster

Dividing in a given ratio

This spread will show you how to:

- Divide an amount in a given ratio
- Solve multi-step problems involving ratio

A **ratio** allows you to compare two amounts.
5 : 2 means 5 parts of one thing compared to 2 parts of another.
You can simplify a ratio, similar to how you simplify fractions.
10 : 15 = 2 : 3 (divide both sides of the ratio by 5)

You can divide a quantity in a given **ratio**.

Example

Sean and Patrick share £348 in the ratio 5 : 7.
How much money do they each receive?

....

Sean receives 5 parts for every 7 parts that Patrick receives.

Total number of parts = 5 + 7
                      = 12 parts
Each part   = £348 ÷ 12
                      = £29

Sean will receive 5 parts   = 5 × £29
                            = £145
Patrick will receive 7 parts = 7 × £29
                            = £203

Check your answer by adding up the two parts. They should add up to the amount being shared!
£145 ÷ £203 = £348

Some calculations involving ratio and **scale** need to be broken down into smaller steps.

Example

A model is made of a truck.
The length of the model is 28 centimetres.
The length of the real truck is 6.3 metres.
Work out the ratio of the length of the model to the length of the real truck.
Write your answer in the form 1 : n.

....

Step 1
Express the ratio in equal units.

Length of model : length of truck
        28 cm : 6.3 m
        28 cm : 630 cm
           28 : 630

Step 2
Express the ratio in the form 1 : n.

÷28 (28 : 630) ÷28
     1 : 22.5

The scale is 1 : 22.5.

When a ratio is expressed in different units, convert the measurements to the same unit.

1 Solve each of these problems.

  a The ratio of boys to girls in a class is 4 : 5. There are 12 boys in the class. How many girls are there?

  b In a metal alloy the ratio of aluminium to tin is 8 : 5. How much aluminium is needed to mix with 55 kg of tin?

  c The ratio of the number of purple flowers to the number of white flowers in a garden is 5 : 11. There are 132 white flowers. How many purple flowers are there?

  d The ratio of Key Stage 3 students to Key Stage 4 students in a school is 7 : 6. There are 588 Key Stage 3 students. How many Key Stage 4 students are there at the school?

2 **a** A map has a scale of 1 : 400. A distance in real life is 4.8 m. What is this distance on the map?

  b In a school the ratio of teachers to students is 1 : 22.5. If there are 990 students at the school, how many teachers are there?

  c The model of an aircraft is in the scale 1 : 32. If the real aircraft is 12.48 m long, how long is the model?

> Hint for part **a**:
> For every 4 boys, there are 5 girls.
> 8 boys → 10 girls
> 12 boys → ? girls

3 A map has a scale of 1 : 5000.

  a What is the distance in real life of a measurement of 6.5 cm on the map?

  b What is the distance on the map of a measurement of 30 m in real life?

4 Solve each of these problems.

  a Divide £90 in the ratio 3 : 7.

  b Divide 369 kg in the ratio 7 : 2.

  c Divide 103.2 tonnes in the ratio 5 : 3.

  d Divide 35.1 litres in the ratio 5 : 4.

  e Divide £36 in the ratio 1 : 2 : 3.

5 Solve each of these problems. Give your answers to 2 decimal places where appropriate.

  a Divide £75 in the ratio 8 : 7.

  b Divide £1000 in the ratio 7 : 13.

  c Divide 364 days in the ratio 5 : 2.

  d Divide 500 g in the ratio 2 : 5.

  e Divide 600 m in the ratio 5 : 9.

6 Simplify each of these ratios.

  a 4 : 2   **b** 3 : 9   **c** 21 : 14   **d** 18 : 16

  e 45 : 60   **f** 48 : 36   **g** 80 : 72   **h** 96 : 120

Expanding and factorising

This spread will show you how to:

- Multiply a single term over a bracket
- Take out common factors

Keywords
Brackets
Expand
Simplify

- You can multiply out brackets.
  You multiply each term inside the
  bracket by the term outside.

  $2(x + 4) = 2 \times x + 2 \times 4 = 2x + 8$

$2 \times 4 = 8$

$2 \times x = 2x$

In the picture,
there are normally
x cookies in each
pack.

Example

Expand each expression.
a $4(y + 3)$ **b** $2(3x + 1)$ **c** $n(n + 5)$

....

a $4(y + 3) = 4 \times y + 4 \times 3$
$\qquad\qquad = 4y + 12$

b $2(3x + 1) = 2 \times 3x + 2 \times 1$
$\qquad\qquad\quad = 6x + 2$

c $n(n + 5) = n \times n + 5 \times n$
$\qquad\qquad = n^2 + 5n$

Expand means
'multiply out'.

$n \times n = n^2$

To **simplify** expressions with brackets, expand the brackets and collect like terms.

Example

Simplify each of these.
a $2(p + 2) + 3p$ **b** $m(m + 2) + m$ **c** $3(x + 1) + 2(4x + 2)$

....

a $2(p + 2) + 3p = 2p + 4 + 3p$
$\qquad\qquad\qquad = 2p + 3p + 4$
$\qquad\qquad\qquad = 5p + 4$

b $m(m + 2) + m = m^2 + 2m + m$
$\qquad\qquad\qquad\quad = m^2 + 3m$

c $3(x + 1) + 2(4x + 2)$

$\qquad = 3x + 3 + 8x + 4 = 11x + 7$

Like terms have
the same power
of the same
letter.
m^2 and m are **not**
like terms.

- Factorising is the 'opposite' of expanding brackets.

- To factorise an expression, look for a **common factor** for all the terms.

A common factor
divides into all
the terms.

$$2(x + 4) \;\;\overset{\text{expand}}{\underset{\text{factorise}}{=}}\;\; 2x + 8$$

In number...
a factor is a number that exactly
divides into another number.

2, 3 and 4 are factors of 12.

In algebra...
a factor is a number or letter that
exactly divides into another term.

3 and $2x$ are factors of $6x$.

1 Expand the brackets in these expressions.
   a $3(m + 2)$ **b** $4(p + 6)$ **c** $2(x + 4)$ **d** $5(q + 1)$
   e $2(6 + n)$ **f** $3(2 + t)$ **g** $4(3 + s)$ **h** $2(4 + v)$

2 Expand these expressions.
   a $3(2q + 1)$ **b** $2(4m + 2)$ **c** $3(4x + 3)$ **d** $2(3k + 1)$
   e $5(2 + 2n)$ **f** $3(4 + 2p)$ **g** $4(1 + 3y)$ **h** $2(5 + 4z)$

3 At a pick-your-own farm, Lucy picks n apples.
   Mary picks 5 more apples than Lucy.
   a Write down, in terms of n, the number of apples Mary picks.

   Nat picks 3 times as many apples as Mary.
   b Write down, in terms of n, the number of apples Nat picks.

4 Expand and simplify each of these expressions.
   a $3(p + 3) + 2p$ **b** $2(m + 4) + 5m$ **c** $4(x + 1) - 2x$
   d $2(5 + k) + 3k$ **e** $4(2t + 3) + t - 2$ **f** $3(2r + 1) - 2r + 4$

5 On Monday a shop sells s DVDs.
   On Tuesday the shop sells 6 more DVDs than on Monday.
   a Write an expression for the number of DVDs it sells on Tuesday.

   On Wednesday the shop sells twice as many DVDs as on Tuesday.
   b Write an expression for the number of DVDs it sells on Wednesday.

   On Thursday the shop sells 7 more DVDs than on Wednesday.
   c Write an expression for the number of DVDs it sells on Thursday.

   Give your answer in its simplest form.

6 Find all the common factors of
   a $2x$ and 6   **b** $4y$ and 12   **c** 10 and $20j$ **d** 6 and $12p$
   e 9 and $6q$ **f** $6t$ and 4   **g** $4x$ and 10   **h** $24t$ and 8

> **Hint for 6a:**
> 2 and x are factors of 2x.
> 1, 2, 3 and 6 are factors of 6.
> 2 is the common factor of 2x and 6.

7 Find the highest common factor of
   a $3x$ and 9   **b** $12r$ and 10   **c** $6m$ and 8   **d** 4 and $4z$

8 Find the highest common factor of
   a y^2 and y **b** $4s^2$ and s **c** $7m$ and m^3 **d** $2y^2$ and $2y$

9 Factorise these expressions.
   a $2x + 10$ **b** $3y + 15$ **c** $8p - 4$ **d** $6 + 3m$
   e $5n + 5$ **f** $12 - 6t$ **g** $14 + 4k$ **h** $9z - 3$

A02 Functional Maths

C Booster

Intersection of two lines

This spread will show you how to:
- Plot graphs of functions in which y is given explicitly in terms of x

Keywords
Solution

A straight line graph is made up of an infinite number of points.

- All the points on a straight line **satisfy** the equation of the line.

- Where two straight lines cross, the coordinates satisfy the equations of both lines.

The lines $x = 4$ and $y = -1$ are drawn on this graph.

Every point on the line $x = 4$ has x-coordinate 4.
Every point on the line $y = -1$ has y-coordinate -1.

So the point where they cross is $(4, -1)$.

The point P satisfies both equations: $x = 4$ **and** $y = -1$. It has coordinates $(4, -1)$.

P is the **solution** to the equations $x = 4$ and $y = -1$.

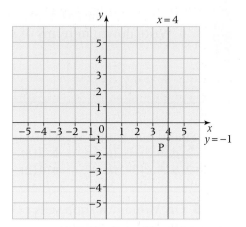

Example

a Draw the graphs of $y = x + 6$ and $y = 2x$ on the same pair of axes.
b Write the coordinates of the point where they cross.
c What can you say about this point?

....

a $y = x + 6$

x	−2	−1	0	1	2
y	4	5	6	7	8

$y = 2x$

x	−2	−1	0	1	2
y	−4	−2	0	2	4

b Graphs cross at $(6, 12)$
c $(6, 12)$ satisfies both equations.
$x = 6$ is the solution to $x + 6 = 12$ and $2x = 12$.

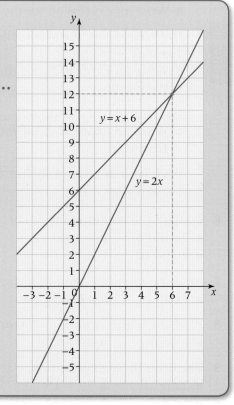

1 Write the coordinates of the points where these lines cross.
Draw graphs to check your answers.
　a $x = 2$ and $y = 3$
　b $x = -1$ and $y = -4$
　c $x = 3$ and $y = 7$
　d $x = -2$ and $y = -4$
　e $x = 7$ and $y = -2$
　f $y = 1$ and $x = 4$

2 For each pair of equations,
decide whether the lines
will cross and then draw the
graphs on a copy of this grid
to check your answers.
　a $y = 2x + 1$ and $y = 4x + 2$
　b $y = 3$ and $y = x + 1$
　c $y = 3x + 2$ and $y = 3x - 1$
　d $y = x$ and $y = -x$

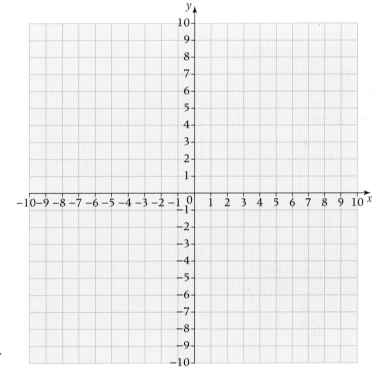

3 For each pair of lines from
question **2** that cross, write
the coordinates of the point
where the lines cross.

4 **a** Draw the graphs of
　　$y = -x + 2$ and $y = 2x - 1$
　　on the same axes.
　b Write the coordinates of
　　the point where the two
　　lines cross.
　c Does the point (1, 2) satisfy
　　both of these equations?
　　Explain how you know.

5 **a** Draw the graphs of $y = 2x - 4$ and $y = x - 1$ on the same axes.
　b Write the coordinates of the point where they cross.

6 **a** Draw the graphs of these two equations on the same axes.
　　　$x + 2y = 8$
　　　$x - y = 2$
　b Where the two lines cross, the x and y values satisfy both these
　　equations.
　　Write these x and y values.

C Booster

This spread will show you how to:
- Solve linear equations that require prior simplification of brackets and fractions

Keywords
Brackets
Expand

- To solve equations with the unknown on both sides and brackets
  - Expand the brackets
  - Use the balance method.

Example

Solve each equation.
a $2(y + 4) = 4y$
b $6r - 2 = 4(r + 3)$

$$
\begin{array}{ll}
\textbf{a} \quad 2(y + 4) = 4y & \text{Expand the brackets.} \\
\quad\quad 2y + 8 = 4y & \text{Subtract } 2y \text{ from both sides.} \\
\quad\quad\quad\quad 8 = 4y - 2y & \\
\quad\quad\quad\quad 8 = 2y & \text{Divide both sides by 2.} \\
\quad\quad\quad\quad 4 = y &
\end{array}
$$

$$
\begin{array}{ll}
\textbf{b} \quad\quad\quad 6r - 2 = 4(r + 3) & \\
\quad\quad\quad\quad 6r - 2 = 4r + 12 & \text{Subtract } 4r \text{ from both sides.} \\
6r - 4r - 2 = 4r - 4r + 12 & \\
\quad\quad\quad\quad 2r - 2 = 12 & \text{Add 2 to both sides.} \\
\quad\quad\quad\quad\quad 2r = 12 + 2 & \\
\quad\quad\quad\quad\quad 2r = 14 & \text{Divide both sides by 2.} \\
\quad\quad\quad\quad\quad\quad r = 7 &
\end{array}
$$

Example

Solve each equation.
a $\dfrac{x}{4} = -3$ **b** $\dfrac{x + 3}{2} = 5$

$$
\textbf{a} \quad \frac{x}{4} = -3 \qquad\qquad\qquad \textbf{b} \quad \frac{x + 3}{2} = 5
$$

$$
4 \times \frac{x}{4} = -3 \times 4 \qquad\qquad 2 \times \frac{x + 3}{2} = 5 \times 2
$$

$$
x = -12 \qquad\qquad\qquad\quad x + 3 = 10
$$

$$
\qquad\qquad\qquad\qquad\qquad\qquad\qquad x = 10 - 3
$$

$$
\qquad\qquad\qquad\qquad\qquad\qquad\qquad x = 7
$$

1 Solve these equations.
  a $2(r + 6) = 5r$ **b** $6(s - 3) = 12s$
  c $4(2t + 8) = 24t$ **d** $5(v - 1) = 6v$

2 Solve these equations.
  a $2(a + 5) = 7a - 5$ **b** $3(b - 2) = 5b - 2$
  c $2(c + 6) = 5c - 3$ **d** $3d + 8 = 2(d + 2)$

3 Solve these equations.
  a $3(2x - 4) = 7x - 18$ **b** $2(3y + 2) = 5y - 2$
  c $4(2z + 1) = 6z + 15$ **d** $-4(6m + 1) = -17m - 18$

4 Solve these equations.
  a $2(e + 3) = 4e - 1$ **b** $4f + 3 = 2(f + 2)$
  c $4(2g + 1) = 6g + 1$ **d** $3(2h + 3) = 5h + 8$

5 Solve these equations.
  a $\dfrac{x}{3} = 3$ **b** $\dfrac{m}{4} = -2$ **c** $\dfrac{-n}{3} = 6$ **d** $\dfrac{m}{5} = 4$

6 Find the value of the unknown in each of these equations.
  a $\dfrac{s}{3} + 5 = 8$ **b** $4 - \dfrac{t}{2} = 1$ **c** $\dfrac{u}{5} + 7 = 5$ **d** $16 = \dfrac{v}{4} + 13$

7 Solve these equations.
  a $\dfrac{2x}{3} + 5 = 9$ **b** $\dfrac{3y}{2} - 5 = 4$ **c** $3 - \dfrac{2z}{5} = -3$ **d** $\dfrac{3q}{2} + 5 = -7$

8 Solve these equations.
  a $\dfrac{x + 5}{3} = 2$ **b** $\dfrac{x - 3}{4} = 2$ **c** $\dfrac{x + 9}{2} = -4$ **d** $\dfrac{10 - x}{4} = 1$

9 I think of a number.
  I divide my number by 4 and add 6.
  a Write an expression for 'I divide my number by 4 and add 6'.
     Use n to represent the number.
  b My answer is 10.
     Using your expression from part **a**, write an equation to
     show this.
  c Solve your equation to find the number, n.

Expression
a = 10

This spread will show you how to:

- Generate and describe integer sequences using position-to-term definitions

Keywords
General term
*n*th term
Position-to-term

- A **position-to-term** rule links a term with its position in the sequence.

For example, the 4 times table: 4, 8, 12, 16, 20, 24, ... can be written as

1st term = T(1)	2nd term = T(2)	3rd term = T(3)	4th term = T(4)	5th term = T(5)	6th term = T(6)
4	8	12	16	20	24

$T(1) = 1 \times 4$
$T(2) = 2 \times 4$
$T(3) = 3 \times 4$
$T(10) = 10 \times 4$

The **general term** or ***n*th term** of the 4 times table is $T(n) = n \times 4$ or $4n$.

You can generate a sequence from the general term.

Example

Find the first three terms and the 10th term of the sequence with general term $3n + 2$.

....

1st term $3 \times 1 + 2 \rightarrow 5$
2nd $\quad 3 \times 2 + 2 \rightarrow 8$
3rd $\quad 3 \times 3 + 2 \rightarrow 11$
10th $\quad 3 \times 10 + 2 \rightarrow 32$

- To find the general term of a linear sequence:
  - work out the common difference
  - write the common difference as the coefficient of n
  - compare the terms in the sequence to the multiples of n

A linear sequence has an equal spacing between terms.

Example

Find the general term of the sequence
5, 8, 11, 14, 17 ...

....

The common difference is $+3$.
The nth term contains the term $3n$.
Compare the sequence to the multiples of 3:

3*n*	3	6	9	12	15
Term	5	8	11	14	17

Each term is 2 more than a multiple of 3.
The general term is $3n + 2$.

Check:
$n = 1 \rightarrow 3 + 2 = 5$
$n = 2 \rightarrow 6 + 2 = 8$
$n = 3 \rightarrow 9 + 2 = 11$
...

1 Find the first three terms and the 10th term of these sequences.

   a $5n + 1$ **b** $3n + 8$ **c** $8n - 4$ **d** $6n - 8$

   e $24 - 2n$ **f** $15 - 5n$ **g** $7n - 20$ **h** $4n - 6$

2 Copy and complete the table of results for each sequence.

   a $3n + 8$ **b** $6n - 15$

Term number	Term
1	11
2	
3	
5	
10	
n	$3n + 8$

Term number	Term
1	-9
2	
3	
5	
10	
n	$6n - 15$

3 Write the first five terms of the sequences with nth term

   a $n^2 + 4$ **b** $n^2 - 2$ **c** $2n^2$ **d** $12 - n^2$

4 **a** Find the common difference for the series 5, 9, 13, 17, 21, ...

   b Copy and complete this statement:

       The nth term contains the term $\square n$.

   c Copy and complete this table to show the sequence and the multiples of n.

Sequence				
$\square n$				

   d Compare the terms in the sequence to the multiples of n and write the general term for the sequence.

5 Follow the steps in question **4** to find the general terms for these sequences.

   a 11, 17, 23, 29, 35, ...   **b** 1, 10, 19, 28, 37, ...

   c 15, 22, 29, 36, 43, ...   **d** $-10, -6, -2, 2, 6, ...$

   e 20, 17, 14, 11, 8, ...   **f** 15, 11, 7, 3, -1, ...

   g 16, 8, 0, -8, -16, ...   **h** 31, 23, 15, 7, -1, ...

6 Find the nth term for each of these arithmetic sequences.

   a 7, 11, 15, 19, 23, ...   **b** $-6, -2, 2, 6, 10, ...$

   c 32, 23, 14, 5, -4, ...   **d** 15, 9, 3, -3, 9, ...

This spread will show you how to:
- Solve linear inequalities in one variable

Keywords
Greater than
Inequality
Less than
Solution set

- In an **equation**, the left-hand side equals the right-hand side.
- In an **inequality**, the left-hand and right-hand sides are not necessarily equal.

  An inequality usually has a range of values.

You use one of these signs to show the relationship between the two sides of an inequality.

<	**less than**	>	**greater than**
≤	less than or equal to	≥	greater than or equal to

You can show inequalities on a number line.

$x < 2$	x is less than 2	
$x > 2$	x is greater than 2	
$y ≤ 4$	y is less than or equal to 4	
$y ≥ 4$	y is greater than or equal to 4	

The open circle shows that 2 is not included.

The filled-in circle shows that 4 is included.

Inequalities can have more than one term, for example $3x + 4 < 19$.

You can solve an inequality to find a set of values for x.

Example

a Solve the inequality $3x + 4 < 19$
b Show the **solution set** on a number line.

....

a $3x + 4 < 19$
   $3x + 4 - 4 < 19 - 4$
      $3x < 15$
       $x < 5$

b

The solution set is $x < 5$.

Sometimes a letter is bounded by two inequalities.

Example

List the whole numbers that satisfy the inequality $-3 < x ≤ 2$.

....

$-3 < x$ means '-3 is less than x,' or 'x is greater than -3'.
$x ≤ 2$ means 'x is less than or equal to 2'.
The whole numbers that satisfy the inequality are $-2, -1, 0, 1, 2$.

1 Show these inequalities on a number line.

a $x < 1$ **b** $x \geqslant 1$ **c** $x \geqslant 5$ **d** $x < -2$

e $x < 1.5$ **f** $x > -4$ **g** $x \leqslant 3$ **h** $x \leqslant -1.5$

2 **a** If $x > 5$, what can you say about   **i** $2x$ **ii** $4x$?

     b If $y \leqslant 6$, write an inequality for   **i** $3y$ **ii** $5y$.

     c If $x \geqslant -4$, write an inequality for $5x$.

     d If $m < -3$, write an inequality for $6m$.

3 Solve these inequalities and show the solution sets on number lines.

     a $2x \leqslant 4$ **b** $2x < 10$ **c** $3x > -6$ **d** $4x \geqslant -16$

4 Match each inequality to a number line.

a    **i** $x < -3$

b 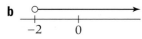   **ii** $x \leqslant 3$

c 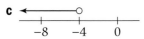   **iii** $x - 1 \leqslant -3$

d 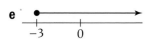   **iv** $x \geqslant -3$

e    **v** $x - 1 > -3$

f   **vi** $x + 2 < -2$

5 Copy and complete these inequalities.

     a If $3x + 2 > 11$ then $3x > \square$ and $x > \square$

     b If $7x - 4 > 31$ then $7x > \square$ and $x > \square$

     c If $2x + 9 \leqslant 11$ then $2x \leqslant \square$ and $x \leqslant \square$

     d If $5x - 3 \geqslant 12$ then $5x \geqslant \square$ and $x \geqslant \square$

6 Solve each of these inequalities.
Show each solution on a number line.

     a $x + 7 \leqslant 12$ **b** $x - 2 \geqslant 4$ **c** $3x + 5 \geqslant 11$ **d** $2x - 5 < 3$

     e $5x + 1 \geqslant -4$ **f** $6x - 2 \leqslant 16$ **g** $3x + 2 > 11$ **h** $2x - 9 \leqslant -5$

7 List the whole numbers that satisfy each of these inequalities.

     a $-3 \leqslant x < 2$ **b** $-2 < x \leqslant 3$ **c** $-1 \leqslant x \leqslant 4$

     d $0 < x \leqslant 5$ **e** $-3 \leqslant x \leqslant -1$ **f** $0 < x < 2$

This spread will show you how to:

- Use the formula to find the area of any parallelogram
- Use formulae of rectangles, triangles and parallelograms to find the area of any trapezium

Keywords
Area
Base
Parallelogram
Perpendicular
  height
Trapezium

You can find the formula for the **area** of any **parallelogram**.

For this parallelogram ...

cut off one triangle ...

and fit it on the other end ... to make a rectangle.

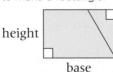

height

base

- Area of parallelogram = **base × perpendicular height.**

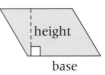

height

base

The height must be perpendicular to the base.

You can find the formula for the area of any **trapezium**.

You can fit two **congruent** trapeziums together to make a parallelogram.

Congruent means identical.

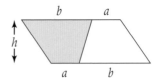

The base of the parallelogram is $a + b$ and the height is h.
Area of parallelogram $= (a + b) \times h$
Area of trapezium = half area of parallelogram.

- Area of trapezium $= \frac{1}{2} \times (a + b) \times h$

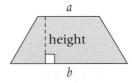

a

height

b

The height is the perpendicular distance between the parallel sides.

Example

Calculate the area of each shape.

a

3 cm

5 cm

b

3 cm

4 cm

7 cm

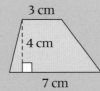

....

a Area of parallelogram $= 5 \times 3$
         $= 15\,\text{cm}^2$

b Area of trapezium $= \frac{1}{2}(3 + 7) \times 4$
         $= 5 \times 4$
         $= 20\,\text{cm}^2$

1 Calculate the area of each parallelogram.

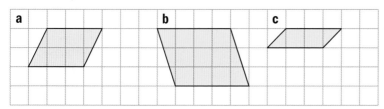

Give your answers in square units.

2 Calculate the area of each trapezium.

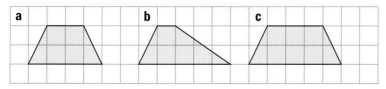

3 Calculate the area of each parallelogram. State the units of your answers.

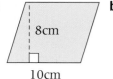 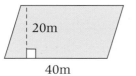 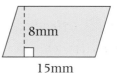 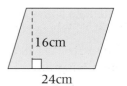

4 Calculate the area of each trapezium. State the units of your answers.

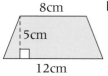 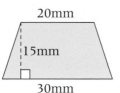 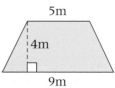 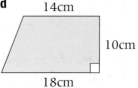

5 The areas of these shapes is given. Calculate the unknown lengths.

   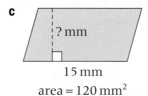 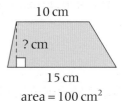

6 a Calculate the area of this shape using the formula for the area of a trapezium.
  b Calculate the area by adding the areas of the triangles and the square.

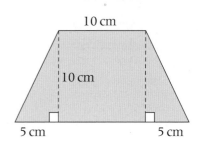

This spread will show you how to:
• Use parallel lines and alternate angles

Keywords
Alternate
Corresponding
Parallel
Vertically
  opposite

When two lines cross, four angles are formed.

• **Vertically opposite** angles are equal.

When a line crosses two **parallel** lines, eight angles are formed.

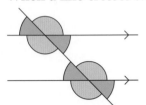

The four red **acute** angles are equal.

The four purple **obtuse** angles are equal.

Acute + obtuse = 180°

Parallel lines are
always the same
distance apart.

An acute angle is
less than 90°.
An obtuse angle is
more than 90° but
less than 180°.

• **Alternate** angles are equal.

• **Corresponding** angles are equal.

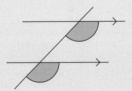

Example

Find the unknown angles in these diagrams.
Give reasons for your answers.

a 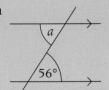   **b** 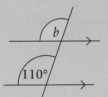   **c**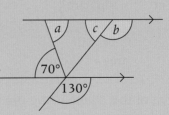

....

a $a = 56°$ **b** $b = 110°$ **c** $a = 70°$ (alternate angles)
  (alternate angles)   (corresponding angles) $b = 130°$ (corresponding angles)
                                                  $c = 180° - 130°$
                                                    $= 50°$ (angles on straight
                                                                        line add to 180°)

430

1 Calculate the size of the angles marked by a letter in each diagram.
Give a reason for each answer.

The diagrams are not drawn to scale.

a

b

c

d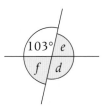

e

2 Find the value of each angle marked with a letter.
Give a reason for each answer.

a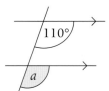

b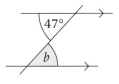

c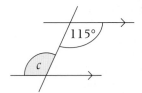

d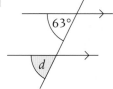

e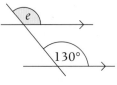

f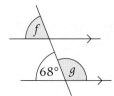

g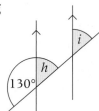

h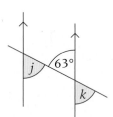

i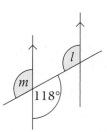

3 Find the value of each angle marked with a letter. Give a reason in each case.

a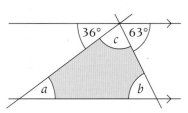

b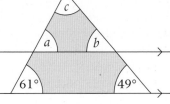

c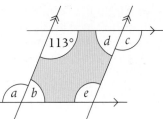

+13 **Similar shapes**

This spread will show you how to:

● Identify the scale factor of an enlargement as a ratio of the lengths

Keywords
Enlargement
Scale factor
Similar

● In an **enlargement**, the object and the image are **similar**,
 – the angles stay the same
 – the lengths increase in proportion.

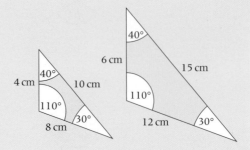

You use corresponding lengths to find the **scale factor**.

● Scale factor = $\dfrac{\text{length of image}}{\text{lengh of object}}$.

Example

These triangles are similar.
Find the length x.

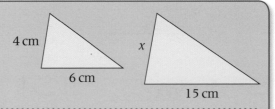

The scale factor is $\dfrac{15}{6} = 15 \div 6 = 2.5$
$x = 4\,\text{cm} \times 2.5 = 10\,\text{cm}$

Example

a Show that triangle ABE is similar to triangle ACD.
b Calculate the value of x.

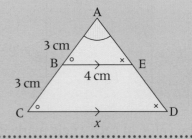

a Angle B = angle C   (corresponding angles are equal)
 Angle E = angle D   (corresponding angles are equal)
 Angle A is common to both triangles.
 So ΔABE and ΔACD are similar.

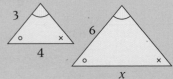

b The scale factor is $6 \div 3 = 2$
 $x = 4\,\text{cm} \times 2 = 8\,\text{cm}$

Similar shapes have the same angles but are different sizes.

1 In each question, the two triangles are similar.
Find the value of the unknown angles.

a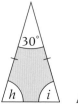

b

> Angles in a triangle add to 180°.

c

d

2 Which of these rectangles are similar to the green rectangle?

For the ones that are similar, give the scale factor of the enlargement.

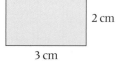
2 cm
3 cm

a
4 cm
6 cm

b
10 cm
15 cm

c
4 cm
5 cm

d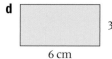
3 cm
6 cm

e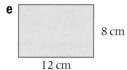
8 cm
12 cm

f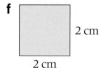
2 cm
2 cm

3 In each question, the two triangles are similar. Calculate the scale factor of the enlargement and the unknown length.

a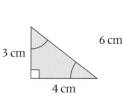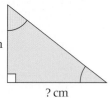
3 cm
4 cm
6 cm
? cm

b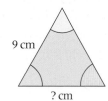
3 cm
4 cm
9 cm
? cm

4 (**Challenge**) Calculate the value of each unknown length.

a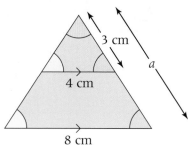
3 cm
4 cm
8 cm
a

b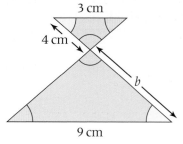
3 cm
4 cm
9 cm
b

> This type of question is unlikely to appear in the Foundation tier exams.

This spread will show you how to:
- Calculate the midpoint of the line AB

Keywords
Coordinates
Line
Midpoint

- The **midpoint M** of a line **AB** is halfway along it.

M is the midpoint.

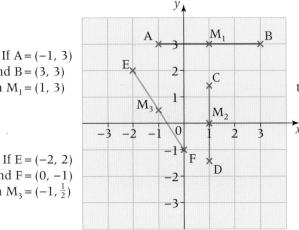

If A = (−1, 3)
and B = (3, 3)
then M_1 = (1, 3)

If C = $(1, 1\frac{1}{2})$
and D = $(1, -1\frac{1}{2})$
then M_2 = (1, 0)

If E = (−2, 2)
and F = (0, −1)
then M_3 = $(-1, \frac{1}{2})$

- If **A** = (x_1, y_1) **and B** = (x_2, y_2) **then M** = $\left(\dfrac{x_1 + x_2}{2}, \dfrac{y_1 + y_2}{2}\right)$.

The midpoint of AB is the mean of the **coordinates** of points A and B.

Example

Calculate the coordinates of the midpoint between the points
a (7, 1) and (−3, 5)
b (4, −1) and (2, −2)

....

a (7, 1) = (x_1, y_1) and (−3, 5) = (x_2, y_2)

Midpoint = $\left(\dfrac{7 + -3}{2}, \dfrac{1 + 5}{2}\right)$

= $\left(\dfrac{4}{2}, \dfrac{6}{2}\right)$

= (2, 3)

b (4, −1) = (x_1, y_1) and (2, −2) = (x_2, y_2)

Midpoint = $\left(\dfrac{4 + 2}{2}, \dfrac{-1 - 2}{2}\right)$

= $\left(\dfrac{6}{2}, \dfrac{-3}{2}\right)$

= $(3, -1\frac{1}{2})$

1 a Draw the points A(1, 3) and B(5, 1) on a copy of the grid.

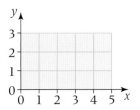

  b M is the midpoint of the line AB.
     Find the coordinates of the point M.

2 Calculate the coordinates of the
   midpoint between the points
   a (3, 1) and (3, 5)
   b (0, 4) and (4, 4)
   c (2, −2) and (2, 4)
   d (3, 1) and (7, 7)
   e (−2, −1) and (6, 7)
   Use a copy of the grid to help you.

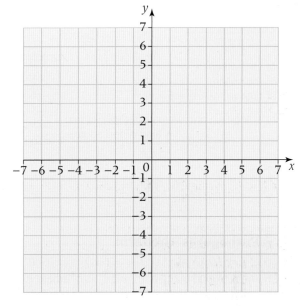

3 The point (3, 4) is the midpoint between (x, 6) and (1, y).
   Find the values of x and y.

4 The point $(1\frac{1}{2}, 5\frac{1}{2})$ is the midpoint between (x, 4) and (2, y).
   Find the values of x and y.

5 The point (0, 2) is the midpoint between (x, 6) and (−4, y).
   Find the values of x and y.

6 The coordinates (−1, 2), (−3, 0), (−1, −2) and (1, 0) are the
   midpoints of each side of a square.
   a Find the coordinates of the vertices of the square.
   b Find the area of the square.

A03 **Problem**

This spread will show you how to:

● Understand, recall and use Pythagoras' theorem

Keywords
Hypotenuse
Pythagoras'
theorem
Right-angled
triangle
Square
Square root

The longest side of a **right-angled triangle** is called the **hypotenuse**.
The hypotenuse is always opposite the right angle.

hypotenuse

This is a right-angled triangle.

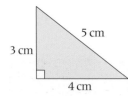

5 cm

3 cm

4 cm

Draw the **squares** on each side.

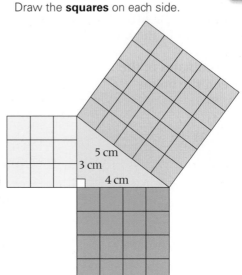

5 cm
3 cm
4 cm

Area of yellow square $= 3 \times 3 = 9\,cm^2$
Area of red square $= 4 \times 4 = 16\,cm^2$
Area of orange square $= 5 \times 5 = 25\,cm^2$

Area of orange square = area of yellow square
            + area of red square.

This is **Pythagoras' theorem**.

a
c
b

● In a right-angled triangle, $c^2 = a^2 + b^2$ where c is the hypotenuse.

Example

Calculate the unknown lengths in these triangles.

a

c
5 cm
12 cm

b
1.5 m
c
2 m

• •

a Label the sides.

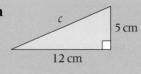

169

c b 5 cm
a   25
12 cm

144

$c^2 = a^2 + b^2$
$c^2 = 5^2 + 12^2$
$c^2 = 25 + 144$
$c^2 = 169$
$c = \sqrt{169} = 13\,cm$

b Label the sides.

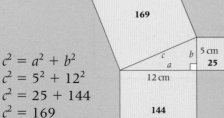

6.25

2.25
1.5 m   b c

a
2 m

4

$c^2 = 1.5^2 + 2^2$
$c^2 = 2.25 + 4$
$c^2 = 6.25$
$c = \sqrt{6.25} = 2.5\,cm$

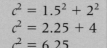

$\sqrt{}$ means
square root.

$\sqrt{169} = 13$
because
$13 \times 13 = 169$.

1 Calculate the area of these squares. State the units of your answers.

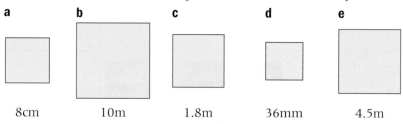

a   b   c   d   e

8cm   10m   1.8m   36mm   4.5m

2 Calculate the length of a side of these squares.
State the units of your answers.

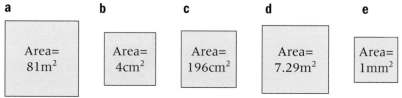

a   b   c   d   e

Area= 81m²   Area= 4cm²   Area= 196cm²   Area= 7.29m²   Area= 1mm²

3 Calculate the unknown area for these right-angled triangles.

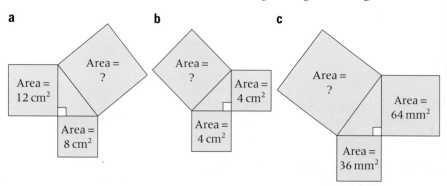

a   b   c

a: Area = ? ; Area = 12 cm² ; Area = 8 cm²

b: Area = ? ; Area = 4 cm² ; Area = 4 cm²

c: Area = ? ; Area = 64 mm² ; Area = 36 mm²

DID YOU KNOW?

Pythagoras was a Greek mathematician most famous for his theorem, who taught his students that 'all things are numbers'.

C Booster

4 Calculate the length of the hypotenuse in these right-angled triangles. State the units of your answers.

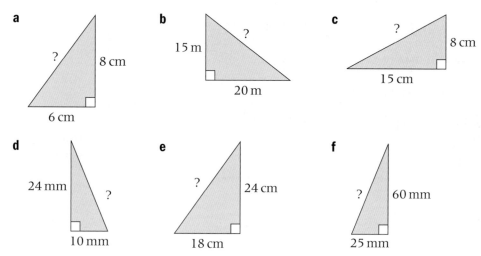

a   ? , 8 cm , 6 cm

b   15 m , ? , 20 m

c   ? , 8 cm , 15 cm

d   24 mm , ? , 10 mm

e   ? , 24 cm , 18 cm

f   ? , 60 mm , 25 mm

This spread will show you how to:
- Identify different mutually exclusive outcomes
- Know that the sum of the probabilities of all the outcomes is 1

Keywords
Mutually
  exclusive
Outcomes

The possible **outcomes** when a dice is rolled are 1, 2, 3, 4, 5, 6.

These outcomes are **mutually exclusive** because if you get one outcome, you cannot get another one.

The probability of rolling a 4 $= \frac{1}{6}$

The probability of rolling a 5 $= \frac{1}{6}$

The probability of rolling a 4 **or** a 5 $= \frac{2}{6}$

Notice that

P(4 or 5) = P(4) + P(5)

$$\frac{2}{6} = \frac{1}{6} + \frac{1}{6}$$

$P(4) = \frac{1}{6}$

$P(5) = \frac{1}{6}$

Or means either of the outcomes 4 or 5.

Example

A spinner is made from a regular pentagon and numbered from 1 to 5. Calculate

a P(3)   **b** P(3 or 4)   **c** P(3 or an odd number)

....

a There is one 3. There are 5 possible outcomes. P(3) $= \frac{1}{5}$

b P(3) $= \frac{1}{5}$ P(4) $= \frac{1}{5}$
The outcomes are mutually exclusive and so
P(3 or 4) $= \frac{1}{5} + \frac{1}{5}$
$= \frac{2}{5}$

c P(3) $= \frac{1}{5}$ P(odd) $= \frac{3}{5}$

The events are not mutually exclusive so you can't just add their probabilities.
A list of the five possible outcomes is

$$\binom{1}{\text{odd}} \quad \binom{2}{\text{even}} \quad \binom{3}{\text{odd}} \quad \binom{4}{\text{even}} \quad \binom{5}{\text{odd}}$$

P(3 or an odd number) $= \frac{3}{5}$

There are three outcomes that are OK.

1 Events are mutually exclusive if they cannot occur at the same time.
State if these events are mutually exclusive.
a spinning a Head and spinning a Tail with a coin
b rolling a 2 and rolling a 3 with a dice
c rolling a 2 and rolling an even number with a dice
d rolling a 2 and rolling an odd number with a dice
e rolling a 2 and rolling a prime number with a dice
f winning and losing a game of chess
g sunny and rainy weather
h taking out a red ball and taking out a blue ball, when taking out
one ball from a bag.

2 This is a net of a tetrahedral dice. The dice is made and
rolled. What is the probability of rolling
a a 3
b a 2
c a 2 or a 3?

3 A bag contains 4 red discs, 5 blue discs and 1 white disc.
One disc is taken out.
Calculate the probability that the disc is
a red
b blue
c white
d red or white
e blue or white
f red or blue or white.

4 Five names are written on cards and placed in a bag.
One name is taken out of the bag at random.
Calculate the probability that
a the first letter on the card is H
b the first letter on the card is G
c the first letter on the card is H or G
d the card has 5 letters written on it
e the card has 5 or 6 letters written on it.

This spread will show you how to:

- Understand and use relative frequency
- Compare experimental data and theoretical probabilities

Keywords

Biased
Equally likely
Estimate
Experiment
Fair
Relative
 frequency
Trial

- A dice is **fair** if the numbers are all **equally likely** to be rolled.
  You would normally expect a dice to be fair, as each face is identical.
- A spinner is **biased** if the colours are **NOT all equally likely to happen**.
  This spinner is not fair as the size and shape of each colour are
  not identical.

It is not always possible to calculate the theoretical probability.

- You can **estimate** the probability from experiments.

Example

Sam knows the probability of a Head when spinning a coin should be $\frac{1}{2}$ (or 0.5).
She thinks the coin is biased and so she spins the coin
50 times. The results are shown in the frequency table.

	Frequency
Head	35
Tail	15

a Estimate the probability of getting a Head when
 spinning the coin.
b Do you think the coin is biased? Explain your answer.

••

a Sam got a Head on 35 out of 50 occasions.
 Estimated probability of getting a Head $= \frac{35}{50} = \frac{7}{10} = 0.7$

b The spinner could be biased as 0.7 is significantly larger than 0.5. However, Sam
 needs to spin the coin a lot more times before she can make the decision.

- Estimated probability is called the **relative frequency**.

Each spin of the
coin is called a
trial.

In the example, if
Sam calculated the
relative frequency
of getting a Head
after each spin, she
could graph the
results.

Highest relative
frequency is 1.

Lowest relative
frequency is 0.

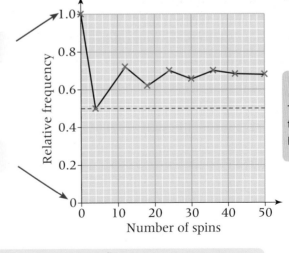

$P(Head) = \frac{1}{2}$
$= 0.5$
This is the
theoretical
probability of
spinning a Head.

- The estimated probability becomes more reliable as you increase the number of trials.

1 The colours of 50 cars are recorded. The colours are shown.

Blue	Red	Other	Silver	Blue	Red	Silver	Silver	Blue
Other	Red	Silver	Silver	Blue	Red	Red	Other	Silver
Silver	Red	Red	Silver	Silver	Blue	Blue	Silver	Silver
Red	Red	Other	Blue	Red	Red	Other	Red	Red
Red	Silver	Blue	Blue	Blue	Other	Silver	Other	Other
Other	Silver	Red	Red	Blue				

a Copy and complete the frequency chart to
   show the 50 colours.
b State the modal colour.
c Give an estimate of the probability that
   the next car will be
   i blue   **ii** red   **iii** silver.

Colour	Tally	Frequency
Blue		
Red		
Silver		
Other		

2 A spinner is made from a regular pentagon.
The scores are recorded

1	2	3	4	3	5	1	2
5	4	2	1	3	1	5	4
2	2	3	1	4	5	4	2
3	1	2	2	4	4	5	5
1	2	3	4	2	4	1	1

a Draw a frequency chart to show the scores.
b State the modal score.
c How many times is the spinner spun?
d Estimate the probability of scoring
   i a 1   **ii** a 2   **iii** a 3   **iv** a 4   **v** a 5.
e If the spinner is fair, how many times would you expect to spin a 3
   from 100 spins?

3 There are 10 coloured balls in a bag.
One ball is taken out and then replaced in the bag.
The colours of the balls are shown in the frequency table.

Colour	Red	Green	Blue
Frequency	9	14	27

a How many times was a ball taken out of the bag?
b Estimate the probability of taking out
   i a red ball   **ii** a green ball   **iii** a blue ball.
c How many balls of each colour do you think are in the bag?
d How could you improve this guess?

This spread will show you how to:

- Use a data collection sheet for discrete data
- Understand and use frequency tables

Keywords

Data
Data collection
  sheet
Frequency table
Tally chart

- You can collect data using a **data collection sheet**.

  This one is a **tally chart**.

Coin face	Tally	Frequency
Head	ⵜⵜ ⵜⵜ ⵜⵜⵜ	13
Tail	ⵜⵜ ⵜⵜ ⵜⵜ	12

ⵜⵜ = 5

Data can also be shown using a **frequency table**.

Example

The number of televisions in each house in my street is shown in the frequency table.

Number of TVs	Number of houses
0	1
1	5
2	12
3	9
4	1

a Calculate the number of houses in my street.

b Calculate the total number of televisions in my street.

c Calculate the mean number of televisions per house.

••

The numbers in the table are:

0, 1, 1, 1, 1, 1, 2, 2, 2, 2, 2, 2, 2, 2,
2, 2, 2, 2, 3, 3, 3, 3, 3, 3, 3, 3, 3, 4

Add an extra column to the table

TVs	Houses	TVs × Houses
0	1	$0 \times 1 = 0$
1	5	$1 \times 5 = 5$
2	12	$2 \times 12 = 24$
3	9	$3 \times 9 = 27$
4	1	$4 \times 1 = 4$

a $1 + 5 + 12 + 9 + 1 = 28$ houses

b $0 + 5 + 24 + 27 + 4 = 60$ televisions

c $60 \div 28 = 2\frac{1}{7}$ televisions per house.

1 a Copy and complete the tally chart to find the frequency of the vowels a, e, i, o, u in this sentence.
  b Which vowel occurs the most often?
  c Which vowel occurs the least often?
  d Calculate the total number of vowels in the sentence.
  e Find a paragraph of writing in a newspaper and complete a similar tally chart.

Vowel	Tally	Frequency
a		
e		
i		
o		
u		

2 Rainfall, measured in millimetres, is recorded daily for the month of April.

4 2 1 0 0 1 2 2 3 5
7 8 5 3 3 2 0 0 0 1
2 3 2 4 6 7 8 8 1 2

  a Copy and complete the tally chart to show this information.
  b State the number of completely dry days in April.
  c Calculate the total amount of rain to fall throughout April. State the units of your answer.

Rainfall (mm)	Tally	Number of days
0		
1		
2		
3		
4		
5		
6		
7		
8		

3 Nails can be bought in bags.
There are approximately 20 nails in each bag.
The numbers of nails in 40 bags are recorded.

19 20 19 21 20 20 20 21
22 19 19 19 21 20 20 21
19 21 21 22 20 19 20 21
20 20 21 21 20 20 22 21
19 19 20 20 21 20 20 20

  a Copy and complete the tally chart to show this information.
  b Calculate the total number of nails in all 40 bags.

NAILS

Approximately 20 nails in this bag

Number of nails	Tally	Number of bags
19		
20		
21		
22		

4 Sophie did a survey to find the number of books being reed by the students in her class. The results are shown in the frequency table.
  a Calculate the number of students in Sophie's class.
  b Calculate the total number of books being read by the whole class.
  c Calculate the mean number of books for each student.

Number of CDs	Number of students
0	1
1	8
2	6
3	8
4	2
5	3

This spread will show you how to:

- Draw and use scatter graphs, and compare two data sets
- Understand correlation and use lines of best fit

You can use a **scatter graph** to compare two sets of data, for example, height and weight.

- The data is collected in pairs and plotted as coordinates.
- If the points lie roughly in a straight line, there is a **linear relationship** or **correlation** between the two **variables**.

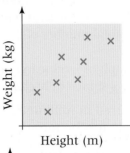

The data can be discrete or continuous.

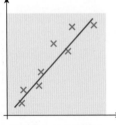
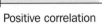

Positive correlation

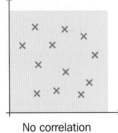

No correlation

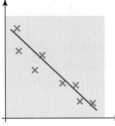

Negative correlation

Plotted points are not joined on a scatter diagram.

The straight line is the **line of best fit**.

The correlation is strong if the points are close to the line of best fit.

Example

The exam results (%) for Paper 1 and Paper 2 for 11 students are shown.

Paper 1	56	72	50	24	44	80	68	48	60	36	20
Paper 2	44	64	40	20	36	64	56	36	50	24	80

a Draw a scatter graph and line of best fit.

b Describe the relationship between the Paper 1 results and Paper 2 results.

c Identify a rogue value and describe how this student performed in the papers.

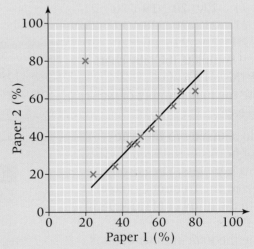

a Plot the exam marks as coordinates. The line of best fit should be close to all the points, with approximately the same number of crosses on either side of the line.

b Students who did well on Paper 1 did well on Paper 2. Students who did not do well on Paper 1 did not do well on Paper 2 either.

c There is a rogue value at (20, 80). This student performed badly in Paper 1 but exceedingly well in Paper 2.

1 Describe the type of correlation for each scatter graph.

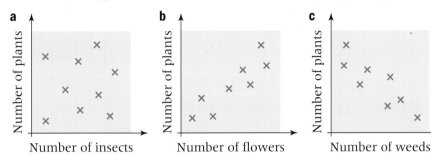

2 The table shows the amount of water used to water plants and the daily maximum temperature.

Water (litres)	25	26	31	24	45	40	5	13	18	28
Maximum temperature (°C)	24	21	25	19	30	28	15	18	20	27

a Copy and complete the scatter graph for this information.

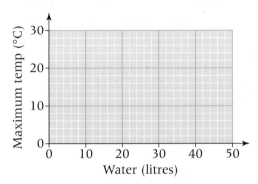

b State the type of correlation shown in the scatter graph.
c Copy and complete these sentences:
  i As the temperatures increases, the amount of water used _____.
  ii As the temperature decreases, the amount of water used _____.

3 The times taken, in minutes, to run a mile and the shoe sizes of ten athletes are shown in the table.

Shoe size	10	$7\frac{1}{2}$	5	9	6	$8\frac{1}{2}$	$7\frac{1}{2}$	$6\frac{1}{2}$	8	7
Time (mins)	9	8	8	7	5	13	15	12	5	6

a Draw a scatter graph to show this information.
  Use 2 cm to represent 1 shoe size on the horizontal axis.
  Use 2 cm to represent 5 minutes on the vertical axis.
b State the type of correlation shown in the scatter graph.
c Describe, in words, any relationship that the graph shows.

This spread will show you how to:

- Gather data from secondary sources
- Use effective methods for random sampling
- Identify sources of bias and plan to minimise it

- A **database** is an organised collection of data, especially in a form that can be used by a computer.

An example might be the records of the Year 11 students in a school.
You can sort a computer database
- alphabetically
- numerically.

You can sort using any or several of the columns (fields).

Number	Surname	Forename	Form	Gender
0001	Smith	Thomas	10E	Male
0002	Jones	Michaela	10B	Female
0003	Chapham	Leah	10A	Female
0004	Clark	Alan	10B	Male

This database has been sorted by number.

Sometimes there is too much data in a database to process all the data, and so a **random sample** is used.

- In a random sample, each person or item must be **equally likely** to be chosen.

If each person is not equally likely to be chosen, the sample is **biased**.

Example

Describe a method to choose a random sample of 30 students from a year group of 120 students.

....

- Number each student from 1 to 120.
- Generate 30 random numbers, by either
  - picking 30 numbers from a bag of 120, numbered 1 to 120, or
  - using the RAN# key on a calculator.
- You can generate random numbers on a calculator using the random function. RAN# generates random numbers from 0.000 to 0.999.
- You can generate a random number from, say, 1 to 120 by using 120 × RAN#.

Use the first three digits of the display.

A02 Functional Maths

1 Sanjit wants to buy a laptop. He creates a database of the 10 laptops he is considering buying.

Laptop number	Speed of processor	RAM memory	Size of hard drive	Screen size	Warranty	Cost
1	2.16 GHz	1 GB	120 GB	15.4″	No	£275
2	2.0 GHz	2 GB	160 GB	14.1″	1 year	£500
3	1.6 GHz	1 GB	120 GB	8.9″	1 year	£220
4	1.8 GHz	2 GB	120 GB	17″	1 year	£350
5	2.0 GHz	2 GB	64 GB	12.1″	3 years	£600
6	2.0 GHz	2 GB	160 GB	15.4″	2 years	£310
7	2.16 GHz	1 GB	120 GB	15.4″	3 years	£345
8	2.0 GHz	4 GB	320 GB	15.4″	3 years	£437
9	1.8 GHz	2 GB	160 GB	15.4″	1 year	£402
10	2.53 GHz	5 GB	500 GB	15.6″	No	£549

a Write down the costs of the laptops in order of price, smallest first.
b Write down the speeds of the processors in order of size, smallest first.
c Which laptop has the smallest processor speed?
d Which laptop has the largest RAM memory?
e List the laptops that have
  i a screen size of 15″ or more
  ii at least 160 GB of hard drive memory
  iii a 2-year or 3-year warranty.
f Sanjit wants a laptop with a screen size of 15″ or more, at least 160 GB of hard drive memory and one with a 2- or 3-year warranty. Which laptop is the cheapest option?

2 A class of 30 students decide to elect a class representative by a random process. State whether these methods of selection are random or biased. Give a reason for each answer.
  a Arrange the class list into alphabetical order and select the first name on the list.
  b Arrange the class list into alphabetical order and select the last name on the list.
  c Put the names of the students on cards of equal size. Put the cards into a bag and pick out one card.
  d Arrange the students in order of height and select the smallest student.
  e Hide a gold star in the classroom, and select the student who finds the star.
  f Number the students from 1 to 30. Roll a dice and select the student with that number.
  g Number the students from 1 to 30. Use a calculator to find 30 × RAN# and take the first two digits on the display.

C Booster

GCSE formulae

In your AQA GCSE examinations you will be given a formula sheet like the blue panel below.

Area of a trapezium $= \frac{1}{2}(a + b)h$

Volume of prism = area of cross section × length

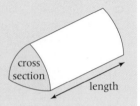

Here are some other formulae that you should learn.
These will not be given in your exams.

Area of a rectangle = length × width

Area of a triangle $= \frac{1}{2} \times$ base × height

Area of a parallelogram = base × perpendicular height

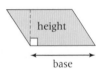

Area of a circle $= \pi r^2$

Circumference of a circle $= \pi d = 2\pi r$

Volume of a cuboid = length × width × height

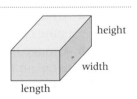

Volume of a cylinder = area of circle × length

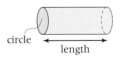

Pythagoras' theorem states,

For any right-angled triangle, $c^2 = a^2 + b^2$
where c is the hypotenuse.

Answers

N1 Check in
1 304
2 **a** 70   **b** −12
   c 5
3 −7°C

N1 Summary
1 **a** Seven thousand three hundred and sixty
   b 14 000   **c** 40
2 28, 45, 56, 79, 121
3 **a** 81 miles   **b** London   **c** 570 miles
4 10 million = 10 000 000
5 £36

D1 Check in
1 **a** 0.2, 0.25, 0.3
   b 0.7, 0.75, 0.8
   c 0.8, 0.85, 1
2 **a** $\frac{3}{4}$ **b** $\frac{3}{8}$
3 **a** 1   **b** 1   **c** $\frac{1}{10}$ **d** $\frac{1}{5}$ **e** $\frac{1}{4}$
4 **a** 0.8   **b** 0.3   **c** 0.1

D1 Summary
1 **a** **i** likely   **ii** impossible   **iii** certain
   b 5
2 **a** around 1   **b** zero
3 $\frac{7}{20}$

D2 Check in
1 **a** 6, 17, 19, 26, 29, 30, 37, 42
   b 106, 115, 118, 121, 130, 135
   c 144, 145, 154, 155, 156, 165, 166
2 **a** 121   **b** 144
   c 252   **d** 413
   e 68   **f** 23
   g 49   **h** 82
   i 189   **j** 266
3 **a** 04 : 58   **b** 20 : 45

D2 Summary
1 **a** **i** for example no time frame
       ii for example not enough options
   b for example tick boxes 0, 1, 2, 3, 4 or more
   c **i** Some letters are a lot more common than others
       ii Method 2—this will ensure that she gets a fair sample

N2 Check in
1 **a** 3000   **b** 2900   **c** 2920
2 **a** 48   **b** 105
   c 815   **d** 229
3 **a** 30   **b** 6   **c** 72
   d 141   **e** 168   **f** 13

N2 Summary
1 **a** **i** £22.08   **ii** 39
2 **a** 270   **b** 300
   c Any of 395, 396, 397, 398, 399, 401, 402, 403
3 £6

D3 Check in
1 **a** 180   **b** 90   **c** 36
   d 72   **e** 60   **f** 30
   g 2   **h** 4
2 **a** 25, 29, 30, 31, 36, 41, 43, 49
   b 234, 243, 324, 342, 423, 432
   c 12.3, 13.2, 21.3, 23.1, 31.2, 32.1
3 150°

D3 Summary
1 **a** Most magazines published at start of the month.
   b Men total 82
       Women total 86. Women buy more.
2 **a** Concert   **b** £200   **c** £75   **d** £50

D4 Check in
1 **a** 26, 29, 31, 35, 36, 40, 41, 48
   b 91, 92, 98, 101, 102
   c 4, $4\frac{1}{2}$, 6, $7\frac{1}{2}$, 8
2 **a** 80, 80 ,80, 82, 83, 83, 84, 84, 84, 84
   b 45, 45, 46, 48, 48, 48, 48, 49, 49, 49

D4 Summary
1 **a** 8   **b** 17 weeks
   c 20 weeks   **d** 13 weeks
   e Lowest value so makes hospital look better.
2 **a** 6   **b** 3   **c** 30
   d ii $\frac{4}{11}$
3 Range = 9 (mode = 0), mean = 2.7 (median = 2.5)
   sensible comment e.g. mean number of absences is only 2.9 students but it varies a lot

N3 Check in
1 **a** $\frac{3}{4}$ **b** $\frac{3}{5}$ **c** $\frac{3}{5}$
2 **a** 0.75   **b** 0.4   **c** 1.25
3 **a** $\frac{3}{5}$ **b** $\frac{1}{4}$ **c** $\frac{1}{5}$

N3 Summary
1 **a** 6 shaded   **b** 2 shaded
2 0.25, $\frac{7}{10}$, 2%
3 Adam 60% so Ben better
4 €900

D5 Check in

1 **a** 2, 3, 5 or 7   **b** 1, 4 or 9
  c 1, 3, 6 or 10   **d** 4 or 8
  e 1, 2, 5 or 10

2 **a** $\frac{2}{3}$ **b** $\frac{4}{5}$ **c** $\frac{1}{4}$
  d $\frac{3}{5}$ **e** 1

3 **a** $\frac{3}{4}$ **b** $\frac{3}{10}$ **c** $\frac{2}{5}$

4 **a** 10   **b** 40   **c** 200

D5 Summary

1 **a** X   **b** W   **c** Y
  d i P (green)   **ii** P(green or blue)
                       or P(red or yellow)

2 175

A1 Check in

1 **a** 9   **b** 4   **c** 16

2 15

3 **a** 7   **b** −1
  c 2   **d** −3

4 **a** −6   **b** −8
  c −2   **d** 4

A1 Summary

1 **a** $7c$ **b** $4x - 3y$ **c** $x + 20$

2 **a** True   **b** True   **c** False

3 $30x + 50y$

4 dimensions must add to $2x + 6$ e.g. $x + 8$, $x - 2$

5 **a** 5   **b** 3

N4 Check in

1 $\frac{2}{3}$

2 e.g. $\frac{2}{4}$, $\frac{3}{6}$

N4 Summary

1 **a i** £5.40   **ii** £4.60
  b £2, £2, £2, 50p, 20p, 10p
  c $\frac{1}{3}$

2 **a** 13   **b** 28 756

3 $\frac{300 \times 4}{6} = 200$

A2 Check in

1 **a** 3   **b** 8
  c 2   **d** 5

2 **a** 8   **b** 5
  c 8   **d** $3\frac{1}{2}$

3 **a** 5   **b** −4
  c 1   **d** 11

4 **a** −1   **b** −5
  c 1   **d** −7

A2 Summary

1 **a i** (0, 2)   **ii** (4, 3)
  b Should be at $\left(2, 2\frac{1}{2}\right)$

2 **a** 8, 12
  b Straight line passing through (0, 6) and (5, 16)

N5 Check in

1 **a** 49   **b** 8
  c 1000   **d** 0.32

2 5

3 Yes, because it will halve twice over (122, 61)

N5 Summary

1 **a** 6, 8 or 10 **b** 9
  c 8   **d** 7

2 **a** 2 numbers from 5, 7, 9, 11
  b 5, 7 or 11
  c 8

3 **a** 42 or 49   **b** 5 and 16

4 **a** $5 \times 5 \times 5 = 125$ **b** 216
  c No $5^3 = 125$ $6^3 = 216$
  d 81

5 12

6 36 seconds

A3 Check in

1 **a** 3   **b** 9
  c 4   **d** 3

2 1, 4, 9, 16, 25, 36, 49, 64, 81, 100

3 **a** 5   **b** 4
  c 7   **d** 6

4 **a** 2   **b** 2
  c 3   **d** 3

5 **a** 8   **b** 6
  c 12   **d** 10

A3 Summary

1 **a** Pattern with 9 sticks
  b 9, 11   **c** 25

2 **a** 23, 27   **b** 43

3 **a** For example, **i** 16 20 24 28   **ii** add 4
  b For example, **i** 30, 45, 60, 75   **ii** add 15
  c i $x + 7$ **ii** 8

4 Possibilities include 8, 16 or 7, 11

A4 Check in

1 **a** $4x$ **b** m^2
  c $4p$ **d** $6x$

2 **a** $5p + q$ **b** $5x + y$
  c $-m + 5n - 4p$ (or $5n - m - 4p$)

3 Grid with points correctly plotted.

A4 Summary

1 **a i** 125   **ii** 2
  b $5a + 6b$

2 **a** 100 miles **b** 5 hours
  c 33.3 miles per hour

N6 Check in

1 $\frac{1}{3}$
2 £24
3 £5
4 10

N6 Summary

1 a $935   b £106.95
2 a 25%   b 12000
3 £160 : £240

A5 Check in

1 a 6   b 15
  c 11   d 3
2 a 4   b 6
  c 8   d 5
3 a 3, 4   b 5, 7
4 a 7   b −1
  c 12   d $2\frac{1}{4}$

A5 Summary

1 a 30   b 4   c 32
2 $x = 8$ $y = 7$ $w = 3$
3 a 6   b 10   c 24

G1 Check in

1 a 7.8   b 9.4   c 5.5
2 a 400   b 14 000   c 31
  d 1340   e 6300   f 40
  g 60   h 4.3   i 0.64
  j 0.31
3 a 45 mm   b 4.5 cm

G1 Summary

1 Around 4.5 m.
2 a i 1.5 kg   ii 1500 g
  b 2 kg + 2 kg + 1 kg
3 centimetres, miles, kilograms
4 a 14 cm   b 2 × 3 or 4 × 1

G2 Check in

1 a 57 mm   b 5.7 cm
2 a around 40°
  b around 130–140°

G2 Summary

1 a 48°
  b any three angles that add to 360°
2 a $\frac{180}{5} = 36°$ b 107°
3 Two possible answers: (3, 1) or (5, 5)

G3 Check in

1 a 180°   b 180°   c 360°
2 a 50°   b 70°

G3 Summary

1 Only 1 pair parallel sides → trapezium
  4 right angles, sides not all same length →
  rectangle
  all sides same length, no right angles →
  rhombus
  opp angles equal, no right angles, sides not all
  equal → parallelogram
2 a cylinder
  b cone
  c Square-based pyramid
3 a 4   b 6   c 4
4 Possibilities include 4 cm × 3 cm × 7 cm
  and 2 cm × 2 cm × 21 cm

N7 Check in

1 47
2 a 1.3   b 0.3
3 a 3.56   b 8.04   c 0.06

N7 Summary

1 a £16.46 b 95p   c £41.98 d £8.75
2 600
3 55.0368
4 a 2.5   b 21 kg   c $\frac{3}{8}$

G4 Check in

1 a 180°   b 270°
  c 90°   d 180°
2 a clockwise b anticlockwise

G4 Summary

1

2 a vertices at (−2, 1), (−6, 1) and (−2, 3).
  b vertices at (−2, −1), (−2, −3) and (−6, −1).

G5 Check in

1 a $x = -2$ b $y = 1$
2 a 90°   b 270°   c 180°

G5 Summary

1 a coordinates (2, −1) (4, −1) (4, 4) (1, 4)
  b rotation 180°, centre (0, 0)
2 a coordinates (−2, −1) (−2, −2) (−4, −1)
  b coordinates (3, 2) (3, 4) (4, 2)

A6 Check in

1 a −3   b +6
  c ÷5   d × 4
2 a $2x + 2y$ b $5p + 2$
  c $\frac{m}{8}$
3 a 12   b 11
  c 4   d 13
4 a $x = 2$ b $x = 5$
  c $y = 2$ d $y = 7$

A6 Summary

1 a $x = 4$ b $5y = 40$ c 1
2 a $x = 6$ b $y = 45$ c $x = 4$
3 a $x = 2$ b $y = 9$
4 $x = 50°$

G6 Check in

1 a 1   b 4   c 4.5   d 1
  e 4   f 1.5   g 1   h 6
  i 0.5   j 1.5

2 a 35–45°   b 160–170°
  c 220–230°   d 125–135°

G6 Summary

1 a 120 km   b 170°
2 a 280 km   b 310°
  c AC is 280 km
    BC is 86 km

G7 Check in

1 a diameter   b circumference   c radius
2 28 cm²

G7 Summary

1 a 21.9 cm²
  b the shaded area has two lines of symmetry.
2 20 000 cm³
3 31.42 cm

Index